Intercultural Dramatherapy

The first overarching work on dramatherapy intercultural practice and research, this book explores the therapeutic encounter between therapists and participants as an intercultural space, highlighting how attending to cultural differences informs care.

Drawing on international voices of practitioners and participants, each chapter seeks to explore how social and political struggles, such as rising global conservatism, nationalism, climate crisis, increasing displacement and the coronavirus pandemic, are experienced in dramatherapy. Main themes covered include the development of intercultural good practice guidelines, therapist transparency – especially through self-disclosure and transference issues for the therapist – and the negotiation of power relationships across identity differences. The book concludes with a section on recommendations for training, supervision and practice.

A resource from which new practice and research can emerge, this book will be valuable to dramatherapy educators, practitioners and students, specifically those interested in intercultural practice.

Ditty Dokter, **PhD**, has worked clinically in adult and young people's mental health and refugee care. Academically she led two masters programmes in dramatherapy and one in dance movement therapy. Her research and publications focus on intercultural arts therapies practice, training and research.

Nisha Sajnani, **PhD**, **RDT-BCT**, is the director of the graduate programme in dramatherapy and the theatre and health lab at New York University. Her body of work explores the unique ways in which aesthetic experience can inspire care, equity and collective human flourishing across the lifespan.

Intercultural Dramatherapy

Imagination and Action at the
Intersections of Difference

Ditty Dokter and Nisha Sajnani

Routledge
Taylor & Francis Group

LONDON AND NEW YORK

Designed cover image: Rael San Fratello, *Teeter-Totter Wall*. American and Mexican families play on a seesaw straddling the Mexican border with US at the Anapra zone in Ciudad Juarez, Chihuahua State, Mexico. Photo by Ronald Rael.

First published 2023
by Routledge
4 Park Square, Milton Park, Abingdon, Oxon OX14 4RN

and by Routledge
605 Third Avenue, New York, NY 10158

Routledge is an imprint of the Taylor & Francis Group, an informa business

© 2023 Ditty Dokter and Nisha Sajnani

British Library Cataloguing-in-Publication Data
A catalogue record for this book is available from the British Library

ISBN: 978-1-138-36347-2 (hbk)
ISBN: 978-1-138-36348-9 (pbk)
ISBN: 978-0-429-43159-3 (ebk)

DOI: 10.4324/9780429431593

Typeset in Times New Roman
by SPi Technologies India Pvt Ltd (Straive)

Contents

"My black body cannot be unseen. It is ever-present. Like all bodies. With nuance and a kind of magic. As dramatherapists, we are concerned with whole body experience and attunement. It has never been more important than 'here and now', for us to learn how to navigate the uncomfortable terrain of institutions, intersectionality, and individual difference. This book springs from the well of Dokter's and Sajnani's deep listening, learning, and restorative action and practice, for 'all' bodies."

– **Samantha E. Adams**, *British Dramatherapist & Lecturer, University of Roehampton, London, UK*

"The field of Dramatherapy has long awaited this book, an artistry of cultural responsiveness and candour, Sajnani and Dokter reveal 'both the strengths and shadows of dramatherapy heritage.' Situating Dramatherapy within the various sociopolitical contexts in which we live and work, this research illuminates how Dramatherapy can attend to structural oppression and colonization within clinical spaces, affirm cultural identities and work towards disrupting the systematic devaluing and erasure of the experiences and cultural values of minoritized people. A unique treasure and a must read for all Dramatherapy students and seasoned professionals, it is books like these that make our profession a better place."

– **Jessica Bleuer, PhD(c), RDT**, *Graduate Program Director, MA Drama Therapy, Concordia University, Montreal, Canada & Past Diversity Chair, North American Drama Therapy Association*

"A timely book that will surely stimulate essential dialogue and self-examination in our field. The book is beautifully inclusive – in its exploration of many facets of identity (race, gender, age, language, sexual orientation, religion, class, nationality, and ability), and in bringing together perspectives from the North American Drama Therapy Association and the British Association of Dramatherapists, along with vignettes from drama therapists and clients around the globe. Written in a thoughtful, accessible, and inviting manner, *Intercultural Dramatherapy* inspires cultural reflection, humility, skill, and expanded awareness and action – for practitioners and supervisors – especially in relation to working across difference."

– **Renée Emunah, PhD, RDT-BCT**, *Founder/Director, Drama Therapy Program at the California Institute of Integral Studies*

"An essential text for students, practitioners and teachers of dramatherapy. This book offers both a theoretical orientation and practical starting points for the intercultural practice of dramatherapy. It is written with reflexivity and rigour and draws on consultations with drama therapists across the world. While the book is aimed at those based in the UK and USA, insights are adaptable to other contexts. The chapter on decolonising dramatherapy is particularly relevant to those interested in working in the global south responsibly and ethically."

– **Maitri Gopalakrishna**, *Dramatherapist, Counselling Psychologist and Trainer Parivarthan Counselling Training and Research Centre, Bangalore, India*

"The authors share their own lived experiences of inequality, attending then to disparity that can occur in dramatherapy practice more generally. They encourage co-creation, listening to client voices and signs of their internalised oppression in a broadly white and privileged profession. Both writers model activism and cultural humility, addressing attitudes towards dis/ability, racism, ageism, homophobia and further biases which promote othering. Professional and student readers will gain self-awareness through selected vignettes from practitioners and clients combined with skilful questioning as chapters end. The authors subtly guide the reader, enabling silenced voices to be heard and curricula to be re-focused. A brilliant and timely book."

– **Joanna Jaaniste, PhD**, *Adjunct Fellow, Western Sydney University, Australia*

"An amazing book showing how dramatherapy practitioners cross their geo-political boundaries, integrating, and internalizing Other cultures, placing dramatherapy in an intercultural domain. The current complex global scenario of migration, wars, poverty, and marginalization, makes this a *must* read text, for all mental health professionals. This book contains rich descriptions regarding the benefits of dramatherapy practice within culturally diverse settings, enabling to view each individual and the human society as *Pluralist*."

– **Ravindra Ranasinha PhD**, *Director, Research Centre for Dramatherapy, Colombo, Sri Lanka*

"This is an excellent book and essential reading for dramatherapists and students who care about intercultural perspective communication in relation to dramatherapy theory and practice, including supervision and training. Invisible something has a voice!"

– **Tae-Seung Lee, PhD**, *Lecturer MA Drama Therapy, Yong-in University, So.uth Korea*

"This book is a vast and thoughtful resource that explores and grapples with experiences and complexities of intercultural dramatherapy. Drawing from case studies, interviews, personal communications, literature, personal and professional narratives, it covers a range of intersectional considerations and perspectives regarding dramatherapy training, practice, and supervision. Each chapter offers the reader a relevant set of questions that prompt contemplation and self-reflection at the intersection of positionality and perspective. Dokter and Sajnani have written an important text for dramatherapy students and seasoned clinicians alike."

– **Britton Williams**, *Adjunct Professor, Program in Drama Therapy, New York University, USA*

"This book establishes for the reader salient concepts and praxis in cross-cultural/intercultural dramatherapy. The clear structure of the chapters, the balance of the findings from the research study in conversation with practitioner interviews and current research and writing in the profession, makes a thick and complex topic accessible. The book also demonstrates where the gaps are in the current literature, in our ever-changing world, and where more work and research need to be focused. It will be an outstanding textbook for teaching and for dramatherapists who wish to develop their capacities in centering difference in their work, as it thoughtfully reminds us that all clinical practice may indeed be intercultural work."

– **Maria Hodermarska, MA, RDT-BCT, CASAC, LCAT**, *Clinical Associate Professor of Drama Therapy, New York University, USA*

"Simultaneously personal and political, this publication draws out the urgency of transcultural understanding in dramatherapy training and practice. Vignettes are accompanied by scholarly comment, addressing problems of inequality, intransigence, and implicit codes in training and clinical contexts. There is disruption to dramatherapy tropes and challenges to orthodoxy. It is an exciting and vital read and one which prompts reflection and action – both in ourselves and our communities. This is a core text for dramatherapists, arts therapists, educators and professionals interested in the shadows and strengths of their practice."

– **Richard Hougham**, *MA Principal Lecturer, Royal Central School of Speech and Drama, University of London, UK*

"'What is foregrounded, made visible in dramatherapy, theory and practice and what remains invisible?'. This question posed in the introduction, supports the reader in making sense of the complexities of power dynamics and the intersections of identity and how these may play out in the therapy space. True to its title, 'imagination and action' are at its heart, offering creative approaches and practical ideas to explore content so painful that it can easily be pushed aside. This book honours the voices and multiple perspectives of a range of professionals and their clients, exploring ways in which the power dynamics of race and racism, age and ageism and social class for instance, can manifest in the therapy room. It will help practitioners and clients create safer ways of initiating important conversations which may otherwise have been avoided. The book, strengthened by the North American and European perspectives of the authors, will serve as a much needed guide and practical tool for therapy clients, arts therapists, psychotherapists, trainers and clinical supervisors."

– **Mandy Carr**, *former Dramatherapy Senior Lecturer,*
Anglia Ruskin University, Cambridge, UK and former
Convenor of the Equality and Diversity Sub-committee,
British Association of Dramatherapists

Foreword

This book sets a new agenda for dramatherapy theory and practice.

Fascinating, thorough and illuminating, in one volume Dokter and Sajnani provide a journey through crucial territory and provide an innovative guide for negotiating complex areas. This is essential reading for every dramatherapy practitioner or trainee, and the book will help the field to rethink how all relationships between clients and therapists form and develop.

The ways in which oppression, silencing, power and prejudice feature in the lives of therapist and client are brought alive by vignettes and descriptions of practice. These can be areas that create tension, anxiety and fear of an absence of knowledge on how best to act. This book takes us into clear routes and "practical strategies" (p. 7) to build new ways of thinking, responding and working. Starting from the question, "How does culture influence dramatherapy?" (p. 5), the different chapters raise awareness and help the therapist to examine their knowledge, understanding and actions. Chapter 4 identifies a 'need' that permeates the approach of the book: "to examine how our interactions and the materials we use, the stories, case examples and approaches, may risk reinforcing notions of colour blindness, Eurocentric norms, and/or ask racialised students and clients to replace their experience once more with those of their white counterparts" (p. 54). It supports movement into alive and fertile ways of being creative in areas connected to the relationships between class, race, gender, disability, sexuality, age, belief and privilege. In writing about weaving in the Incakunaq Ruwaynin Project, Peru, del Solar talks about it as involving many dimensions: a "system of ideas that underlies the weaving process", as "one of the most important means to learn, communicate and reproduce aesthetic and cultural values" (Franquemont, Franquemont and Isbell 1992: 48, cited by del Solar, 2019, p. 175), as well as being described by women weavers as "what they know how to do with their hands" (2019, p. 173). In Chapter 11, Dokter and Sajnani propose the image of the therapist as weaver in their analysis of "practice examples", to show how dramatherapists "weave between" the complex "intersections" (p. 151) explored. Such a vision of the therapist echoes well with del Solar's descriptions of weaving as both deep structural reflection of ideas and values at the same time as the practical "how to do with their hands" (2019, p. 173). This weave is everywhere in the book, as the authors illuminate concepts by showing how they interconnect with the everyday practices of therapy: the dramatherapist as "cultural broker" (p. 122); the empowerment of clients, "the promise of interculturalism" (p. 16) and the potentials of the dynamics between "therapist self-awareness, client world-view, the therapeutic relationship and advocacy" (p. 178).

The careful detail and consideration of context avoid the dangers of essentialising the learning and development the book facilitates. Dokter and Sajnani demonstrate the values of what Zilliacus, Paulsrud and Holm have called "context-sensitive analysis" – which enables the combating of "ethnocentrism and marginalization and to enhance equality and co-existence" (2017, p. 167). This approach allows us to understand the relevance of the deep, broad structural questions asked of us, but also to understand the ways these feature within, and illuminate, the different and varied contexts that therapists and clients experience. Combining information, research, questions and guidance, *Intercultural Dramatherapy* avoids easy answers: instead, it provides chapters that provoke stimulating reflection. Reading it is akin to being in lively dialogue with a knowledgeable and questioning colleague, teacher and supervisor – all woven together within the book's voice.

Phil Jones is Professor of Children's Rights and Wellbeing at the Institute of Education, UCL's Faculty of Education and Society and is author of Child Agency and Voice in Therapy (with Cedar, Coleman, Haythorne, Mercieca & Ramsden), Rethinking Children's Rights (with Welch), The Arts Therapies and Drama as Therapy.

References

Del Solar, M. E. (2019). Highland peasant weavers: Empowered women, heritage keepers and home providers. Incakunaq Ruwaynin Project, Cusco, Peru. *TEXTILE*, *17*(2), 168–181. https://doi.org/10.1080/14759756.2018.1474003

Zilliacus, H., Paulsrud, B. & Holm, G. (2017). Essentialising vs. non-essentialising students' cultural identities: curricular discourses in Finland and Sweden. *Journal of Multicultural Discourses*, 12(2), 166–180. https://doi.org/10.1080/17447143.201 7.1311335

Acknowledgements

This book would not have been possible without the generous support, critical reading, examples of practice and editorial assistance from our community of family, friends, colleagues and students.

Thank you first to our research assistants at New York University. Opher Shamir assisted with the technical infrastructure of the study and data collection. Monica Gamboa assisted with data analysis and sourcing our cover image. Akhila Khanna assisted with referencing and indexing. We are also thankful to our editors at Routledge for your support throughout this process.

Thank you to those who contributed interviews, reflections on practice and critical reader reflections, including, in alphabetical order: Samantha Adams, Bruce Howard Bayley, Eva Boorsma, Jessica Bleuer, Ryan Campinho Valadas, Mandy Carr, Aileen Cho, Carol Cumberbatch, Simon Driver, Jean Francois-Jacques, Alida Gersie, Maitri Gopalakrishna, Ruth Goodman, Maria Hodermarska, Richard Hougham, Joanna Jaaniste, Shoshi Keisari, Heidi Landis, Tae-seung Lee, Kristin Long, Roshmi Lovatt, Sarah Mann-Shaw, Caroline Miller, Joan Moore, Charlie Moritz, Beau Pirie, Susana Pendzik, Emma Ramsden, Adam Reynolds, Anna Seymour, Mary Smail, Hailey Southern, Cathie Sprague, Adam Stevens, Jordan Stewart, Marlize Swanepoel, Chanaphan Thammarut, Dana Trottier, Britton Williams, Linda Winn and Eleanor Zeal.

Notes to Reader

Co-first authorship: Ditty Dokter and Nisha Sajnani contributed equally to this book.

Confidentiality: All participant names in vignettes are anonymised and use pseudonyms. Individual practitioners are not named unless they requested to be named.

Use of language: English language used in this publication is a mix of US and UK English to reflect the different authorial voices, but UK English spelling is privileged in general discursive text.

Limitations: Our perspectives arise from the contexts in which we have lived, trained and worked. Therefore, readers will find that the majority of examples offered in this text come from the UK, Netherlands, US and Canada. The sample size for the survey that informed the organisation of this book was small as compared to our global community. We have sought to balance these limitations with self-reflexivity, interviews, vignettes and references to research that offer insights on intercultural practice from other vantage points. We acknowledge these limitations and offer this book as a catalyst to invite more stories of intercultural vitality and struggle from participants and providers of dramatherapy.

Part I

Framework

Chapter 1

Introduction

I was a young dramatherapist in the 1980s in my first dramatherapy job newly working on an acute ward for people struggling with eating and mood disorders in an academic hospital. I attended the ward round with the multi-disciplinary team, chaired by a white, male psychiatric consultant. A client I was working with was discussed and introduced by the consultant as "a young woman with a borderline personality, eating and sexual orientation disorder". The client herself was called in later, so she did not hear herself described in these terms, but I noticed that, when she came in, the vivacious talkative young woman I knew was as silent as I was in that ward round. It was tempting to see this as medical male hierarchy versus female powerlessness. I could find solace in identifying with my client. However, as someone who worked as part of this team, I was ashamed that I was not able to voice my indignation at the way she was described. I allowed myself to be silenced. That shame has stayed with me. It reminds me that at times, I find myself unable to challenge power driven ways of categorising and pathologising people, denying the value of the relationship. I prioritised my place in the team, the wish to be accepted and to avoid the outsider position, easily taken and given as a non medic and immigrant professional who spoke English as a second language.

Dramatherapist, UK

This story, like all stories, is a fractal of its surrounding social context. The three players in this scene are two young White women and a middle-aged White male. The professional backgrounds are university student, dramatherapist and university psychiatric consultant. The sexual orientation is hidden for the professionals and pathologised for the client. The dramatherapist is a migrant and English additional language speaker, whilst the other two players present as majority White British. Dilemmas around diagnosis vs human condition, status and class within a medical context are present as subtext. The young dramatherapist reflects the role training she received about how to conduct herself as a young immigrant woman, a new dramatherapist and member of a psychiatric team. Her words reveal an internalisation of power dynamics stratified in relation to age, gender, professional identity, language, sexual orientation, and race that resulted, in her words, in an alienating

DOI: 10.4324/9780429431593-2

silence embodied by both client and dramatherapist. A seemingly parallel process occurs as we read about how the client was othered through diagnoses reflecting the social biases of the time just as the dramatherapist experienced the othering of being a non-medical, immigrant professional.

This moment reveals the central themes of this book in which we cast the space between the dramatherapist and participant, whether they be referred to as a client or patient in clinical care or participant in community-based practice,[1] as an *intercultural space*. In a time in which we are reminded daily of the traces that we leave on each other and are increasingly aware of the differential impact of systems we encounter across racial and economic lines, our hope is that the stories, ideas, and analysis offered in these pages offer useful perspectives on how culture and difference, understood in relation to past and present expressions of power, informs care. In this introduction, we begin with sources of inspiration for this book, the methods we used to gather research for this text together with selected findings and the organisation of the chapters that follow.

The inspiration for this book

This book arose from a series of conversations between the authors about the influence of culture in dramatherapy during a period of rising global conservatism, White supremacy, concerns about climate change, increasing numbers of forcibly displaced persons, the coronavirus pandemic, resurgent efforts to advance racial justice and protect reproductive rights and the war in Ukraine. As a species, we have struggled to coexist with each other and with the planet, and it is within this struggle that we wanted to focus our efforts. As authors, we want to examine where and how this struggle is expressed in our field and in our intersubjective encounters with each other and those with whom we work. What is foregrounded, made visible in dramatherapy theory and practice, and what remains invisible? Some voices may be silent or silenced; how do we become aware of the absent voices in dramatherapy? How do we attend to our own cultural experience and that of those we work with in a way that does not repeat dynamics of silencing and marginalisation in the classroom, clinic and other spheres of professional engagement? We wanted to find our way into these seemingly enormous challenges and ground them in everyday moments of practice.

We are influenced by different but complementary theoretical frames of reference. Before training as dramatherapists, Ditty had been trained in social anthropology and youth work and drew heavily on interculturalism (Dokter, 1998a, 2000a; Dokter & Hills de Zárate, 2016), whereas Nisha was influenced by her background in applied theatre and critical race feminism, including intersectionality (Sajnani, 2012a, 2013, 2016b). These theoretical and practical frames of reference are explained further in Chapter 2, but it is worth mentioning here that our frames of reference overlapped in that we shared an understanding of culture as going beyond essentialist notions of nationality, race or ethnicity towards a dynamic expression of patterns and possibilities arising from interactions within the myriad social groups with which we identify within the context of an unequal society.

Each of us brought extensive previous experience in both writing about and bringing together dramatherapists working within and between cultural spaces where issues relating to identity, difference, power, privilege and oppression were salient (Dokter, 1998a, 2000b, 2005/2006; Dokter & Khasnavis, 2008; Dokter & Hills de Zárate, 2016; Sajnani, 2004, 2009, 2012a/b, 2016b, 2017). We both remain invested in how social justice concerns are integrated into the training of dramatherapists, having been course leaders of MA dramatherapy programmes. At the time of writing, Nisha was and still is at New York University in the US, and Ditty recently retired from her post at Anglia Ruskin University in the UK. We collaborated on the development of *intercultural practice guidelines* for the British Association of Dramatherapists (2016) and *cultural responselability guidelines* for the North American Drama Therapy Association (2016), co-facilitated workshops on intercultural practice and training (Sajnani & Dokter, 2015) and co-authored a chapter on experiential intercultural training in dramatherapy (Sajnani & Dokter, 2017). The feedback that we received following these efforts, the development of practice guidelines in particular, highlighted the need for examples of where cultural influences could be brought into conversation with dramatherapy training, practice, supervision and research. We heard the need for examples of where we get stuck, what practices have been helpful, where potential opportunities may lie and where questions should be raised.

Methodology and selected findings

Our primary research question was *how does culture influence dramatherapy*? We undertook mixed-method research in order to triangulate data from a survey of dramatherapists and clients of dramatherapy, semi-structured interviews and vignette research on dramatherapist perspectives. The study was reviewed and approved by NYU Institutional Review Board (IRB-FY 2019-3100) and distributed through social media networks and to the membership of the North American Drama Therapy Association (NADTA) and British Association of Dramatherapists (BADth). All those who began the survey were offered a definition of culture that made it clear that we were looking at culture from the perspective of one's membership in specific social groups rather than locating it within a concern with ethnicity alone.

Of a total of 167 respondents, 66 completed the survey. Of these 66, 48 respondents identified as people with the dual experience of having received and provided dramatherapy, 15 reported only providing dramatherapy and three reported only receiving dramatherapy. Of those who had provided dramatherapy, 48% had been practising for more than ten years, and approximately 10% of respondents were in training. Geographically, respondents were from Northern America (37), Europe (18), Asia (4), South Africa (1), the Middle East (1) and five chose not to answer. We did not ask respondents which country they trained in, so there are variations in this sample. When asked which aspects of identity most inform and influence their experience of dramatherapy, responses revealed the following: race and ethnicity highest, gender as second; age, language, sexual orientation and spirituality shared third place, followed by political beliefs, socio-economic status, professional identity, family composition, nationality and citizenship and then disability.

Of the 66 respondents, 12 agreed to be interviewed. The interview methodology was semi- structured, elaborating on some of the survey questions.[2] Our approach to these interviews was phenomenological in that we were interested in their experience of cultural influences in dramatherapy. These interviews were transcribed and manually coded using descriptive and consensual coding (Saldaña, 2016) by both co-authors and a research assistant. Excerpts from these qualitative accounts have been used as opening vignettes and examples to ground each chapter in the lived experience of practising dramatherapists and to reflect the complexity of how culture and context intersect and arise in the context of care work (Yep & Mutua, 2015). Additionally, vignettes of dramatherapists' accounts of practice in the UK, US, South Africa, South Korea, Australia, New Zealand and the Netherlands collected by Jones and Dokter (Jones, 2009a) have been integrated into the text.

As authors and culturally situated subjects (Marotta, 2014), we have also aimed to be transparent and self-reflexive with each other about our own cultural horizons, prejudices, standpoints and the ideologies that inform them, to identify helping and hindering processes in our own understanding of this work. To this end, we have included a section in each chapter where we locate ourselves in relation to the topic. We acknowledge and appreciate that we are two cisgendered, bisexual women who have migrated to countries that occupy significant influence in a geopolitical context and in the context of our field. Ditty is a Dutch, White woman living in the UK, and Nisha identifies as a South Asian–Canadian immigrant to the US. We grew up with dramatherapy (becoming) recognised as a profession with available training programmes in each of our respective countries. Both of us have sufficient cultural, social and economic capital within our professional context to be able to disseminate our ideas. Therefore, there will likely be instances where, despite our attempts to remain self-reflexive, the privilege that we carry as researchers and authors attempting to examine spaces of marginalisation and complicity in our work clouds our vision and interferes with our analysis.

With this in mind, we designed a methodological approach with various checks and balances. Vignette and interview contributors were asked to member check and critically provide feedback on chapters, whilst extra critical readers with expertise in the chapter themes and topics read and provided additional editing suggestions. However, limitations remain in that, with the exception of our vignettes, we drew on a British and North American sample for the survey, and the survey was only in English.

Organisation of the book

This book is organised into three sections comprising a total of 16 chapters. The first section contains three chapters. Following this introduction is a chapter on theoretical influences followed by a chapter that presents a discussion of the guidelines. The second section of the book contains nine chapters that each privilege a facet of identity as a lens from which to discuss intercultural and intersectional issues in dramatherapy. These chapters are presented in the order in which they were prioritised by respondents who were each asked to consider which aspects of identity informed their experience of dramatherapy. Chapter 4 focuses on race and racialisation, followed by chapters on gender, age, language, sexual orientation, spirituality and religious beliefs, socio-economic status, national identity and migration and dis/ability. Concerns related to family composition have been subsumed in our discussion of gender and socio-economic status, and issues related to professional identity and political beliefs have been woven throughout the text. This is not to suggest a hierarchy of identity or oppression but rather, as Hays (1996) has argued in her *Addressing* model of addressing cultural complexities in counselling, to offer different entry points into an examination of culture, identity and equity. At the same time, the order of chapters in Part II, again informed by how respondents prioritised these aspects of identity, acknowledges race as an organising factor in our experience of dramatherapy and disability as emerging in our collective consciousness as a profession steeped in the practice and politics of care. Each chapter ends with practical questions for further exploration. Part III of the book consists of four chapters focused on implications for pedagogy, supervision, practice and a conclusion.

Conclusion

Our hope in writing this book is that it equips students and professional dramatherapists with discursive and practical strategies with which to better understand and explore the influence of culture in dramatherapy. We are indebted to our colleagues who shared their stories with us of where work went well, where they struggled and where complex questions remain. They have helped us collectively work toward increasing ethical practice. There are many aspects of identity and experience that are not included in this book which we accept as one of the many ways in which this work is incomplete. Yet, we hope that this book offers a springboard for useful explorations and conversations about our coexistence in a greater ecology.

Notes

1 For discussion on the use of the word 'client' in dramatherapy, see Sajnani (2018).
2 To view the survey and interview questions, please use this link: https://bit. ly/3lfr7HA.

Chapter 2

Dramatherapy through an intercultural and intersectional kaleidoscope

From the very moment that client comes into my office, I'm reading their body and they're reading my body...even before a word is spoken. As the client tries to acclimatise and see...you know...is this a space where I can be vulnerable? Part of someone answering that question is...who is the therapist? How can I set this framework where we can work across differences? What makes sense to disclose in terms of our culture, or my cultures, in terms of similarities and differences? How do I create a space where clients know that we are going to talk about this and that it is a perfectly normal part of therapy to talk about who I am and who they are – and what it is like to do this work together? What parts of who I am and who they are make this work more challenging or more vulnerable? When will I not understand where they are coming from and how do I create a space where they can say to me that I missed what they are saying? Culture is infused in every part of the session even if we're not talking about culture. For example, when we're talking about depression, of course the understanding of depression is culturally mitigated. ... What is my understanding of depression and what is their understanding of depression?

Jessica Bleuer, Dramatherapist, Canada

The dramatherapist in this vignette reveals their close observation of their client and the questions that are alive for them as they walk into the room. She describes the intersubjective space in which experience, expectations and meanings may be shared, as an intercultural encounter. In this chapter, we consider the field of dramatherapy through an intercultural and intersectional kaleidoscope, drawing on our own experience and ideas about interculturalism in adjacent disciplines such as theatre, sociology, anthropology and psychology, as well as theatre based-practices that have been influential in our work. We discuss interculturalism in relation to intersectionality as guiding theoretical influences for this book.

An intercultural profession

From its inception, our profession of dramatherapy has benefitted from an intercultural exchange of ideas and ways of working. The development of dramatherapy as a formal profession arose from the 1960s onwards in the

DOI: 10.4324/9780429431593-3

UK, US and the Netherlands through increased contact between individuals and the creation of professional associations and trainings alongside state registration, such as the Health and Care Professions Council (HCPC) in the UK (Andersen-Warren & Grainger, 2008; Dokter & Gersie, 2016) and licensure in the specific states and provinces in North America (Gaines & Butler, 2016). The European Consortium of Arts Therapies Training and Education (ECArTE), formed in 1989, played an important role in the European Union in developing courses and contacts between countries. The European Federation of Dramatherapy (EFD) was founded in 2013 following a period of consultation and exchange with European professional associations. The World Alliance of Dramatherapy (WADth), founded in 2017, now brings together 18 professional dramatherapy associations representing 36 countries. These efforts at collaboration continue to cultivate a conducive environment for developing relationships, shared aims, exchanging ways of working and discussing standards of education and practice.

We have had a history of intercultural research in the field upon which this text has relied. Sue Jennings' (1995) examination of drama and ritual amongst the Temiar people in Malaysia was an early example. Jones (2007) argued that drama and ritual are connected by both theatre practitioners and anthropologists as both a core process of dramatherapy and a specific approach (Mitchell, 2016; Schrader, 2012). The first volume of intercultural arts therapies research (Dokter & Hills de Zárate, 2016) combined phenomenological and ethnographic methodology to study intercultural communication in a dance therapy training group (Panhofer et al., 2016), whilst others use a more traditional ethnographic (Singer et al., 2016) or auto-ethnographic (Mullen-Williams, 2016) approach. Snow's (2022) articulation of ethnodramatherapy brought together ethnodramatic and dramatherapeutic processes with adults with varied abilities and needs. Alongside these efforts have been attempts to illuminate how differences in racialisation, citizenship, gender identity and expression; sexuality; age; religion; dis/ability; and artistic influences, for example, are expressed within our profession in ways that inform professional identity, aesthetic choices and the dynamics of care (Beauregard et al., 2016; Dokter, 1998a; Dokter & Hills de Zárate, 2016; Hodermarska, 2013; Makanya, 2014; Mayor, 2012; Sajnani, 2012a, 2013; Snow et al., 2017; Valadas & Carr, 2018). These efforts have often attempted to link the personal with the political as we will do, albeit partially, in the section that follows.

Situating ourselves in our profession

As co-authors, we grew up in third spaces between seemingly crystallised dichotomies of Black and White, east and west, foreign and familiar, rich and poor. We also grew up in dramatherapy, a profession that encouraged and enabled playful, embodied and guided explorations of identity and experience as changeable constellations of real and imagined images, roles, scenes and stories. Viewing dramatherapy through an intercultural lens seemed to come naturally as two people who have experienced a pronounced sense of difference within the contexts in which we lived. We were curious about how our ways of working may be shaped by our lived experiences in the cultural groups to which we belong. We wondered about how our intersecting identities and social groups contribute to how we see and move in the world as care providers. Which aspects of ourselves do we foreground or background in a particular context? Which hidden aspects do we make transparent in a therapeutic relationship, which are visibly present without any choice? When is it easier to own one's 'oppressed' as different from 'oppressor' identities? What was at stake in the work? For example, migrant, English as a second language and an increasingly older woman are aspects of Ditty's identity that are visible/audible in the therapeutic relationship. Being disabled, a bisexual woman married to a man and coming from a working-class background are less so. For Nisha, being a woman of colour is apparent, though being a Canadian immigrant to the US and a bisexual woman in a lesbian relationship is not. Our artistic, spiritual and political backgrounds and politics may be equally invisible. Both of us will sometimes use aspects of our identities to connect to clients' experiences of oppression as a way of showing empathy but also recognise the need to be careful that we do not only work with those aspects of identity where there is 'sameness', as there are plenty of 'othering' ones left. Reflecting on our authorial voices, we will offer a brief excerpt of our own intercultural audit to highlight cultural influences and to examine where some aspects of our identities may influence our (in)ability to notice differences. As authors we want to explore those aspects we are less comfortable with, aiming to share struggles rather than position ourselves as 'experts'. We will return to this in subsequent chapters, aiming to be as transparent as possible about our own challenges when working interculturally.

Nisha: At the gates of the empire

I stood at the gates of Buckingham Palace, both hands wrapped tight around the wrought iron rails, staring at the guards. I had walked through Victoria Memorial park around to each of the three formal entrances marked by tributes to previous imperial possessions: Canada, Australia and South and West Africa. I remembered a story about the Kohinoor, the largest diamond known to have been stolen from India by the British in the 1800s. How should we deal with the colonial legacy of theft? What is owed to whom and why did it matter to me, a first-generation Canadian born to parents who were forcibly displaced following the end of British rule in India prior to migrating to Canada. The moment lasted only a few minutes and I wasn't alone. A friend was with me. A tall, White, male, older friend. He witnessed this moment of postcolonial angst, making it all the more accessible in my memory. I released my grip. It could be that what felt stolen was a sense of geographic, linguistic, economic, cultural place but also true might have been the function of my gaze in preserving my role as an outsider. Now I live and work in the US, a coloniser-settler country with a terrifying legacy of anti-Black racism, sexism, homo and transphobia, ageism, xenophobia and ableism that requires an exhausting vigilance of how oppressive dynamics may be at work and a commitment to taking down material and psychological gates to belonging. It is tempting to assume the outsider role as a Canadian and a woman of colour in this space, to be the one looking in…critiquing a centre of power while remaining outside the fray…binge-watching *The Crown* during a pandemic.

When I stood at those gates, I was in the process of completing my doctoral studies. I had come across Amita Handa's *Of Silk Saris and Miniskirts* (2003) on the experience of South Asian women walking a tightrope between host and home cultures. I could relate to this tension between ballet and bharatanatyam, two classical dance forms I trained in simultaneously as a young person. She wrote of hybridity, centres and peripheries, decolonisation and third spaces, concepts popularised by postcolonial theorist Homi K. Bhabha (1994). Of course, these very concepts may be critiqued for their Eurocentricity as they depend upon the presence of the empire with its gates in the first place (Brians, 2008). Other South Asian theorists like Angela Aujla (2000) had helped me to flip the script on displacement and understand "the advantage of in-betweenness, the straddling of two cultures and the consequent ability to negotiate the difference" (Hoogvelt, 1997, p. 158). Black feminist scholars like hooks (1989) and Crenshaw (1988) helped me to understand marginalisation as a space of power. I remember feeling that it had taken until that point in my education to read about realities that I could identify with and that this was both exhilarating and infuriating. I suppose my search for these voices also reflected a particular phase of my own acculturation and racial identity development as a person of colour living in predominantly White communities for most of my life (Berry, 2005).

Like many dramatherapists, theatre became the art form and the platform from which to express myself from early on. Three roles stand out as reflective of phases of my own acculturation. The first was the title role in *Moo*, a play by White, Canadian playwright Sally Clark (1989). *Moo* offered access to a feminist yearning in the form of a woman who was both bold yet obsessed with a man who did not love her and who, in the end, committed her to an asylum against her wishes. The fact that 'Moo' was a White woman was never discussed except for when the director pointed out that her choice to cast me was the 'non-traditional choice'. This reinforced Whiteness as the invisible norm necessitating *assimilation*, the valuing of majority culture over one's own (Berry, 2005). The second role was 'Kamala' (Ophelia) in *Samsaria*, an Indian adaptation of Hamlet, which still reified a Eurocentric theatre canon but also signalled a *separation*, a pull towards preserving one's own culture

(Berry, 2005). Berry's third phase involved true *marginalisation*, the experience of losing cultural contact and identification with one's culture as well as the majority culture. I can't point to a specific role that embodies this phase but recognise both its loneliness and liminality. The third role was in a socio-biographical performance that I co-created with four close friends, one who identified as White and American, one who identified as Polish-Canadian and two others who identified as Iranian-Canadian. *Sounds Like Canada* combined verbatim and gestural theatre styles to convey personal stories relating to the intersections of national and gender identity (Sajnani, 2003, 2013). This role, and the project as a whole, signalled a kind of *integration* when viewed through the lens of acculturation theory in that it involved valuing the complexity and contradictions in our own cultural heritage and majority culture (Berry, 2005).

Beyond my experience with roles were formative experiences with applied theatre, an umbrella term for forms of theatre that deliberately engage with people in their own spaces to create work that reflects and seeks to address their concerns and interests (Prentki & Abraham, 2020). My experience of working with applied theatre forms such as Playback Theatre and Theatre of the Oppressed had a great influence on my practice as a dramatherapist in that these practices privileged voice, agency and cultural dialogue while also calling attention to the dynamics of audience interaction (Sajnani, 2009, 2012b). Devising theatre that reflected sources of strength as well as a spectrum of systemic, interpersonal and internalised harm as a woman of colour with a community of South Asian youth in Montreal offered reference points for later work as a dramatherapist working with newcomer and refugee women (Sajnani & Nadeau, 2006). Interculturalism within applied theatre will be discussed at greater length later in the chapter. Finally, my training in Developmental Transformations (Johnson & Pitre, 2020) is what facilitated an internal capacity to embrace complexity and difference while noticing my own tendencies for power and control in destabilising encounters.

At the time of this writing, Kamala Harris, a biracial woman of Jamaican and Indian heritage, was elected vice-president in the US. In her acceptance speech, she encouraged children to "dream with ambition, lead with conviction, and see yourself in a way that others might not see you, simply because they've never seen it before" (Harris as cited in Stevens, 2020, n.p.). What I like about this quote is her emphasis on our capacities to imagine ourselves in ways that exceed the constraints of present experience, that disrupt dominant narratives. Isn't this what we do in dramatherapy? These authors and playwrights reflected unspoken realities in their writing and, in so doing, inspired me to render the invisible, visible. Yet, what I perceive as invisible, marginal and otherwise needing attention, is influenced by my own privileges and complicities. How do I attend to the Other? How can we better attune ourselves to the gates of internalised empires, each other's and our own? How do our practices enable us to attend to the material gates that restrict agency and collective flourishing?

Ditty: On being white in countries with colonial heritage

"Have you swapped babies?" The question was asked of my mother and her sister-in-law in the health centre in the late 1950s. It was based on hair and skin colour. My mother was White with ash blond wavy hair and blue eyes, my aunt had an Asian complexion with the dark straight hair of someone born in Indonesia, of Javanese descent. My baby cousin was blond and blue-eyed like my mother, I was olive-skinned with dark eyes. My mother and aunt told us this story laughingly when my cousin and I were growing up. I always wondered about the possible subtexts but did not feel able to ask. There were tensions in the family about skin colour, although my father's racist comments tended to be focused on people of African rather than Asian descent; he made clear he did not want me to have an African partner or mixed-race children; what did this say about my mixed-race cousins? My aunt and cousins familiarised me with the Dutch colonial heritage, but more as a taken-for-granted historical reality rather than a present-day embodiment of continued exploitation and oppression.

As a White Dutch national who migrated to the UK, I wonder how my aunt felt about her migrant Indonesian identity in the Netherlands of the mid-20th century. I never knew her migration history. We had Indonesian female neighbours who were being helped by the families in our apartment block of council flats. Dutch working-class culture can have a somewhat aggressive helpfulness that tends towards the paternalistic. In this working-class neighbourhood, it was not easy to distinguish the various levels of underprivilege that coexisted. I was aware that being of a different skin colour and female meant that neighbours tended to be somewhat condescendingly helpful. The Dutch tradition of St Nicholas, the White bishop with Black helpers (played by White people with blackface) was very popular, with a similar blindness to the implications of the tradition for non-White Dutch.

Racism is a belief system developed by White Europeans to justify a trading system that implemented the oppression of non-White peoples, be they in the form of slavery, colonialism, apartheid, occupation or other forms of violence. This made sense of some of my Dutch experiences in a wider European context; the Dutch have a history of colonialism and benefitting from slavery in both the Caribbean and Indonesian contexts (Mbeki & van Rossum, 2017; Nimako & Willemsen, 2011). In my second country the UK, the history of colonialism, slavery and systemic racism is equally toxic. The COVID-19 crisis made the, for White eyes often invisible, inequalities very visible. In the UK Black, Asian and Minority Ethnic groups have been at highest risk of dying from Covid-19 even after adjusting for deprivation and health (Razaq et al., 2020). The intergenerational impact of trauma and disease on underprivileged communities is also a part of my heritage, which can make it hard to own my identity as a privileged White European. I struggle to own my responsibility as traumatiser whose privilege is paid for by others' oppression, underprivilege and discrimination. White privilege is an absence of the negative consequences of racism (Eddo-Lodge, 2017). The idea of White privilege forces White people to confront their own complicity in its continuing existence (not to confuse racism and prejudice; racism can be described as prejudice with power). The White moderate shallow understanding of people of goodwill can deny the impact of White privilege. The description of UK racism made me understand my Dutch family dynamics with mixed-race children a bit better when reading "white privilege is never more pronounced than in our intimate relationships, our close friendships and our families" (Eddo-Lodge, 2017, p. 102). Much of White supremacy's power is drawn from its invisibility, the taken-for-granted aspects that underwrite all other political and social contracts. I am White privileged in the fact that I struggle with the term White supremacy and associate it with White hate groups, but have to face that that difficulty only serves to protect the processes it describes, it stops me from seeing the mechanisms of racial inequality (DiAngelo, 2018). When thinking about cultural racism, the development of White superiority from childhood, I struggle with questions of whether I felt superior to my cousins, especially my girl cousin with the same name and Javanese features. DiAngelo's criteria for how race shapes the lives of White people are interesting: born into the culture with a sense of belonging; freedom from the burden of race, freedom of movement; theories about human development based on my race as the norm; White solidarity; reminiscing that the past is 'good'; White racial innocence and segregated lives. When I arrived in the UK in the 1980s, I was employed in both the National Health Service (NHS) and social care systems in Greater London where anti-racist consciousness-raising was part of my employment contract; facilitating groups for White mothers with Black babies and conflict resolution groups for parents in schools to address racist incidents. Things that had been invisible to me became more visible. Working with refugees during the 1990s and early 2000 (Dokter, 1998a) further developed my awareness of race as a factor in 'othering' and oppression. I resonate with DiAngelo when she says, "Most of us would not choose to be socialised into racism and white supremacy. While there is variation in how these messages are conveyed and how much we internalise them, nothing can exempt us from these messages completely" (DiAngelo, 2018, p. 69).

White defensiveness, as part of White fragility, can show a good/bad binary; as racism is bad, being a racist is a moral defect, from which the White response can only be defensive. "This hides the structural nature of racism and makes it difficult for us to see or understand it" (DiAngelo, 2018, p. 73). If we keep thinking of racism as individual hateful acts, we will not acknowledge our actions as racism. When I look at my story, it reflects that I am a product of my socialisation: primary, secondary and racial/ethnic. What does this stop me from seeing?

Racism is so deeply woven into the fabric of our society that I am part of it in both my countries. Like Nisha, I like the image of being on a continuum, a dramatherapy structure I often use. That concept for me acknowledges both the transgenerational elements of racism and the possibility of trying to address it rather than unquestioningly repeating it in action or non-action, as a silent bystander. In exploring my identity as a migrant in different life stages through autobiographical theatre (Dokter, 2021, 2022), I explored the inter-action between choices made by and for me in this process. My father would have been horrified to know that his attitudes towards Black people mirrored those of the Nazis who oppressed him; he lived in hiding to escape forced labour during the war. His love of my mixed-race cousins was in contradic-tion to his racist attitudes towards my imagined partner. How do I co-exist with my contradictions, can I move along the continuum with my clients?

Interculturalism and applied/theatre

We offer this abridged history of interculturalism in theatre and applied the-atre to reflect on the ideas and practices that we have inherited and deploy in dramatherapy, as well as possibilities we may still benefit from exploring fur-ther. In the context of theatre, *interculturalism* refers to "theatrical attempts to bridge cultures through performance, to bring different cultures into pro-ductive dialogue with one another on the stage, in the space between the stage and the audience, and within the audience" (Knowles, 2010, p. 1). This approach assumes that *culture*, "the day to day, lived realities of a peoples in specific spaces and at specific times" is embodied, enacted, and made visible through our ordinary (daily acts) and extraordinary (ritualised and staged events) performative activities (p. 1). The focus here has been on the history of how cultures and cultural forms have been negotiated, incorporated and remixed through performative acts, in an increasingly globalised and multi-cultural context.

Of course, the context of exchange has never been equal and must be understood in relation to the realities of colonisation, appropriation and cul-tural imperialism. Thus, the term *interculturalism* in theatre is a contested term (Chaudhuri, 1991; Chin, 1991) as it has, in western discourse, reified unquestioned, ahistoricised cultural 'discoveries' of non-European symbols, forms and techniques for the purpose of revitalising western aesthetic tradi-tions. Such practices tend to exotify and reinforce rather than disrupt other-ness. Influential examples include Antonin Artaud's essay "On the Balinese Theater" (Savarese & Fowler, 2001) inspired by his encounter with Balinese dance at the Paris Colonial Exposition in 1931 and Bertolt Brecht's encoun-ter with Chinese acting which was central to his understanding of *Verfremdungseffekt* (defamiliarisation or alienation effect). The first use of this term appeared in a 1936 essay entitled "Alienation Effects in Chinese Acting" (Brecht, 1936). Knowles (2010) and Schechner (2002) credit these two theorists and practitioners as the progenitors of interculturalism in the context of theatre, albeit with differing aims. While Brecht was concerned with historical critique and material change, Artaud was invested in a universal aesthetic that could, in his view, transcend culture. Artaud's ideas influenced notable directors like Peter Brook, Ariane Mnouchkine, Robert Lepage and Jerzy Grotowski who have all benefitted from and been critiqued to varying degrees for their decontextualised use of cultural forms in which internationalisms are on display with variable effort to hire actors from groups represented on stage (Barucha, 1993; Innes, 1993; Vaïs, 2019). Jerzy Grotowski used small immersive embodied performances to provide different perspectives for his audiences after the Second World War, a way of facilitating his Polish audience to start facing the atrocities committed on their soil and that of other European countries (Wolford & Schechner, 1997). Brooke emphasised action and was influenced by Artaud's theatre of cruelty, aiming to abolish the separation between the performance and audience space, aiming to shock the audience into revelation, a new perspective. Stanislavski and Brooke influenced the early development of UK dramatherapy, whilst Grotwoski continues to influence with his emphasis on embodiment and ritual.

However, in the context of theatre, the promise of *interculturalism* may continue to fall short of its ideals until those whose lived realities have been marginalised are in control of the funding and spaces necessary to represent their own realities and make decisions about the conditions of exchange. There are increasingly more examples of this happening possibly because of the growing number of platforms and technologies that make such sharing possible. Early examples include Spiderwoman Theatre, an indigenous women's performance group founded in 1976 that privileged indigenous urban performance practices of storytelling and storyweaving as the basis for their creative work (Spiderwoman Theater, n.d.). Another example is Montreal's Teesri Duniya Theatre, a company "dedicated to producing and presenting socially and politically-relevant theatre, promoting interculturalism and creating new forms of theatre based on cultural experiences of visible minorities living in Canada" (Teesri Duniya Theatre, n.d.).

In place of an interculturalism characterised by a binary of "west and the rest" are emerging ecologies of performance practice that critique or reinterpret 'canonical' works (e.g. Nisha's description of *Samsaria* on p. 000) or bypass "white brokerage" altogether (Knowles, 2010, p. 58). Such spaces are what Holledge and Tompkins (2000), in *Women's Intercultural Performance*, call 'new identity spaces'. They disrupt essentialist notions of culture and function as politicised sites in which diasporic identities may be reconstituted, valued and presented to audiences characterised by their hybridity and intersectionality rather than to constituents of the dominant culture alone. A relatively recent example of this has been the use of 'blackout' nights in which productions oriented around the experiences of Black peoples strategically plan on Black-only audiences, in some ways mirroring the freedom to cast the audience that drama therapists employ in performance-oriented drama therapy and therapeutic theatre. Writing about *Slave Play*, written by Jeremy O. Harris, Tran writes,

> On Sept. 18, *Slave Play* set aside all 804 of the seats at Broadway's Golden Theatre for Black theatregoers, and Black theatregoers only. … To have the majority of a Broadway audience consist of people of colour is undoubtedly a rarity (according to the Broadway League, 75 percent of Broadway ticket buyers are white). But to have a house that is only Black is almost certainly unprecedented. … Asked what the performance was like, Harris says it was like being "transported" to "some new place in the future where this was a standard, not a possibility. It felt like we turned the 'hallowed' space of a theatre into just a building – a building with new possibilities and rules."
>
> (2019, n.p.)

In the UK, the recent *Death of England* production, written and directed by Black artists Williams and Dyer, about working-class culture and racism was performed as a monologue from a White perspective in the first production and a Black perspective in the second; a reviewer themed his experience as 'tangled roots' (Benjamin, 2020). Kwei-Amah, playwright and director of the Young Vic theatre, committed himself to a programme of Black work to reopen the theatre in autumn 2020 and emphasised the importance of carrying this forward, to not just be a Black Lives Matter moment:

> We have to create an environment that does not make people feel like a theatre is not a place for them. There were Egyptian mystery plays 2000 years before the Greek dramas we know, so I am not an invader, as I used to feel. … I was welcomed as a foreigner, but there is a flow through to stage culture from African work too.
>
> (Thorpe, 2020, n.p.)

Practices that fall under the banner of *applied theatre* have also responded to intergroup conflict and the need for intercultural dialogue by creating theatre with, for, and about real concerns faced by communities (Prentki & Abraham, 2020). Proponents have emphasised the need to work *in context* to better understand how interactions in a project may reflect larger social dynamics and the value of working across difference without eradicating difference, what Kuftinec (2009) has referred to as turning 'Others' into 'others'. The benefits of theatre in these projects have been conceptually, and at times empirically, linked to the process of collaborating on a shared project and the behind-the-scenes process of negotiating differences (van Erven & Gardner, 2011), the new perspectives that arise from the aesthetic translation of conflict (Kuftinec, 2009; Rowe, 2007; Volkas, 2009), and the value of modelling intercultural dialogue on stage (Thompson et al., 2009). Most recently, scholar-practitioners have explored the potential of play in exploring differences and enabling productive encounters and relationships to form between people with a history of oppression (Leffler, 2022).

Interculturalism in social and anthropological theory

In defining culture, we were drawn to several definitions. From cultural theory, we have drawn on Stuart Hall's description of *culture* as "those patterns of organisation, those characteristic forms of human energy which can be discovered as revealing themselves…within or underlying all social practices" (Hall, 1986, p. 36). There has been a long history in anthropology and sociology of studying individuals who live between two or more cultures (Gough, 1968; Marotta, 2014), resulting in current conceptualisations of multicultural, intercultural and transcultural identities. Marotta argues a close affinity between these concepts as they adopt an anti-essentialist conception of culture that questions whether there is such a thing as a self-sufficient culture separate from others. Critics of the term *multiculturalism* focus on its emphasis on identity politics and accuse it of fuelling communitarianism. This is reflected in the Council of Europe's (COE) contrasting of interculturalism with multiculturalism, which has, according to COE, overemphasised diversity over commonalities, thus contributing to group conflict. Similarly, Vertovec and Wessendorf (2010) provide a critique of multiculturalism when emphasised as a singular, fixed ideology or dogma. They claim that many immigrants, encouraged by multicultural orthodoxy, retreat into their differentness. Bottomley (1997) in her turn critiques such an 'essentialist' approach to cultural identity as it requires "an other who is different, a drawing of boundaries that excludes challenges" (Bottomley, 1997, p. 44). She emphasises the differences within ethnic identity, as well as, for example, gender, sexuality and class. Peréz-Torres (1993) highlights the multiplicities of identities across various positions, subject to constant negotiation "an endless engagement with contradictory positions" (Peréz-Torres, 1993, p. 185).

Transnationalism is the idea that flows of trans-state migrants and their symbolic and material accoutrements as bi- or multidirectional, as well as ongoing. That is, where previous generations of migrants tended toward making a "clean break" with their societies of origin, many contemporary migrants continue to have ongoing ties with the communities from which they migrated. Transnationalism has been defined in anthropology as "the process by which immigrants forge and sustain simultaneous multi-stranded social relations that link together their societies of origin and settlement… many immigrants today build social fields that cross geo-graphic, cultural and political borders" (King, 2005, pp. 2220–2221). The negative side of transculturalism can be the emphasis on assimilation, which overlooks imbalances in power. The contact and subsequent mixing between cultures is not always an equal process. Ortiz (1947) describes transculturalism as a process in which one culture or people 'impose transculturation'; colonialism epitomises this process. Consequently, the process of transculturalism is an ambivalent and dangerous process, especially for subordinate cultures. Transculturalism can also be idealised as having 'supracultural creativity' (Epstein, 2009, p. 330). This can lead to emphasising the importance of distancing for awareness and understanding to become possible. Dramatic distancing is of course one of the core concepts in dramatherapy (Landy, 1986). Dramatherapy in its early years validated its practice by referencing ritual and drama as healing in 'other' cultures (Grainger, 1990; Jennings, 1987).

Joppke (2018) critiques this perspective of interculturalism vs multiculturalism and distinguishes a Canadian vs European version, which yields opposite visions of liberal cosmopolitan vs parochial segregationist. Interculturalism, although heavily contested, has been firmly institutionalised in Europe, as the COE report reflects, including the emphasis on intercultural professional competencies. The stress on communication and dialogue is characteristic of interculturalism, but it has been critiqued for the multiplication of identities and ignoring that some identities are more painful and disadvantaging than others (Modood, 2016).

The depiction of the intercultural comes more from hermeneutics and philosophy (Marotta, 2009) perceiving the world through multiple perspectives and a lens of double belonging (Ariarajah, 2005). To be intercultural is to resist universalising practices (Mall, 1998), whilst problematising an identity model where only insiders can comprehend the insiders' worldview (Mall, 2000). In Bernstein's intercultural imagination (1991), interculturalism becomes a foundation for dialogue across differences in which we are sensitive to the sameness of others with ourselves and the radical alterity that resists the reduction of the other to the same, whilst maintaining difference and boundaries between self and other. Interculturality derives from the understanding that cultures thrive only in contact with other cultures, not in isolation (COE, 2016). Cultural differences refer to variations in attitudes, values and perceptual constructs that result from different cultural experiences (Zane et al., 2004). The COE contrasts interculturalism with assimilationist approaches, which seek to obscure and ultimately eradicate diversity.

Interculturalism in relation to intersectionality and critical race theory

Intersectionality is a concept that was put forward by Crenshaw (1988), an African American civil rights advocate and critical race theorist who deployed the term as a recapitulation of foundational ideas in Black feminism about how forms of oppression, such as classism, sexism, and racism, interlock and rely on one another to persist (Hill-Collins, 2000). Specifically, she observed that Black women were subjugated to racism and sexism under the law. She drew on an employment lawsuit brought against General Motors St Louis by a group of Black women in order to demonstrate that the plaintiffs lost because the company was able to show that it was not racist (because it hired Black men) or sexist (because it hired women). Under the rigid categories of the Civil Rights Act of 1964, the court could not examine a combined claim of race and sex discrimination, and so could not offer a remedy specifically for Black women. In her own words, Crenshaw describes how intersectionality grew out of trying to conceptualise the way the law responded to issues where both race and gender discrimination were involved.

> What happened was like an accident, a collision. Intersectionality simply came from the idea that if you're standing in the path of multiple forms of exclusion, you are likely to get hit by both.
>
> (Crenshaw, 2004, p. 2)

The goal of this argument was to enable an analysis of lived experience from an intersectional rather than isolated perspective without losing sight of the fact that groups are not homogeneous and an individual's experience within them may change over time and in different contexts (McCall, 2005; Young, 2000). An intersectional interculturalism helps us and those we work with to think about what it means to belong to particular social groups especially those unique groups that exist at marginalised points of intersection while also examining relationships to other groups (Sajnani, 2013). Intersectionality also presents a challenge to what has been referred to as the 'race to innocence' (Fellows & Razack, 1998) or the 'oppression Olympics' (Walby et al., 2012,) where the goal becomes about whose subordination is the worst. Proponents of intersectionality encourage alliances between and within groups in order to document and consider how everyday encounters, resource-allocation and decision-making power may force social groups, such as social workers and creative arts therapists, full-time and part-time faculty in a university, or White women and women of colour, for example, to compete for places of respectability and inclusion in patriarchal society.

An intersectional analysis has also been instrumental in organised efforts to advance equity that take into account the complexity of human experience (Thornton-Dill & Zambrana, 2009). For example, it has been actively used in arguments for affirmative action in job training, education, hiring, and promotion (Steinbugler et al., 2006), to demonstrate the specificity of intercultural queer experience (Chan & Erby, 2018), and in efforts to illuminate how racism, sexism and ableism intertwine to produce unique forms of inequity and resistance in the lives of families of colour who have children with disabilities (Ben-Moshe & Magaña, 2014; Frederick & Shifrer, 2019).

Intersectionality is used as an approach to analyse multifaceted power structures and processes that produce and sustain unequal health outcomes (Kapilashrami & Hankivsky, 2018). Intersectionality moves beyond individual factors such as biology, socio-economic status, sex, gender and race. It focuses on the relationships and interactions between those factors and across multiple levels of society to determine how health is shaped across population groups and geographical contexts. The slogan 'we are all in this together', used often in the Covid-19 context during which this book was written, contrasts with existing social inequalities and systemic exclusion. More recently, the awareness that all may be in the same storm, but not the same boat has surfaced control issues and the 'us and them' dynamics of scapegoating. Victim blaming is one way of defending against the guilt of privilege and White fragility (DiAngelo, 2018). In both the UK and US, it is recognised that people of colour are at highest risk of dying from Covid-19, even after adjusting for deprivation and health (Razaq et al., 2020). Splits by gender and class, the greater impact on women of domestic violence, the closure of schools and childcare. Job loss is worse for young adults, the lower educated and those in the gig economy. The impact of the crisis on the homeless, poor and dispossessed; no, we are definitely not in the same boat. We hear echoes of Primo Levi's fear of categorisation, that a person is judged for the group they accidentally belong to rather than who they are, where boxes become deadly (Goldstein, 2015).

When we encounter 'differences', we are compelled to examine how our perspectives are informed by particular experiences and situated social locations (Sorrells, 2015). This requires self-reflexivity to understand how we have become who we are. Both intersectionality and positionality play a role: intersectionality illustrates the multiplicity of social forces that inform our experiences and identities, whilst positionality points to the fact that our identities are always relationally shaped within hierarchies of power.

Interculturalism in psychological therapy

Intercultural psychotherapy is a term used in the UK context (Kareem & Littlewood, 1992) to indicate the interactive element in cultural dynamics between the different parties involved in therapy. Kareem established the Nafsiyat Intercultural Therapy Centre in 1983 because diverse religious, cultural and ethnic communities in London at that time were struggling to gain access to psychotherapy, whilst traditional psychotherapy and counselling were not adequately able to respond to the needs of diverse communities.

The profession of dramatherapy offers evidence of interculturalism in our field as we draw on a broad range of psychological and psychotherapeutic theories (Jones, 2021; Karkou & Sanderson, 2006). However, as with theatre, psychological theories predicated on male, White, upper-middle-class perspectives prevail also in our field. Karkou and Sanderson (2006) interviewed UK arts therapists and identified the theoretical influences for dramatherapy as theatre based, humanistic, Jungian, developmental and psychodynamic. Jones (2007) identifies the main psychological influences across the arts therapies as cognitive behavioural, humanistic and psychodynamic. In the second edition of his book (2021), he looks at the dialogues between arts therapies and analytic psychotherapy, developmental approaches and mindfulness. He emphasises the arts therapies dialogue with different therapeutic paradigms, but that the arts communicate the therapeutic relationship and are an indicator of change. The client's needs are the main influence on the approach chosen, leading to a great variety of approaches. Milioni (2001), a drama-therapist, critiques the focus on particular paradigms, emphasising that the meaning for the client is more important than the theory-prescribed imposition of meaning. Clients also voiced their critique of theory-driven meaning in other research (Dokter, 2010). In an intercultural context, this imperative is even greater. The challenge pushes the traditional knowledge cultures of arts therapies (Talwar, 2016, p. 118) in "ways that are committed to diversity and inclusion." Jones (2021) raises that the emphasis on the arts therapist as artist and that of the client as not needing prior experience of the art form sets the scene for potential inequality, but also raises the complexity of the therapists' role in providing access to the arts and the creative potential of the client. Skaife (2000) considers issues of acculturation and the potential power of the therapist in relation to the clients' work. In many societies, the relationship clients have with art forms is different from their relationship with the spoken word. The engagement between client, therapist and art form connects to the social and political dimensions of the client's experiences and life (Jones, 2021). Offering opportunities for expression and creativity may be different from providing opportunities to redress political imbalance in access to the arts, according to Jones, but he also follows this with "whilst this may be an important element within arts therapists' practice" (Jones, 2021, p. 273). The power aspect of the 'teacher-pupil' aspect of the therapeutic relationship where the therapist becomes the expert and the client the novice may be worked with differently according to the psychological orientation: in cognitive behavioural practice, this aspect might be minimised through the focus on the client finding their own means of expression, whilst in the psychodynamic orientation, this aspect of the relationship would be made visible and explored.

The psychodynamic psychotherapeutic perspective has been critiqued as grounded in the Euro-American worldview, which focuses on values such as individual autonomy, the scientific method and the protestant work ethic (D'Ardenne & Mahtani, 1999; Sue, 1998). Tuckwell (2002) summarises its orientational strengths as offering a framework for examining complex dynamics related to the client's inner world, including racial and cultural beliefs about self and others in interracial mixed interactions. Its weakness is that it does not recognise racial/cultural factors in psychological functioning, uses intrapsychic constructs which are antithetical to many non-western cultures and takes no account of sociopolitical issues. The two other main psychotherapeutic theoretical frameworks used by dramatherapists (Jones, 2005, 2021; Karkou & Sanderson, 2006) are the humanistic and integrative ones. Humanistic strength is a therapeutic relationship in which the conditions enable the clients to change and grow, whilst the integrative one offers a broad, diverse approach based on a range of theories and models combined to best meet the needs of the clients. Their weaknesses are shared with the psychodynamic orientation as focussing on a western philosophy of individual autonomy and fulfilment, taking no account of sociopolitical issues, or considering them only in an individual context. Both humanistic and psycho-dynamic approaches do not tend to consider racial/cultural factors in individual functioning and identity. Within the different orientations, exceptions can be found such as Dalal (2002) in the psychodynamic group analytic, whilst more recent literature has also expanded on racial/cultural factors and collective identity as part of psychological functioning and the need for multicultural therapeutic competencies. Issues of power in the theoretical frameworks tend to be underemphasised in the older literature. Ryde (2009) notes, "Maybe one of the most important aspects to acknowledge when working across cultures as a white professional is the power in the room – and how it is distributed" (p. 44). She cites Jacobs (2000) and Lago (2006) in emphasising the importance of acknowledging and identifying issues of power and culture.

Conclusion

An intercultural lens asks us to examine when, why, where, how and to whom culture, always understood in relation to power and equity, matters in how we conceive of therapy, the role of the therapist and the therapeutic process. What is the subjectivity of the therapist, what is the intersubjectivity between client and therapist, teacher and pupil, supervisor and supervisee, reader and author? Together we co-produce an intersubjective intercultural space, some of it consciously, and some of it unconsciously (Thomas, 2019; Tuckwell, 2002).

We acknowledge that we have been trained and socialised into a 'sociology of dominance' (DiAngelo, 2018, p. 113). What was present in dramatherapy training and what was missing, both in the training received and those we devised and delivered? Where did we collude with the silence, and where did we allow ourselves to be silenced? Dramatherapy, while it has its roots in ancient embodied, enacted practices, came to be known in the past century through a predominantly White, Eurocentric lens. Who and what is silenced in dramatherapy, and can this analysis make something visible that often stays invisible or does not have a voice? How might we co-create partnerships with those we work with towards disrupting old binaries of the carer and cared for? These are some of the questions that lay at the heart of this book's exploration.

Chapter 3

Developing intercultural good practice and cultural response/ability guidelines for dramatherapists in North America and the United Kingdom

One day, David (16yrs) wanted his hair woven by Naomi, a classmate, who worked in a hairdressers at the weekends. David struggled with literacy and had already served a sentence for a stabbing. He'd come occasionally for sessions before and enjoyed destroying things that could safely be destroyed [such as] cardboard boxes that could be...destroyed and soft toys that could be disembowelled. They announced they would be coming to my room (dramatherapy session room) that day. We agreed on a time. This was going to be real, not play hairdressing. Naomi had all her combs and brushes in her bag. Afro-Caribbean hairdressing can take hours and hairdressers are often culturally important meeting places with extended opening times and a relaxed, family-friendly atmosphere. They arrived, arranged cushions and chairs to create a comfortable, functional hairdressing corner and gave me permission to sit nearby. Naomi declared the group an all-black one. I'm white, Welsh. Naomi is from Sierra Leone and David is British with family from Jamaica.

They chatted as they might in the hairdressers. David asked for a mirror in which he gazed in fascination throughout the session. My offers of roles and scenarios were rejected. ... I offered to be someone else in the hairdresser (another customer, hairdresser, neighbour). This was rejected. They wanted a sort of net-curtain, a separation and I had the feeling that if I changed my role Naomi would have struggled even more with my presence. She was trying to work me out as myself, as a therapist. She wanted me to stay put. She made it clear they [other students] would not be allowed that session. ... I was part of the group but Naomi feared that I would align myself with the white students. She was banning them, because she had chosen who would attend. ... I did feel privileged that I was allowed in this black group. My skin colour was permitted. She had quite a negative view of white people and I had been allowed in. They seemed to want me to be someone who attended to their needs and who understood that I was to stop talking if I started "chatting shit." ... They started to talk, with minimal prompting, about recent experiences. [David] was looking at his face and really enjoying what she was doing. ... I think I asked about school and their experiences at school. From that they discussed being told they were naughty and bad from the word go. I probably asked if they remembered being small. David had clearly been shaken by

DOI: 10.4324/9780429431593-4

the violence he'd encountered in prison and he showed me how many feet away from a murderer he'd slept. He'd been told he was a thug but saw a "good" face in the mirror. Naomi talked despairingly about her homelife and confusing relationship with her mother. At this point she showed me a sharp hair instrument and said I would feel it if I stepped out of line. She said she wished her skin were lighter, she wished she was not black. We talked about racism, including the differences in our experiences because our skin is either white or black.

Dramatherapist, UK

This chapter describes the history leading up to the articulation of cultural response/ability guidelines in the North American Drama Therapy Association (Sajnani et al., 2016) and intercultural good practice guidelines in the British Association of Dramatherapists (Bilodeau et al., 2017). The impetus for these guidelines arose out of experiences like the one described in the account above which offers us an example of how the therapist and client(s) orient and re-orient themselves to each other across lines of constantly shifting visible, invisible, imagined, projected, symbolised and enacted differences in identity and power. This particular vignette is discussed in greater detail in Chapter 4 on the impact of race in dramatherapy. However, we included it here because it highlights the value of working out how we, as professionals in a caring profession, deepen our knowledge about and attend to cultural differences and the dynamics of inclusion and exclusion that are present within our own community and in the lives of the people in our care. We then take a look at points of comparison between these guidelines, their reception within our professional community and what has emerged since.

Developing guidelines in support of intercultural good practice

The development of guidelines of intercultural good practice must be understood in relation to the social and political context from which they arise. The guidelines endorsed by the North American Drama Therapy Association (NADTA) and the British Association of Dramatherapists (BADth) arose in a context of significant social struggle and transformation. In the past five years, constituents of both organisations have contended with debates concerning immigration, citizenship, marriage equality, transgender rights, racial justice and religious freedoms amongst other intersecting issues such as healthcare, labour rights and climate change. Many of these issues were at the fore of debates surrounding 'Brexit', the decision to withdraw the UK from the European Union. Similar issues came into focus during Donald Trump's presidency in the US. The political leanings of therapists are not often discussed in the context of training, supervision, or professional development despite the fact that they may influence, insofar as such leanings reflect moral and ethical perspectives, the therapeutic process (Sajnani, 2016b). Indeed, in our survey of dramatherapists and clients, 64% indicated that their political beliefs influence their experience of dramatherapy from their choice of therapist to how and whether certain topics are brought up and worked with in therapy. As helping professionals, we attend to this reality by adopting a code of ethics which constitutes normative statements that provide guidance on values, issues and choices that a drama therapist may encounter in their professional work. The development of guidelines reflects a further commitment to offer guidance concerning issues that people tend to have very strong feelings about and about which we may not always agree. The American Psychological Association offers useful guidance in differentiating between guidelines and standards such as those found in a code of ethics:

> *Guidelines* differ from *standards*. *Standards* are mandatory and, thus, may be accompanied by an enforcement mechanism; *guidelines* are not mandatory, definitive, or exhaustive. *Guidelines* are aspirational in intent. They aim to facilitate the continued systematic development of the profession and to promote a high level of professional practice.
>
> (APA, 2015)

We acknowledge that this chapter is limited in scope, as we are only offering a comparison of guidelines from two major dramatherapy associations with which we have been involved. At the time of writing, efforts are underway to compare ethical codes and similar guidelines across professional associations affiliated with the World Alliance of Dramatherapy.

Historical development of cultural response/ability guidelines in North America

The evolution of the NADTA's commitment to cultural humility, equality, diversity and inclusion has been documented (NADTA, 2019) with selections described here as they pertain to the development of what became referred to as 'cultural response/ability guidelines' (Sajnani, et al., 2016). In 1999, in an effort to create a culture of welcome prompted by a new Canadian training programme in Montreal, a Canadian representative was established on a then all-American board of what was the National Association of Drama Therapy (NADT). This change, amongst others, illuminated the need for focused attention on diversity. The first informal diversity committee was convened by Sherry Diamond and Carlos Rodriguez-Perez at the annual conference in 2000. The passing of Raymond Jacobs, a drama therapist who was a strong advocate for HIV/AIDS at a time when neither the association nor the US was responsive to the crisis, led then NADT president Alice Forrestor to create a memorial diversity award in his name.

In 2002, the NADTA convened its first conference focused solely on the theme of diversity in Albuquerque, New Mexico. Armand Volkas was invited to give the keynote address where he presented on the subject of intolerance and oppression. During this conference, attendees participated in affinity groups based on identity and social groups for the first time, and Roslyn Taylor O'Neale, a nationally recognised diversity trainer, was brought in to give a conference-wide training assisted by Nisha Sajnani and Zeneida Disla. In 2003, under the leadership of then president Sherry Diamond, the board conducted an analysis of the strengths and weaknesses of the organisation, which revealed the need for an international caucus for international members who had voiced feeling like outsiders and the establishment of a formal diversity committee (now referred to as the Cultural Humility, Equality, and Diversity Committee) chaired by Nisha Sajnani. In 2007, this committee led the first all-conference diversity forum focused on the influence of intersecting identities (e.g. race, sexual orientation, gender, age, language, geography, national identity, dis/ability) in dramatherapy. Since then, similar forums have been held at every annual conference and throughout the year using online meeting platforms.

In 2009, the NADTA board, led by President Kate Hurd, engaged in a consultation about increasing accessibility to conferences for those who are hearing impaired. In 2011, the membership voted in favour of a change in name from the National Association for Drama Therapy to the NADTA to better include Canadian members. This prompted discussion about the languages used within the organisation and the relationship of the NADTA to Mexico and other countries to the South. In 2012, the annual membership survey was revised per the recommendations of then diversity co-chairs Daniela Bustamente and Amber Smith to include questions pertaining to the diversity of the membership. In 2013, the NADTA hosted its first bilingual (English and French) conference in Montreal. The board approved policy concerning accessibility and approved changes to the code of ethics concerning cultural competency and gender-neutral language. The NADTA president Nisha Sajnani proposed the creation of a permanent diversity chair and research chair to ensure sustained focus in these areas and Michelle J. Buckle was appointed as the first diversity chair.

In 2014, Michelle contacted Ditty Dokter to invite collaboration between the NADTA and BADth to jointly develop intercultural good practice guidelines. The BADth Equality and Diversity (E&D) committee was interested in collaboration, so an exchange began in which the previous and next NADTA diversity chairs participated, whilst Sarah Bilodeau, Mandy Carr and Dokter participated from the BADth side.

In 2014, Nisha Sajnani, Jessica Bleuer, Patrick Tomczyk and Jami Osborne co-led a diversity forum using legislative theatre practices (Sajnani et al., 2021) to elicit and explore stories of when drama therapists felt challenged in their capacities to navigate issues related to identity, inclusion and equity. These examples were then grouped into focus areas such as self-awareness, practice, supervision, teaching, advocacy and organisational responsibilities. This group compared these findings with other guidelines for responsible practice developed by allied practitioners in Canada and the US from fields such as counselling, psychology, social work, music and art therapy (AATA, 2011; AMCD, 1996; APA, 2020; CAMT, 1999; CSJ, 2011) and drafted language for the NADTA guidelines. Several suggestions were incorporated before the guidelines were finally ratified by the board of the NADTA on June 18, 2015 (Sajnani et al., 2016).

In the autumn of 2015, the NADTA held its second diversity-focused conference. At this conference, Nisha Sajnani, in collaboration with then diversity chair Jessica Bleuer, engaged the membership in a process of reviewing and discussing the newly ratified guidelines to learn about which areas resonated with them and which required further development. The diversity committee offered continuing professional development (CPD) in the years that followed to focus on various aspects of identity, culture and issues relating to diversity, equity and inclusion.

Historical development of intercultural good practice guidelines in the UK

Historically, dramatherapy training in the UK recruited students both nationally and internationally. As they were part-time, day-release trainings, students outside the EU had difficulty obtaining student visas, so most non-UK students tended to be from Europe. Trainers might be from migrant backgrounds (Dokter, 1998a; Gersie, 1997a), whilst UK trainers also travelled abroad to offer dramatherapy training (see Chapter 13 for more discussion on training). In the 1980s, an Erasmus exchange programme at the University of Hertfordshire offered time-limited training in dramatherapy and art therapy to students from Mediterranean countries in particular. A follow-up study aimed, through interviews, to ascertain the difficulties and possibilities of this training to be applied in their country of origin (Dokter, 1993). In the early 1990s, the war in the ex-Yugoslavian countries meant that European dramatherapists found themselves working with refugees from those countries and wished to exchange lessons they had learned from working interculturally. Bringing together these therapists as authors culminated in an edited publication and a conference where the book was launched (Dokter, 1998a), whilst the conference proceedings were published in 2000 (Dokter, 2000b). Dramatherapy developments in this field occurred in parallel with developments in the other arts therapies, occasionally through collaboration. The book on arts therapists, refugees and migrants (Dokter, 1998a) was edited in parallel to a book published about art therapy, race and culture (Campbell et al., 1999), and exchanges about their proposed content facilitated complementarity.

In 2006, the British Association of Dramatherapists rekindled their E&D Committee, with Mandy Carr as chair. In 2009, Dokter facilitated a workshop at a BADth conference on intercultural practice related to her doctoral research in progress (Dokter, 2000b). Carr took part in the workshop. A workshop structure using a parachute to explore commonalities and differences in participant backgrounds found her excluded from the parachute 'igloo' created by the group. This re-enacted previous painful experiences of outsider identity. In a debriefing post-workshop, Carr invited Dokter to join the new E&D committee to work on intercultural practice developments. A special issue of the *Dramatherapy* journal, focused on the impact of cultural identity in dramatherapy, was guest edited by Dokter and published in autumn 2009 (Dokter, 2009).

In 2012, the annual BADth conference focused on bridging cultures: sensitivities, competencies and opportunities in working across cultures. A special London-based CPD day focused on the cultural background of the dramatherapist and its impact on the therapeutic relationship. Participants outlined some of the benefits as gaining insight into how dramatherapists work with cultural issues, a deeper understanding of the dynamic of working with an interpreter, the importance of looking more deeply into English culture and the support and camaraderie of the group which itself fostered a sense of belonging. All felt that they would like more CPD days on these issues, particularly practical ways of dealing with controversial cultural issues (Carr & Andersen-Warren, 2012).

Carr and Dokter co-facilitated a workshop at the BADth 'Bridging Cultures' national conference to share intercultural practice experiences and start formulating good practice based on those experiences. Post-it notes towards good cultural practice were produced by the workshop participants, including more questions than answers, but all provided attention points for future development. In collaboration with the BADth E&D committee, a document was formulated and published on the BADth website. It reflected dramatherapist preoccupations and questions when working interculturally, such as which dramatherapy structures to use to explore identity and how to work with communication diversity, including different languages; provide relational safety and containment in the therapeutic relationship; provide client choices about therapists; explore differences in expectations between therapist and client; facilitate joint cultural learning between therapist and client, including around issues of shame, making mistakes and tolerating not knowing. Other concerns were raised regarding when the therapist should self-disclose about their own background and how to work with the fact that the therapist systemically is part of oppressive systems.

The Equality Act of 2010, with its nine protected characteristics, had accelerated the impetus for practical action, supported by the law. Particularly as the 2009 survey of BADth members' backgrounds had highlighted a disproportionately low number of practitioners from ethnic minorities. Haydn Ford, an active member of BADth for many years, complained to the then chair of BADth, John Hazlett Dickinson, about the need for prioritisation about the lack of visibility of ethnic minority dramatherapists. This became a springboard for the organisation to forefront E&D, starting with a strategic orientation day entitled "Is There a Cultural

Elephant in the Room?" Attendance by members from diverse backgrounds and senior members of the BADth executive was significantly higher than usual on such a day. A five-year plan was devised and further developed by the E & D committee, which prioritised regular liaison between the BADth executive committee and the E & D members, as well as collaboration with NADTA.

Further CPD events took place to elaborate on and explore the issues outlined in the next few years. In 2014, following an invitation from Michelle Buckle, then diversity chair for the NADT, both the BADth E & D and the NADTA diversity committee undertook a consultation process. Bilodeau compiled for BADth a 'compare and contrast' document drawing in the UK on codes of ethics (ADMP, 2013; BAAT, 2014; BACP, 2013; HCPC, 2013; UKCP, 2009) and in the US (AATA, 2011; AMCD, 1996; AMTA, 2013; APA, 2003, 2020; NADTA, 2013). Headings under which the different guidelines were compared and contrasted were ethics, therapist competencies, therapeutic relationship, consent, therapist bias and assumptions, sensitivity to different value systems, religion, biculturalism and language. The BADth intercultural good practice guidelines were launched in 2016 (Bilodeau et al., 2017).

Inspired by the NADTA guidelines launch, BADth agreed to a 90-minute creative consultation session with all delegates at the 2016 annual conference. The allocation of a specific slot solely for a prioritised area of practice was new and may have influenced a slightly higher representation of therapists from diverse backgrounds on the 2019 executive committee, the major decision-making engine of the organisation.

Points of comparison

There are several points of similarity and variation between the NADTA and BADth guidelines which will be presented here. The full guidelines can be found on www.badth.org and www.nadta.org and consist of six NADTA guidelines and five BADth guidelines.

NADTA

Guideline one: Commitment to cultural awareness and knowledge of self and others

Guideline two: Commitment to cultural response/ability in dramatherapy practice

Guideline three: Commitment to cultural response/ability in dramatherapy training

Guideline four: Commitment to cultural response/ability in dramatherapy supervision

Guideline five: Commitment to cultural response/ability in dramatherapy research

Guideline six: Commitment to cultural response/ability in advocacy and organisational change

BADth

Guideline one: Cultural awareness and knowledge of self and others

Guideline two: Dramatherapy practice and supervision

Guideline three: Dramatherapy training and continuing professional development

Guideline four: Research

Guideline five: Advocacy, professional relationships and systemic change

Similarities

Both the NADTA and BADth indicate that the published guidelines of each association do not replace their respective code of ethics but should be viewed as complementing relevant aspects of the code by which dramatherapists practice. The relevant portions of these codes are as follows:

> A drama therapist does not engage in unfair discrimination based on, but not limited to, age, gender, identity, race, ethnicity, culture, national origin, religion, sexual orientation, disability, socioeconomic status, physical appearance or attributes, or any basis proscribed by law.
>
> NADTA Code of Ethics, Article 5a

> Dramatherapists should monitor their practice to ensure that they are not making discriminatory decisions based upon a client's race, culture, nationality, gender, marital status, physical or mental ability, physical appearance, religion, political opinions or sexual orientation.
>
> BADth Code of Practice (BADth)

Both the NADTA and BADth use terms like *recommend* and *commit* to stress that the guidelines aim to *encourage* all dramatherapists to strive towards greater accountability in a dynamic social and political environment in which ideas about equity and inclusion are constantly being negotiated with real, material consequences.

Both sets of guidelines adopt a dynamic definition of culture. BADth, in an addendum about cultural competency and the challenge of defining culture, emphasises that culture is dynamic "always changing and shifting and in the process of being created" (Krause, 1998, p. 174). The NADTA defines culture as a dynamic worldview of learned and transmitted beliefs, values, norms and social institutions, including psychological processes (Fiske et al., 1998). Each set of guidelines, albeit with different language, includes an acknowledgement that "we see the world and each other through our own cultural filters" (Dokter, 1998b, p. 147). However, they strive to go beyond acceptance of our multiplicity and cultural relativity towards a practice of contextualising differences.

> As drama therapists, we are sensitive to the power and influence of stories, roles, and repeating patterns in our lives and in the lives of those with whom we work. These guidelines are intended to encourage drama therapists to remain responsive to the presence and impact of implicit and explicit bias in the contexts in which we practice towards avoiding "unfair discrimination" *and* to encourage us to contribute to cultivating relationships and environments in which all people are treated with dignity.
>
> (Sajnani et al., 2016, p. 142)

> Dramatherapists aim to develop their understanding and skills to address cultural differences with regard to touch, communication styles and the emphasis on a playful approach, as well as openness and empathy towards a multiplicity of narratives and meaning. This may mean incorporating systemic thinking and reflection on the impact of external systems (such as environment, religion, unconscious political / historic and current contexts). The practice of dramatherapy acknowledges and respects diversity.
>
> (Bilodeau et al., 2017, p. 3)

With this in mind, both documents adopted the Arredondo et al. (1996) definition of cultural competency which encourages practitioners to deepen self-awareness, knowledge, and skills that increase the ability to notice and work with implicit biases as well as to serve diverse individuals (Arredondo et al., 1996). The NADTA connects cultural competency to the concept of *cultural humility*, which refers to "a lifelong process of self-reflection, self-critique, continual assessment of power imbalances, and the development of mutually respectful relationships and partnerships" (Tervalon & Murray-Garcia as cited in Gallardo, 2014). BADth's guidelines encourage a similar stance and encourage drama therapists "to be open to the variety of human experience and culture, to challenge their own assumptions and views when necessary, and to strive towards a non racist and non discriminatory identity" (Bilodeau et al., 2017, p. 3).

The NADTA encourages their members to demonstrate their respect for the clients' Indigenous, religious and/or spiritual beliefs and values, including attributions, symbolic traditions and preferred methods of treatment because they may affect worldview, psychosocial functioning, expressions of distress and perspectives on touch, roleplay and other dramatherapy activities. BADth encourages its members to recognise that help-seeking behaviours,

healing practices, communication patterns, preferred methods of treatment, expression/manifestation of distress/pain, perspectives on touch and
dramatherapy activities may be influenced by culture, and therapists need to
be flexible to adapt to client needs. The formulations may differ, but make the
same point of needing to be responsive, flexible and adaptive to the client's
historical context, worldview, aesthetic preferences and presenting needs.

Variations across the Atlantic

Perhaps the most obvious difference is that the NADTA guidelines are
framed as *cultural response/ability guidelines*, whereas the BADth guidelines
are framed as *intercultural good practice guidelines*. An excerpt of the reason-
ing for each is presented with the full text available in the preamble (NADTA)
or addendum (BADth) of each document:

> The concept of cultural response/ability refers to responsive and respon-
> sible training, research, practice, supervision, advocacy and organisa-
> tional change in drama therapy.
>
> (NADTA)

> Intercultural psychotherapy is a term used in the UK context (Kareem &
> Littlewood, 1992) to indicate the interactive element in cultural dynam-
> ics between the different parties involved in therapy.
>
> (BADth)

The NADTA guidelines are in narrative form, whilst the BADth guidelines
have numbered points to consider. Both associations formulate that they
encourage and advise their members. However, the NADTA guidelines oscil-
late between normative and aspirational statements. The normative statements speak to what dramatherapists do rather than what they ought to do
or are encouraged to do and are, for the most part, statements that reinforce
article 5a of the code of ethics.

The first guideline concerning self-awareness reflects similar encourage-
ments to examine the impact of bias, to need to reflect on our own background, to seek out knowledge to understand cultural oppression, to assess
its impact or benefit and to consider personal, organisational and other contexts that may impact on the asymmetry in the therapeutic relationship.
BADth adds two points which include awareness of specific cultural resources
to support the client and the need for the therapist to familiarise themselves
with the arts forms, imagery, festivals (UNESCO 'intangible cultural heritage') of the client's culture and to explore the meanings this may hold for the
client in a secular and non-secular context. NADTA elaborates on these two
points in its second guideline.

Guideline two varies in the NADTA emphasis on cultural response/ability
in dramatherapy practice, whilst BADth combines guidelines two and four

(dramatherapy practice and supervision) and omits the emphasis on cultural responsibility. The NADTA stresses early in its second guideline that it is important for dramatherapists to avoid cultural appropriation, defined as

> a dominant group's use of the signs and symbols of people who have been systematically oppressed for personal gain in status or otherwise [in contrast to] cultural exchange, which is the mutual or permitted sharing of symbols and practices between groups.
>
> (Sajnani et al., 2016, pp. 144–145)

Cultural appropriation is mentioned in guideline 2.4 as one of many oppressive options: "Therapists also need to be responsive to cultural experiences and biases that may affect a client, i.e. appropriation, acculturation, discrimination, racism, oppression, heterosexism, classism, ageism and transgenerational trauma" (Bilodeau et al., 2017, p. 4).

One element highlighted in NADTA which is not mentioned in BADth is the potential bias in assessment and evaluation instruments, which require interpretation of findings in the light of the client's cultural and linguistic characteristics. Guideline two concludes in the NADTA with dramatherapists needing to reflect on the limits of their competencies. In the BADth guidelines, the role of supervision is highlighted with differentiated roles for the supervisor and the supervisee.

The third guideline considers training, both CPD and the responsibilities of trainers and students. In the UK, BADth is able to refer to the Health and Care Professions Council standards of proficiency (HCPC, 2013), which stress the need for dramatherapists to understand the cultural background of health and the influence on the therapeutic relationship arising from variations in culture, assessment of intercultural relations, cultural differences in understanding symbol and metaphor and the ability to address dynamics that may result from cultural differences. The NADTA stresses the importance of being educated about relevant identity development models, social discriminatory practices, global sociopolitical and intergenerational issues affecting clients. BADth echoes this when outlining the responsibilities of trainers and students whilst also encouraging work with clients from different backgrounds than their own. Knowing one's limitations is stressed by BADth at the end of the training guidelines.

NADTA and BADth encourage dramatherapy educators to provide critical perspectives, to identify privileged world views and to refer students to resources that aid their understanding of cultural considerations. BADth stresses that educators need to aim to attract and retain students and staff members from diverse backgrounds – an issue that may also need to be addressed in guideline five (BADth) and guideline six (NADTA). The NADTA stresses the importance of educators practising cultural humility.

NADTA supervision guidelines encourage supervisors to reflect on sources of comfort and discomfort with cultural differences and commonalities, as well as practising cultural humility and referring supervisees to further resources. BADth phrases the same concerns slightly differently and places the exploration both between the supervisor and the supervisee and the supervisee and the client.

The research guidelines are very similar between the NADTA and BADth. They elaborate on cultural issues around consent and the need to include excluded voices in research, as well as the need to be familiar with relevant research pertaining to the impact of discrimination on health and culturally relevant practices.

The final guideline on advocacy and organisational change (NADTA)/ advocacy, professional relationships and systemic change (BADth) throws up some interesting variations. The NADTA guideline encourages dramatherapists to contribute their knowledge and skills to their professional association, as well as involve themselves in acts of solidarity within their communities. BADth advises dramatherapists to be aware of systemic factors, including institutional barriers, sociopolitical and global discriminatory systems, similar to those stressed by the NADTA in earlier practice and education guidelines. BADth also encourages its members to be active in transforming their professional association but also to be agents of change in their professional relationships, employing organisations and related areas.

Membership involvement and response to the guidelines

When the guidelines were launched at an all-conference event at the NADTA conference in 2015, the guidelines were printed on large paper and given to small groups. Members reflected on the relevance of the guidelines in their own contexts and stressed feeling a mixture of gratitude for their articulation, overwhelmed by the need to "get it right," and a desire to anchor the guidelines in vignettes that could reflect the need behind each guideline.

Vignettes were made available at the BADth guideline launch workshop in 2016. Members asked for the guidelines to lean more towards encouragement and the possibility of learning from 'getting it wrong', whilst also committing to non-discriminatory practice. The earlier stage of draft formulation was in the form of many questions; the members were aware of how much there is to learn in this field and wanted to stress this. The BADth E&D committee had developed written scenarios for paired semi-structured improvisations on stage with actors drawn from the BADth and NADTA diversity committees who were present. These are provided in the following sections to facilitate further exploration.

Scenario guideline 1 cultural awareness and knowledge of self and others

A comfortably off dramatherapist, born and living in central London very close to a tube station, is working with an international trainee who has been given a small grant to study by her home country, Taiwan, which is experiencing a lot of political tension. The trainee lives in zone 6, outer London, and is periodically late, sometimes missing whole sessions because of transport issues, including cancelled and delayed trains. Epilepsy prevents the trainee from driving, and cabs are unaffordable. The dramatherapist feels very frustrated about this, wonders if the client takes the therapy seriously and brings up the issue in the session.

Dramatherapy consulting room

DRAMATHERAPIST: "I wonder if it may be useful to think about the number of sessions you're missing..."
TRAINEE: ...

Scenario guideline 2 dramatherapy practice and supervision

A dramatherapist has a history of mental health problems and is becoming increasingly depressed. They have just started to work with a young client from Afghanistan who is seeking asylum and does not know the location of her parents. The clinical supervisor is concerned about the dramatherapist's emotional well-being and whether their depression could be negatively impacting on the clients. The dramatherapist's sessions have been fruitful and supportive of their clients. However, the dramatherapist is now apprehensive about exploring client issues and particular about what it brings up for them personally, fearing that the supervisor may view them as unfit to practise.

Supervisor's consulting room

DRAMATHERAPIST: My client hasn't seen her mother for over a year. She has not really expressed her feelings about this.
SUPERVISOR:

Scenario guideline 3 dramatherapy training and continuing professional development

A dramatherapy student from a mining (now unemployed) family in the north of England was the first member of the family to go to university. As a postgraduate dramatherapy student, she is struggling financially. People have noticed that she eats little, works very long hours in a café and is understandably tired much of the time, but says she is ok. Does the university encourage her to explore her psychological needs when her physical needs don't seem to be adequately met?

Tutorial in university office

DRAMATHERAPY TUTOR: How are you?
DRAMATHERAPY STUDEN: I'm very well, thanks. Very well indeed...

Scenario guideline 4 research

A dramatherapy researcher from an ethnically minoritised background, is researching discrimination in mental health settings. S/he is unsure how to accommodate the fact that 70% of the service users of a particular psychiatric ward are from ethnically minoritised backgrounds, and 80% of the managing, diagnosing and medical staff are white. S/he consults an academic supervisor about this.

Academic supervision in university café

DRAMATHERAPY RESEARCHER: I'm starting to feel uncomfortable on the ward. I'm angry that every single cleaner seems to be black or Asian. It's just awful. Especially when I see that most of the consultants strutting about the ward seem to be white. I don't think I can continue this research. … It's too upsetting.

ACADEMIC SUPERVISOR:

Scenario guideline 5 advocacy, professional relationships and systemic change

In a hospital outpatients' dramatherapy group, a patient diagnosed with depression is very angry about the state of the world. He has channelled his anger into left-wing politics. He tends to be cynical about expressing emotions in the group and can't bear to think about himself as having any substantial problem when, with the current wars and inequalities, he feels in a very privileged position. He discloses to the group plans to participate in a political demonstration, only slightly breaking the law, but for a good cause. The dramatherapist also believes that this is a good cause but is worried about their client and takes the issue to supervision.

The supervisor's consulting room

DRAMATHERAPIST: The police haven't given permission for this demonstration. So it's effectively illegal. Do I have to inform someone? Is it in my client's interest? What about the other group members? Can I participate in it?

SUPERVISOR:

The feedback from members was that they found the improvisations very useful, illustrative material for the guidelines. In both consultations with the membership of the NADTA and BADth, the aspirational nature of the guidelines was sometimes interpreted as prescriptive, politically correct moral high ground or too 'theoretical'. The majority of members expressed satisfaction that the associations now had formulated guidelines, but felt much more needed to be done to work out what this would mean in practice. Those who had personal experience of difference were more likely to identify than those who identified with the 'majority culture', where difference might be more invisible.

Conclusion

What knowledge, skills, attitudes and actions do we need to engage in to provide culturally responsive and culturally effective care? The development of practice guidelines in each of our respective associations offers multiple entry points into this lifelong process. Our hope is that anchoring each guideline in accounts of lived experience and encouraging conducive environments within which to explore our challenges will help to bridge the divide between theory, policy and practice.

Research on culture, identity and equity issues in dramatherapy

Part II

Research on culture,
identity and equity issues
in dramatherapy

Chapter 4

Race and racism in the clinical space

I had been working with a white woman in her late 70's who struggled with depression for approximately three months in the context of weekly individual psychotherapy/dramatherapy in a private practice that specialised in trauma. She had been volunteering for a survey company that conducted large polls on political opinions and, on one occasion, she brought up Barack Obama's 2008 U.S. presidential campaign. In the context of recounting one of her experiences, she looked at me and said "that monkey will never be elected". I was caught off-guard. I had heard the word monkey as a racist signal. I glanced away and she shifted in her seat. I remember not knowing what to say but not wanting to let the comment disappear into the silence between us lest it be misinterpreted as agreement on my part. I felt my face get hot. What was the significance of that sentence? Did my being a brown skinned therapist have something to do with why she thought she could express her views in this way? Did she feel the same way about me? Was it ok to feel uneasy about this? How would this get in the way of our therapeutic alliance and the work? These were some of the questions that I brought to supervision following this session. My supervisor reminded me that it was appropriate to assert a social norm aligned with values of social justice while also inquiring about potentially relevant clinical themes such as her thoughts and feelings about black men, men in authority, and our relationship. Near the beginning of the next session, I said that I had been thinking about our last session and her comment about Obama and wondered about her experience with black men. It wasn't a perfect way to get into this exploration. I expected her to tell me that she wasn't racist and that she didn't mean to use that word whether or not that was true. I suppose I was feeling a bit defensive. She shared that where she grew up, "Obama would have never had a chance". She spoke about growing up in a rural, poor, predominantly white community where overt anti-black racism continues to be the norm. I wondered about this complexity.

Dramatherapist, USA

In this vignette, race and racialisation intersect with age, socio-economic status and political leanings. It offers insight into how cultural and clinical considerations may operate in tandem with each other. The therapist, who identifies as a person of colour, reports the physiological and emotional

DOI: 10.4324/9780429431593-6

impact of signs of racism as they emerge in the clinical space. They seek out and have access to supervision, which offers a space to reflect on this experience while also organising a way forward. How do we prioritise important values whilst also leaving space for both the client and the dramatherapist to explore the nature of their relationship? How do we work dramatically with experiences of racism in the clinical context? This chapter attempts to respond to these questions through a discussion of themes arising from dramatherapist and client perceptions of the impact of race and racism in dramatherapy from the survey and reflections on practice from vignettes and interviews.

In our survey, we asked respondents to identify which aspects of identity had an influence over their experience of dramatherapy. Race and ethnicity were identified as the most influential factors with 65% (n = 43) of respondents. This affirms and also illuminates a contradiction that other dramatherapists have observed: race is always in the clinical space whether or not the clinician or client is a person of colour, yet race and ethnicity, as a lens from which to understand practice, are often absent from training, supervision, and continuing professional development (Adams, 2020; Maynard, 2018; Mayor, 2012; Sajnani, 2012a; Stevens, 2021; Thorn, 2011; Williams, 2018b).

On race, racism and ethnicity

The concept of race is distinct from ethnicity and nationality though these terms are often conflated with each other (for discussion around nationality, see Chapter 11). The key difference is that *race* is sometimes erroneously assumed to be an objective, assigned and measurable category, while *ethnicity*, often regarded as a self-defined social group sharing a perceived common ancestry, history and cultural practices, is seen as dynamic and changeable (Cornell & Hartmann, 2006). The idea that race is something physical, unchanging and permanent persists in the face of evidence of genetic variation that cuts across visible racial divides (Gutin, 1994). From a psychological perspective, this persistence may be understood as arising from an existential tendency to minimise distinctions within groups and increase distinctions between groups (Tajfel, 1981; Vietze et al., 2013). As Dalal (2002) writes, "Whatever race is, it is used to sort varieties of humankinds" (p. 9). However, it is critically important to examine the function of maintaining racial categories and specifically who benefits from their preservation. As Toni Morrison writes in *The Origin of Others*, "[B]ecause – there are such major benefits in creating and sustaining an Other, it is important to 1) identify the benefits and 2) discover what may be the social / political results of repudiating – those benefits." (2017, p. 40). Indeed *racism*, at its root, is "an ideology of racial domination" (Wilson, 1999) in which, as Clair and Denis (2015) write,

> the presumed biological or cultural superiority of one or more racial groups is used to justify or prescribe the inferior treatment or social

position(s) of other racial groups. Through the process of racialization, perceived patterns of physical difference such as skin colour or eye shape are used to differentiate groups of people, thereby constituting them as races.

(p. 857)

Racism and the ideology of White supremacy, originating as a system of exploitation with European colonialism (see Chapter 2) have been documented in every social sphere of organisation from schools, to housing, education, justice and government (Clair & Denis, 2015). Race may be a social construction (Dalal, 2002), but the impact of constant monitoring, differential levels of access to education and housing are material, continuous and cumulative. As the disproportionately high number of deaths of ethnically diverse people from years of police brutality and, most recently, from Covid-19 indicate, racism is lethal (Mackey et al., 2020; Razaq et al., 2020). It has been declared a public health issue by the American Medical Association amongst other authoritative bodies and its documented impacts on mental health require our collective attention and responsibility (DeGruy, 2017; Wallace et al. 2016; Williams, 2018b). Racial discrimination has also been highlighted as an adverse childhood experience contributing to trauma (Brennan et al., 2019), including intergenerational trauma (Thomas, 2018).

Racialisation as a social process

Socialisation refers to the process of learning how best to behave around other human beings (Clausen, 1968), but who informs that 'best behaviour', and is there room for only one dominant cultural narrative? Primary socialisation is a term that describes the learning that takes place in the home, from a child's direct experience with their parents or other caregivers, by observing their caregivers and siblings interacting, and by others' reactions to their own behaviour. Secondary socialisation is what is learned from interactions outside the home: in school, places of worship and work contexts and from other sources such as social media, television and music. Here, children learn how to function in groups, how to deal with unknown adults and how to handle new norms and expectations. Other sources of secondary socialisation include group activities such as team sports, unstructured play with peers and messages from media, political and religious organisations. Ideally, children are unconditionally loved and accepted during primary socialisation. However, there are various reasons why children may not be unconditionally loved and accepted in their primary socialisation. In families where intergenerational trauma is present and children face adverse childhood experiences, the socialisation processes can be much more complex and challenging. Several introductory vignettes in the following chapters highlight these complexities (e.g. see Chapter 5).

Racial socialisation, or *racialisation*, describes the mechanisms by which we acquire concepts of race and racism (Hughes et al., 2006). This can happen in the context of our primary or secondary socialisation into adult-hood where we may receive implicit or explicit messages about the meaning of race, or our skin colour or ethnicity. Dramatherapist Adams (2020, p. 6) put it this way,

> With the ongoing Windrush scandal and those being unfairly deported, it began to occur to me that perhaps the relationship with one's colo-nial motherland was bound up in a kind of insecure attachment, like a mother who is nuanced and not readily accessible to her distressed child. I was in danger of being overwhelmed by socio-political tides of rising racism, in society and Parliament, where the narratives seem to be, Black people were still no longer welcomed – the hostility they were met with after being recruited by Britain to come and help rebuild after the war, remains over 5 decades later.

Other examples of this would be the anti-Black messages Ditty recounted in Chapter 2 or the messages that students received about their black skin in the opening vignette from Chapter 3:

> They discussed being told they were naughty and bad from the word go, at home and outside. I probably asked if they remembered being small. David had clearly been shaken by the violence he'd encountered in prison and he showed me how many feet away from a murderer he'd slept. He'd been told he was a thug but saw a "good" face in the mirror. Naomi said she wished her skin were lighter, she wished she was not Black.

Naomi's wish to be lighter skinned also points to the psychologically damag-ing effects of negative racial socialisation such as *internalised racism* (David et al., 2019; Pyke, 2010) and *racialisation*, which "becomes racism when it involves the hierarchical and socially consequential valuation of racial groups" (Clair & Denis, 2015, p. 857). This passage calls attention to the internal resources necessary to recover and sustain a vision of oneself as good enough, as David does despite having been told otherwise repeatedly either directly or indirectly.

Adults may intentionally tailor the types or amounts of messages they give to their children based on their children's characteristics (such as gender, age, skin tone, sexual orientation) in order to better prepare them for experiences they anticipate for their children. For example, a mother may buy her daugh-ter books with main characters who look like her. Ta Nehisi-Coates' (2015) *Between the World and Me* offers another example; the book is written as a letter to his teenage son, warning him of the realities associated with being Black in the United States.

Other times, such socialisation is accidental, such as a son observing his care providers looking disturbed when watching a news broadcast about an unarmed Black boy being shot by police or an incident of anti-Asian vio-lence. Some parents may not realise that racialisation occurs whether they talk about race or not. Even choosing not to explicitly discuss race, race-re-lated values or current events, communicates values and beliefs about race. The absence of explicit conversation may communicate the message that not 'seeing' race is preferable to noticing it at all, sometimes referred to as 'colour blindness' (Bartoli et al., 2016), or that it is too difficult or dangerous to talk about.

Dramatherapist perspectives

In this section, we present excerpts from interviews and findings from our survey of dramatherapists and clients with regard to their perceptions about the influence of race and ethnicity in dramatherapy. We begin with demo-graphic data and then discuss salient themes in relation to relevant literature.

Demographics: Racial and ethnic identity

When asked about racial and ethnic identity, respondents to our survey self-identified as White (20), Black (4), Mixed (6), Asian (1), Gibraltarian (1), Jewish (2), Latinx (2) and Other (5), whilst 24 left the question blank. Those who wrote 'other' offered a variety of responses. For example, one drama-therapist responded to the question of racial and ethnic identity with "I feel strongly that we are all a mix of different races and that this needs to be respected". Another wrote "human". There is a tension here as, on one hand, such responses affirm the misguided and racist underpinnings of dividing people into 'races'. However, at the same time, not 'seeing' race is a privilege only afforded to those for whom race, and more specifically racialisation, has not resulted in unequal treatment. As someone who had received dramather-apy wrote, "It is very important that I can trust the therapist to explore her/his assumptions [about race] with me".

Another dramatherapist wrote, "[S]eems like [therapy] is more difficult if they come from different places". Here, the term 'they' calls up notions of the other, migrant or otherwise not from 'here,' an example of where place and nationality come to be conflated with racial and ethnic identity. Other responses to 'other' from both therapists and clients reflected the impor-tance of context in understanding racial socialisation. For example, one dramatherapist wrote, "Due to the intergenerational trauma of apartheid, we have to be cognisant of every race in the room and the stories we bring with us".

Competence

Several responses to the survey called attention to how racialisation informs the perception of competency. One dramatherapist who identified as being a person of colour wrote, "[M]y white patients are often more aggressive towards staff and other patients of colour, often yelling slurs and being more combative". Another dramatherapist who identified as White wrote, "Assumptions are made about me, having competence are the norm…am seen as the therapist, just walking by the room with my whiteness. …I am unfairly given authority from this perspective". It is well documented that healthcare providers of colour are not afforded this same privilege. Racialized therapists' faces are mistaken for clients, receptionists or students and have their competence questioned more often than their White peers (Abrams, 2018; Williams, 2018a). How do we, as individuals and as a community, support the authority and leadership of colleagues of colour?

Lack of representation

Some respondents spoke to an "appalling lack of ethnic minority representation amongst British dramatherapists" though the same could be said about the field as a whole. This may be very slowly changing. Two BADth surveys of dramatherapists' backgrounds undertaken in 2007 and 2015 revealed a shift in respondents who identified as White from 75% to 69.3% (Dokter, 2016; Dokter & Hughes, 2007b), whilst dramatherapists who identified as Black (2%), Asian (1.06%) and Mixed (4.5%) increased to 7.5% from 5%, whilst the general UK population numbers 11% of people who so identified in the 2011 census. The NADTA surveys members each year and includes demographic questions. However, at the time of writing, these data were unavailable.

A lack of representation places an undue burden on students and professionals of colour; as one respondent wrote,

> I am one of four clinicians of colour in a team of 15 counsellors. Granted we are nearly a third of the department, but we still do not accurately reflect the student demographic. I am often called upon to reflect or consult on issues related to race and tolerance.

Another dramatherapist wrote,

> I feel being a queer male of colour has made me stand out. As such, I am often called upon to be a representative or expert. At times this is a welcome experience, and also there are instances where I feel exploited, unsafe and the product of exoticism.

These quotes speak to the ways in which dramatherapists of colour have felt tokenised or unduly put in a position to speak on behalf of an entire community – a community that is seen as a monolithic entity devoid of internal diversity.

Reflecting earlier points relating to having one's competence questioned and illuminating this need for representation, dramatherapist Williams (2018a) writes,

This particular week the participants were new to us and as my partner, a white woman, introduced the group she would gesture to me at times recognizing that we were working together. At some point, one of the clients interrupted my colleague and turned to me to say, "I'm sorry...I am just confused by you. Are you one of the group leaders? The way you talk and the way you are dressed, you look like a group leader. But, I mean, you look like us". As she spoke the last sentence, she pointed to the other black women clients sitting in the room. I remember feeling at that moment that this client believed she was speaking more about how she viewed me by naming "the way I talk" and "the way I dressed", and yet she had actually revealed more about how she perceived herself. As I have thought more about this encounter over the years, I also realise that this was reflecting the field to which I belong. The truth is that the majority of people who walk in the room as a doctor, clinician or administrator are not likely to be persons of colour. That sends a message, and that message is downloaded and internalised.

(p. 229)

Discussing identity in silos will not help us unpack the complexity of why this lack of representation persists. We discussed the roots of racism and socio-economic disadvantage in relation to colonialism in Chapter 2, but also need to consider how racism and socio-economic mobility work in tandem with other circumstances, including intergenerational trauma. We will examine the perspectives available in dramatherapy trainings in Chapter 13 and how these communicate a sense of belonging or otherness. As one respondent wrote, "I feel many of the texts that have been offered are through the lens of whiteness. Throughout my education many of my professors are white. On an organisational level the professional association is overwhelmingly white". How are practitioners of colour engaged, valued and leading the field? How is the White, Eurocentric preference expressed in classroom materials and in professional development contexts?

Racial bias in healthcare and the need for advocacy

Several responses highlighted the urgent need to advocate on behalf of clients and patients of colour. One respondent wrote about the need to advocate on behalf of clients and patients of colour "since we work in a predominantly white staffed hospital and there are microaggressions that staff display towards them". Indeed, implicit bias and racism in healthcare are well-documented facts (Hall et al., 2015). The consequences can be lethal as the recent Covid-related death of Black physician Dr. Susan Moore, who was denied care and whose pleas for pain relief were ignored, reveals (Sykes, 2020). Dramatherapist Williams (2018a) writes about the danger of implicit bias in a clinical context:

I am reminded of a moment when a colleague returned from a group saying that a patient had been acting "bizarre" because she was "banging her head" throughout the group. The patient, a black woman, was some-one I had worked with and engaged in a group earlier that day. When I questioned my colleague regarding the client's behaviour, they showed me exactly how the patient was hitting her head. Recognizing the action, I suggested the client may have been scratching her scalp because it is difficult for individuals with braids to reach the scalp without disturbing the hair. My colleague thanked me for sharing this because they had planned to include the "bizarre" behaviour in the patient's chart. This is an example of how a cross-cultural gap in understanding could have clin-ical consequences for a patient. Had this observation made its way into the patient's chart, it might have impacted her treatment as the doctor could have read this action as a self-injurious gesture, an indication of psychosis, or a need for change in medication.

(p. 224)

Racial and cultural bias in psychiatric diagnoses has been flagged up for some time (Littlewood & Lipsedge, 1982), but racial bias continues to emerge in sub-tle ways such as the unjustified mention of race in case presentations; race is mostly mentioned in cases where patients are not White (Nawaz & Brett, 2009). It may manifest, as it did in Williams' vignette, where an absence of cultural knowledge could have led to dire consequences. It may also manifest as the denial and absence of care as it did in the case of Dr. Moore. These examples illuminate the prevalence of racial bias in clinical practice, the importance of representation and cultural response/ability in clinical teams and the advocacy that dramatherapists, like other health practitioners, may need to engage in.

The 'good white person'

Several respondents emphasised the inheritance and continued presence of a good White person narrative in our field where a light-skinned hero saves the day. As one respondent wrote,

I think the theme or image of the "Good white person" is still critical and present in the world of dramatherapy. I often have the feeling of wanting to hide some of our elders (particularly the men) in the attic or something. I quiver a bit anticipating my own ageing and growing into their ranks; how will the younger generation need to corral and control my bad impulses?

In this response, the issue of age, gender and heritage are a subtext to rac-ism. Wanting to acknowledge the previous generation, whilst distancing from their beliefs, can also be a way of not seeing what we have received in the passing of the baton.

Some responses reinforce the implicit assumption of whiteness as neutral 'just normal' (Dyer, 1997; Ryde, 2009), even as they point to the need for change. As one respondent put it, "As therapists it helps to be aware of who and what we embody...with my skin comes perceived power and privilege and I represent the race of a violent oppressor". However, when the benefits of this power and privilege are acknowledged and addressed, it may be met with resistance, as another dramatherapist writes,

> My politics are generally poorly understood. Colleagues (dramatherapists and other professionals) frequently say things that reveal we live in different worlds. Lots of white fragility, guilt, defensiveness, dismissiveness etc. ...it's very alienating.

As Robin DiAngelo (2018) writes in her book *White Fragility*, it is hard to deviate from the story of the good White person. It can feel like a threat to one's sense of self, purpose and agency in the world. Can we examine both the strengths and the shadows of our dramatherapy heritage and own them, develop along the continuum rather than disown or avoid taking ownership of that heritage and the context of structural oppression and White supremacy in which we live and practice?

Grappling with privilege

Several respondents wrote about trying to work through the privileges that come with whiteness and how these prompt efforts at change. One dramatherapist wrote,

> I enjoy working with different racial or ethnic identities, I love to learn about people. I find the effects of privilege difficult as I work in a place of extreme poverty. I have to watch myself in terms of comparing experiences and feeling angry at privilege. I work within a white supremacist culture, I challenge when I can and try to work on myself and the environment to expand awareness and inclusivity.

Being interested in people, along with making a difference and wanting to help people, is often one of the reasons for wanting to become a therapist. The shadow side of these motivations can be heard in "wanting to learn about others" and "being angry at privilege". Others wrote about how privilege obscures realities faced by others and the challenge of working through this. As one respondent wrote,

> As a white cis guy I struggle a bit how to navigate my privilege and how it relates to my own experiences of competence and success. At times I have benefitted from sexism and white supremacy and I know my identity can complicate my capacity to see ways in which I can address this

on a larger scale. I feel way more (imperfectly) competent in dealing with the issues clinically but in my social and professional circles, I feel quite gummed up.

This phenomenon of being "gummed up" reflects an earlier point concerning the lack of collective socialisation with regard to speaking openly about issues relating to race and racism and examining how they may obscure racial dynamics at play. Dramatherapists also named the impact of working in a White-dominated field with resistance to talking about racism as '\"we then have to address the shame and unconscious bias within". It is also important to note that clients value the capacity of therapists to have open conversations about power, privilege and identity. A respondent who identified as a client of dramatherapy wrote, "I speak to my therapist about her privilege as a white person".

In the strategies for practice chapter in Section 3, we discuss issues around therapist self-disclosure and non-verbal communication; issues around working with 'extremist' views are discussed in Chapter 8. Next, we will look at practice; given the emphasis of the survey perspectives on racism, bias and privilege, how do dramatherapists in practice work with these issues?

Dramatherapist reflections on practice

The reflections on practice in this chapter come from two dramatherapists, self-identified as African Caribbean and White from one of the minority UK countries, both working in England in Pupil Referral Units. These are alternative education options for children excluded from school. Black pupils are disproportionately met with disciplinary measures, lasting from a day to several weeks, that often lead to permanent exclusions in England (Richardson, 2020). In the US, racial disparities in education have been demonstrably linked to racial biases; students are similarly subjected to disciplinary action at rates disproportionate to their White counterparts (Riddle & Sinclair, 2019).[1] These reflections on practice suggest that the experience of working within this context differs for dramatherapists along the lines of race.

Vignette I

Carol Cumberbatch, a dramatherapist who self identifies as African Caribbean, reflected on her own experience of being in this clinical space:

> I know the experience of being different, having been born here makes no difference, people judge what they see. On the street it is the way I look and walk, in the therapy room it is what the clients are bringing with them. ... Sometimes they are really interested in my heritage, speak to me in patois…the difficulty is that they bring just the negatives of my culture and share it with me as if it is nothing.

Her reflections call up the ways in which notions of race are performed and negotiated in every encounter (Mayor, 2012). She describes how, in group work, she can struggle with the swearing and the misogynistic lyrics in the music the clients bring. In her words,

> Sometimes we can listen together, find the understanding of the lyrics, finding language that is not offensive to either of us, not laughing when someone is murdered. It can be quite dark with young people unfortunately, especially with all the stabbings that are going on within the black community. Labels of white and black can create stereotypes.

She related how a young man of Pakistani heritage used the "n word" in the session. The group with this boy had been running for a year until this incident. He was a young man with autism who used to rest more through the sessions, but over time had become more involved. He gradually built up his confidence and was more able to speak up. His peers, who were all White, froze and said, "[Y]ou cannot say that". The dramatherapist tried to explain why it was offensive, and he said, "[B]ut they sing it in all the songs". He referred to US rap songs, and the therapist highlighted that the experience of African Caribbeans in the UK is different from the African American one. She discussed with him what the term would be in his culture and, if that term was used, whether he would be angry. Finding a word of equal offence in his own culture was crucial to his understanding, as it was only then that it made sense to him. He asked, "[W]hy would people use these terms if they find them offensive?" The therapist reflected further on her understanding of this process:

> I understood it was used against us during colonisation for so long. … Some people using it may find it empowering, not every person of African heritage will think and feel the same. I am not trying to own it. It is still not easy, because I believe strongly that words are powerful, so saying negatives builds negatives. To explain why is hard. … If a Caucasian person uses it, it becomes what it was, so it is complex…you cannot say that because of the history.

The dramatherapist also reflected on the impact of adopting American cultural dress and lyrics on the perception of Black people in the UK, whilst the experience of African Caribbeans remains more invisible. She finds that the lyrics maintain the colonial perception, often accompanied by misogynistic attitudes towards women. She perceives this as disempowering.

This dilemma of whether or not to reclaim words once used as racial slurs by the dominant group is taken up by dramatherapist Stevens in his US work to empower Black youth in a high school for students with varied abilities. In a video demonstration, Stevens explores how a young Black man's reclamation of the "n word" contributed to his empowerment (Stevens, 2021).

Vignette 2

Another example comes from a White drama therapist working in the pupil referral unit whose vignette was presented in the opening of Chapter 3. The therapist in that vignette felt privileged that she was allowed in.

> My offers of roles and scenarios were rejected. ... I offered to be someone else in the hairdresser (another customer, hairdresser, neighbour). This was rejected. They wanted a sort of net-curtain, a separation and I had the feeling that if I changed my role Naomi would have struggled even more with my presence. She was trying to work me out as myself, as a therapist. She wanted me to stay put. She made it clear they [other students] would not be allowed that session. ... I was part of the group but Naomi feared that I would align myself with the white students. She was banning them, because she had chosen who would attend. ... I did feel privileged that I was allowed in this black group. My skin colour was permitted. She had quite a negative view of white people and I had been allowed in. They seemed to want me to be someone who attended to their needs and who understood that I was to stop talking if I started "chatting shit".

In turning the tables, it seems as though Naomi gave the therapist an opportunity to experience being on the receiving end of excluding power dynamics.

> Naomi talked despairingly about her homelife and confusing relationship with her mother. At this point she showed me a sharp hair instrument and said I would feel it if I stepped out of line. She said she wished her skin were lighter, she wished she was not black.

The therapist stressed that, in her approach, she tries to keep the possibility of play alive and work with 'discrepant communication' (Johnson, 2009) but also indicates feeling threatened when Naomi held up the scissors in a way that suggested that she needed to protect herself from becoming hurt. It is interesting to note that the dynamic in the session changed after discussing racism. The vignette session continues:

> When they grew tired of hairdressing they decided they needed a rest and arranged the cushions accordingly, demanding blankets and that I replace them every time they kicked them off, which became a game, one that might be played with preverbal babies. I enquired about their earlier experiences. Both said they were bad babies, born bad. I countered this, covered them up a few more times and they fell asleep, leaving me to watch over them.

The therapist reflected that she was asked to take the role of White mother to two Black babies. She felt that she was shown the sharp implement to keep her in her place so that they could feel safe enough to be babies. She said that the clients seemed to want to be with someone who attended to their needs and who knew when to stop "chatting shit" (usually in connection with something emotionally charged). The therapist understood this in relation to Naomi's neglect by her mother. Internalised racism may also play a role, and discrimination on the grounds of skin colour can also be enacted within and between communities.

As Olumide writes, "[I]t is important to recognise that darker-skinned Black women may have harsher experiences as they are further away from the Eurocentric idea of beauty than lighter skinned Black women are" (Olumide, 2016). Naomi, who came from a central African refugee heritage and privileged African background, had to fight to become higher status amongst the Black predominantly Caribbean pupils in the school. Her earlier experience of privilege may also have contributed to her confidence to articulate her experience.

What cultural significance did therapeutic mothering have? It is possible to think about racial socialisation as discussed earlier, but it may also be useful to think about these interactions in the context of ethno-cultural transference (Tuckwell, 2002). Tuckwell highlights the complexities and the potency of racial and cultural phenomena, which can touch deep unconscious feelings that may be enacted in the transference. The transferential processes are often associated with internalised attitudes of White superiority and Black subservience, and these may serve as a catalyst for major therapeutic issues such as trust, anger, acknowledgement of ambivalence and acceptance of disparate parts of the self. These dynamics are present and worked with through metaphor and the use and meaning of language. Tuckwell names mistrust, suspicion and hostility, often rooted in anxiety about being misunderstood and ambivalence in the transference (struggling with negative feelings towards the therapist whilst also having an attachment to them). Both are present in the vignette. A Black woman's anger has many layers of meaning, expressing exposure and resistance to external and internalised racism (Thorn, 2011), challenging the stereotype (hooks, 1990). The therapist started from a developmental approach to address early mother-baby attachment (Wilt, 1993), but the experience of racism also needed to be addressed. The White therapist discusses the clients' experiences in attachment and developmental terms alongside her understanding of racism. Her own role as representing White power and culture is less directly explored, although her naming of privilege may be part of her countertransference. Coming from a White working-class background in a minority country, being a female therapist in a patriarchal education system and being White privileged means many layers of meaning interact. It might be difficult to explore this more directly with the clients, given their embargo on her 'talking shit'. Coming from one of the minority UK countries (see Chapter 9 on language) includes an external and internalised experience of being marginalised.

The other therapist identifies as African Caribbean British. She is allowed to explore the meaning of racist terms more directly with the client by getting him to link it to his own experience. She subsequently reflects on her own internalised experience. The White therapist is asked to initially tolerate the experience of being silenced before being allowed to discuss racism. Both therapists mention the importance of understanding particular cultural references, terms and language and the way they intersect with the experience of racism. The Black therapist mentioned that she found it easier to explore issues around racism in an individual than in a group context, the White therapist found diverse groups the best context for discussion. We will return to this in Section 3.

Conclusion

While there are a limited number of perspectives offered in this chapter, there is enough to affirm that the racialisation of dramatherapists is not dissimilar from the rest of society. As the perspectives shared suggest, there are many ways in which the subject of race and experiences of racism may be silenced; it remains difficult to speak about racism openly despite its exceptionally significant impact on the experience of dramatherapy. According to several of the dramatherapists interviewed and surveyed, there is a desire to continue to work through this, but doing so would require acknowledging the shame and unconscious bias within. The practice reflections offered some examples of the way dramatherapists work with that bias, and more spaces are needed to continue this kind of reflection. As one dramatherapist wrote in reference to White privilege, "[I]t is always there, inescapable and requires attending to…there is so much I cannot know because of it. The effort is one of constant humility". The perspectives offered also indicate a need to examine how our interactions and the materials we use, the stories, case examples and approaches, may risk reinforcing notions of colour blindness, Eurocentric norms and/or ask racialised students and clients to replace their experience once more with those of their White counterparts. Finally, there is a need to bring forward the many ways in which dramatherapists and participants of colour actively resist racist and racializing processes; thereby enacting the margins as a spaces of power (hooks, 1989). Race and racist social stratification intersect with many other aspects of identity; threads from this discussion will emerge in other chapters in this book and continue to be explored in strategies for practice, training and supervision.

Questions for further reflection

- What considerations regarding race are illuminated in the two vignettes from practice? How do/might you address this in your own practice?

- What messages about race did you grow up with, and what has changed in your lifetime?
- (How) do you challenge racism, and how do you determine when and how to do so?
- Have you drawn on dramatherapy skills to explore or address race-based assumptions?

Note

1 One of the critical readers for this chapter indicated that it would be interesting to note if this phenomenon is also present in dramatherapy training. We take a closer look at training in Chapter 13.

Chapter 5

Troubling gender in dramatherapy

Zoe is of dual heritage – her father is Pakistani and mother is White British. Her mother had a painful and difficult childhood which included spells in foster care and led to addiction in adulthood. When Zoe was one year old her father left them and returned to Pakistan. I was asked to help Zoe to process and make sense of the events that had led to her being taken to foster care and prepare her for a move to a long foster placement. Social workers had informed me of their concerns that the white British foster carer was showing poor respect for Zoe's heritage and culture. The foster carer had taken Zoe to another town, pointed out women wearing burkas and reassured Zoe that she would protect her from being raised in such a culture. The social workers' fear of challenging the carer, or even informing her of their concerns, left me in an invidious position. Nine sessions took place in the foster home, with the foster carer present. On hearing Zoe's life history the foster carer began to show greater insight. To explore the history with Zoe, I drew a canvas map showing houses she had lived in. Toy figures of people were used to enact scenes from her life story. The facts were repeated via a "water game" in which water symbolised "love" that flows until it gets blocked by "suffering." Zoe showed a lack of curiosity about her father. As a means of discreetly addressing Zoe's confusion about her ethnic identity, I read her a story based on "Romeo and Juliet" that was about rival families of black and white cats. One from each family falls in love and the pair give birth to a litter, which includes a ginger kitten. Zoe remarked that in being "different" to the others, this kitten was like her. I suggested this kitten was the most appealing.

Joan Moore, Dramatherapist, UK

After race, gender emerged in our survey as an aspect of identity carrying the most influence in therapist and client experiences of dramatherapy. As with all aspects of identity and culture, gender must be understood in the context in which it is (de)valued. This vignette does not offer an overt example of gender-specific concerns. However, assumptions and opportunities to consider practice from a gendered lens, as it intersects with racial, ethnic and religious identity, are present throughout. For example, while it is likely that the information may not have been available, the father in this vignette is referred to as uniformly Pakistani, whereas the mother is considered White

DOI: 10.4324/9780429431593-7

British, leading to questions about whether he had British citizenship or if his legal status was a complicating factor in the circumstances of his departure. Neither the gender identity of the "white British foster carer" nor the dramatherapist is available to the reader, and there is an assumption of a cisgendered male-female gender binary throughout. However, we do know that the White carer transmitted many messages in their denigration of women in burqas and, by extension, devout Muslims while casting themselves in the role of saviour. Given the available information, it is not surprising that Zoe would have shown little interest in her father, given his potential abandonment and potential affiliation with an actively marginalised social group. In Chapter 4, we discussed the tensions between primary, secondary and racial socialisation that are so clearly at play in Zoe's case. We can empathise with the dramatherapist Joan Moore who was charged with supporting Zoe in organising her life experiences while simultaneously affirming her cultural identity. This vignette raises questions about the intersecting influence of gender and other aspects of identity and culture in dramatherapy and how these elements might be usefully considered in practice. It also calls attention to the costs of giving and receiving care within white-dominated systems of care (Sajnani, 2012a). Do we implicitly or explicitly collude with these systems? Can we find agency for ourselves and our clients? In this chapter, we focus on gender identity, expression and analysis in connection with the provision of dramatherapy and the experience of dramatherapists.

Sex, gender and mental health

Despite the fact that gender diversity has been present since ancient times across cultures, a gender binary of male and female remains dominant, so we would like to begin with how we as authors currently understand the terms (Koh, 2012; Schilt & Westbrook, 2009; Yarbrough, 2018). Gender is a layered experience drawing on a range of attachments, not a rigid structure meant to hold solid during a lifetime (Beauregard & Long, 2019). The use of language and knowing how to inquire about gender and sexual orientation can be challenging. It is important not to lose the person amongst the ways of coding the body (Salamon, 2010), but also to be aware that young people and their families may not be in alignment around identity and language (Nealy, 2017; Ryan et al., 2010).

In the way we use current terminology, *sex* is a classification of biological and physiological characteristics, such as chromosomes, hormones and reproductive organs, whereas *gender* is a social construct related to biological differences but rooted in culture, social norms and individual behaviour. A *cisgender* person is someone whose *gender identity*, their personal sense of their own gender, matches with their assigned sex at birth. A person who is *transgender* experiences their gender identity as being different from the sex they were assigned at birth. Our understanding of gender, as with other aspects of identity and culture, emerge through *socialisation*, in which interactions within our primary and secondary relationships reinforce expectations, ideas and behaviours associated with gender that either reinforce or challenge existing *gender norms*. This socialisation can be understood in relation to historical and present-day efforts at *gender policing*, the enforcement of normative gender expressions on a person who is perceived as not adequately performing, through appearance or behaviour, the sex that was assigned to them at birth (Bauermeister et al., 2017). Gender policing is part of the process of 'gendering' children, socialising them in a way considered conventionally appropriate to their assigned sex. Once children are taught gender norms and experience their enforcement, they are likely to begin policing others – both their peers and their elders. This occurs across social spheres such as the family, peer groups, social media and broader systems such as healthcare and national service. There are divergences about transgender equality; until very recently, there was a complete ban on transgender service in the US (Baldor, 2021), for example, whilst in the UK, transgender people have been able to serve openly for more than 20 years. Morgensen (2011) suggests that we consider present-day struggles with gender variance in relation to ongoing expressions of colonisation and the specific ways in which settler cultures restricted and commodified Indigenous expressions of gender fluidity such as Two-Spirit identities in North American Indigenous communities or the ancient but ever-present Hijra or Kinnar community in India, people who identify as third-gender (Nanda, 1996).

For example, in my (Nisha) family and in my generation, girls were expected to prize physical beauty, which was often coupled with thinness and whiteness/fairness and education. As a result of witnessing my mother raise me as a single parent, I also came to value a woman's independence and entrepreneurship. However, regardless of that fact, I was aware that fulfilling prescribed gender roles in our family would involve marrying a cisgendered man. Failing to adhere to this script felt like it meant risking important relationships. My mother grew up in an even more patriarchal environment in which daughters were valued less than sons and where women were only visible in relation to their fathers, brothers and sons (Sajnani, 2016a). In my family (Ditty), women worked as carers of children and other family members inside the house, whilst men worked outside to bring in the income. Both genders worked hard for little remuneration in a working-class environment where education was for those who could afford it. My mother had to stop working when she got married. Intergenerational struggles with that expectation – and the workload – might be diagnosed as psychiatric, even when a son understood enough to say, "There were seven of us children. If things got too much she started to cluck like a chicken and was taken to the asylum".

Rival conceptualisations of gender are in flux, creating areas of cultural stress and personal dis-ease (Allegranti, 2013; Hogan, 2020). Gender oppression takes many forms, examples can be gender policing, violence/abuse, medicalisation. It is no surprise that gender policing can have negative mental health consequences (Bauermeister et al., 2017; Yarbrough, 2018). Mental illness, like in Ditty's example, might be understood as a normal response to abnormal expectations and as a form of social protest against rigid gender expectations in which what is associated with feminine has been systematically devalued (Showalter, 1987; Yarbrough, 2018). The cost of failing to fulfil gender norms and expectations remains high (Allen et al., 2009; Showalter, 1987).

The history of medicine and mental health is tied up with gender policing (Busfield & Campling, 1996; Dhingra et al., 2021; Yarbrough, 2018). More often than not, it has been cisgender men who have been enabled to frame the afflictions of cisgender women. Notable examples include Bienville's influential use of the term 'nymphomania' to describe women's sexual desire, Silas Weir Mitchell's rest cure for 'neurasthenic' or nervous women, Jean-Martin Charcot's descriptions of 'hysterical women' or Sigmund Freud's conflation of anatomy with destiny and his views on women (Busfield & Campling, 1996). A complex racial and gender bias continues to exist in healthcare. For example, women, and Black women in particular, are less likely to be given appropriate pain medication in comparison to their white counterparts; their suffering is questioned (Collins, 1990; Hoffman et al., 2016; Weisse et al., 2001). Being transgender was considered a mental disorder (gender identity disorder) by the American Psychological Association (APA) until 2012.

Despite these challenges, there have been some positive developments. The *Diagnostic and Statistical Manual of Mental Disorders*, in its fifth edition at the time of writing, now focuses on *gender dysphoria*, the psychological distress that results from an incongruence between one's sex assigned at birth and one's gender identity. This shift represents an important step towards removing stigma against transgender people. It acknowledges false stereotypes about gender identity and expression and is a diagnosis that has been used to advocate for gender affirmative and trans-related medical care. In another recent and positive shift, the APA ratified a resolution on gender identity change efforts that acknowledges "that gender is a nonbinary construct that allows for a range of gender identities and that a person's gender identity may not align with sex assigned at birth" (APA, 2021, p. 1).

The history of the profession of dramatherapy is deeply intertwined with these evolving gender dynamics. In the UK, dramatherapy was established mainly by self-identified women such as Billy Lindkvist, Sue Jennings and Dorothy Langley, each coming from their own perspectives and experiences of gender socialisation. Billy Lindkvist founded the Sesame Institute on Jungian archetypal principles, including that of the masculine and the feminine (not necessarily gender specific). Sue Jennings has researched the impact of the body on gender identity (2020) and wrote earlier how a gender hierarchy of male and female was reinforced in the mental healthcare system in which psychiatrists were, and to some extent remain, male and at the top of the hierarchy (Dhingra et al., 2021), amplifying what Jennings (1987) and Johnson (1994) referred to as 'shame dynamics' in the field.

> How many times in my life had the doors been closed by men who were either threatened by successful women or believed that women should be at home and have "little hobbies". The pioneering of dramatherapy had meant that I needed to talk with doctors and psychiatrists, the majority of whom are still male. I needed to speak with directors of trusts and charities, prison governors and special school heads. How often the replies had been, "yes it sounds very interesting but it is not what you call essential drama is recreational...it is a luxury...people should have it as a reward...if disturbed people do drama it will make them more disturbed or mad or dangerous." Looking back now I wonder how I managed to withstand the oft-time abuse and cynicism. It came to a head when I had been asked to put together the Handbook of Dramatherapy (Jennings et al., 1993) with a select group of author-dramatherapists. I was discussing the project with my then supervisor who looked quite askance at the idea. "Oh dear Sue, I don't think so, it should be a book on psychotherapy – the handbook of psychotherapy – with a chapter about dramatherapy!"
>
> (Jennings, 2009, p. 6)

Pendzik (2016) offers another example of how gender dynamics are interlaced with founding narratives in the field:

> As opposed to David Johnson's (2009) statement that "in the beginning there was Moreno" (p. 5), ...dramatherapy does not have a "Guru" or single founder who can claim "paternity" over it. The field's conception is grounded in a quest that proceeded along parallel paths, all of which were connected to the innovative use of theatre, drama, play, and the arts, with therapeutic purposes. ... Numerous early pioneers could be mentioned – including Jacob L. Moreno, Vladimir Iljine, Peter Slade, Viola Spolin, Gertrud Schattner, and others.
>
> (p. 306)

Bayley (1999) pleaded more than 20 years ago for a pluralist perspective, based on Samuels' (1989) Jungian understanding and the emergence of Pink Therapy (Davies & Neal, 1996). He asked to what degree dramatherapy training programmes pathologised, medicalised or simply ignored queer sexual and gender identity. In his earlier work with young male-identified sex workers, he used the term 'split gender role conflict' to describe how they refused to conform to the male-female gender binary, embracing gender ambiguity, gender fluidity, transvestism and transsexuality instead (see Bayley, 2003). He later favoured the concept of gender transgression in his doctoral work (2000), where he drew on Butler's (1990) and others' advances in gender and performance studies. He wrote about transgressive queer performance in his doctoral thesis, which he defined as "any behaviour, presentation or embodiment in performance that would stem from an individual's refusal to conform to the categorisations, social roles and images that are implicit in any dominant hegemony" (p. 37). In the next chapter on sexual orientation, more current work will be discussed, but it is interesting to note that the implications of queer theory for dramatherapy continue to develop (Tomczyk, 2020).

Bayley's early example of dramatherapy work has developed in a range of ways over the past two decades. Bergman (2001), Dinitino and Johnson (1997) and McAllister (2011) examined internalised sexism and gender dynamics in their work with male-identified perpetrators and victims of violence in forensic and outpatient war veteran centres. Haen (2002) examined the ways in which boys are socialised into particular roles and characteristics. Landers (2002) examined the use of Developmental Transformations in dismantling and working through violent masculinities. Hubbard and Mann Shaw (cited in Jones, 2007) offered insight into how dramatherapists encourage clients to play across set gender roles, often within metaphor. Beauregard and Moore (2011) explored gender variance in dramatherapy work with boys from marginalised communities, as well as attitudes towards the LGBTQ+ community within the North American professional community of dramatherapy (Beauregard et al., 2016, 2017). Daccache (2016) situated patriarchy as a primacy clinical concern, while Sajnani (2012, 2013) emphasised the importance of examining the gender implications of clinical and community-based work in dramatherapy from a critical race feminist lens within the context of feminist movements. Dramatherapists have examined presenting clinical concerns from the lens of gender, including Dokter (1994) in her work with women with eating disorders, Novy (cited in Jones, 2007) and Stamp (2000) in their work with women involved with the criminal justice system, Dix (2015) and Bannister (1997) in their work with survivors of sexual abuse, Landis (2014) in her work with refugee women and youth and Zoabi and Damouni (2016) in their work with Palestinian women suffering a dual blow of being devalued as women and as citizens in Israel. Wilkinson emphasised the transformative potential of embodied processes in dramatherapy where we can "use our bodies to replicate gender norms and stereotypes", as well as change patterns of being and relating (Allegranti cited in Wilkinson, 2018, p. 155). Finally, the influence of dramatherapy has been incorporated in other practices focused on liberation from gendered norms such as *drag therapy* (Silvers, 2021).

All of these authors place their work within a sociopolitical context where it is important to look at both external oppression and internalised *sexism* in their embodied work. However, as Curtis (2013), in her editorial for a special issue on gender in the creative arts therapies, and Beauregard et al. (2016, 2017) concluded, work remains to be done to bridge open and affirming attitudes with individual and systemic actions that acknowledge and account for the influence of gender and gender diversity in our field. In the next section, we will examine dramatherapists perspectives on the influence of gender in practice.

Dramatherapist perspectives

In this section, we present excerpts of interviews and findings from our survey of dramatherapists and clients with regard to their perceptions about the influence of gender in dramatherapy. We remind readers that these thematic categories are indicative of how we, as co-authors, have grouped responses to our survey and not an exhaustive set of considerations pertaining to gender in dramatherapy. Where possible, we have made reference to writing from dramatherapists about the influence of gender in the field to guide further inquiry.

Demographics: Gender identity

Consistent with rapid cultural changes concerning how we think about and perform gender, responses to our question concerning the gender identity of respondents received the greatest variety of responses. Of 66 respondents, 14 identified as female, 4 identified as cis-female, 2 identified as being cis-males, 1 identified as nonbinary, another 1 identified as female with "fluctuating expression" and 4 responded with their sexual orientation further reinforcing how gender and sexual orientation are often treated interchangeably even though they are different. Others chose to leave this question blank or offered contextual responses. For example, one respondent wrote, "I identify as male. The local dramatherapy community is mostly female". Another wrote, "I'm a feminist and have women's issues at the heart of my work".

Sex and gender preference in dramatherapy

The question of whether sex or gender matching facilitates greater satisfaction in the course of therapy has been taken up in research over the past 50 years (Kirshner et al., 1978, Jones & Zoppel, 1982; Lambert, 2016). However, to our knowledge, we do not have studies within dramatherapy that consider the impact of gender similarities between practitioner and participant. So, it is noteworthy that respondents who left substantial comments with regard to the influence of gender all identified as having been clients in dramatherapy. One respondent indicated that they had been "drawn to therapists of different genders, depending on my needs at the time". Another respondent questioned the influence of sex and gender in their experience of dramatherapy.

> I noted earlier my request to have a male therapist but being assigned a female. I have worked with male and female. To date and to my knowledge I have not encountered a trans practitioner and I have invested and engaged with the therapist rather than the gender. I'm wondering how themes have been explored "differently" in relation to gender, but as each alliance in therapy cannot be compared to working with another gender with the same issues…this comparison cannot be made.

Others expressed a desire for gender to be referenced in the course of treatment in order to facilitate greater reflection.

> I'm a cis guy and my therapist was a cis woman. Initially we played a great deal about my decision to have a female vs. male therapist, but we never came back to this topic significantly as our relationship deepened. In retrospect I would have appreciated the chance and prompting to explore gender issues more deeply.

Others wrote of explicit preferences fearing further discrimination. One respondent wrote, "I identify as queer so need to feel comfortable that a therapist is not making wrong assumptions about me". This statement may be understood to reference sexual orientation, an aspect of identity we take up in Chapter 6, but it may also reference the experience of being *genderqueer*, which refers to a person whose gender identity falls outside of the gender binary of male/female or is experienced as fluid and changeable over time.

Gender privilege and equity

Consistent with the observations made by several colleagues writing about gender in dramatherapy (Beauregard et al. 2016, 2017; Pendzik, 2016; Sajnani, 2012a, 2013, Wilkinson, 2018), respondents wrote about the material privileges associated with gender such as being able to live and work within systems that reflect their own gender identity and expression. As one respondent wrote, "[A]s a cisgendered person it is important for me to recognize the unearned privileges I have when working with trans and gender-non-conforming, gender diverse clients". Another wrote, "[A]s a cis-woman, I can choose or not to think a lot about my cis-ness and have to actively educate myself on issues impacting trans and non-binary folks".

Gender privilege is the privilege of not having to worry about how one's gender will be perceived or whether their lived experience will be valued and protected in the same way as others. One dramatherapist commented on workplace culture as a source of concern: "I have been questioning my gender for a long time now but do not feel safe expressing it at my job or with my patients due to the location I work". We do not know the context or workplace, but it may be interesting to think of professional association support systems and advocacy to address some of these concerns.

One respondent who identified as a client in dramatherapy commented on the "lack of facilities for people transitioning" as being particularly challenging. Concrete expressions of *gender equity* may include gender-neutral bathrooms and documentation, such as intake forms that offer multiple options concerning gender identity or options to self-identify gender pronouns. Another important material expression of gender equity is career opportunities and salaries, which we take up next.

Gender bias in professional advancement

Some respondents wrote specifically about their perception and experience of *gender bias* in professional dramatherapy settings. For example, one respondent wrote, "[A]s a woman I think that times where I have taken on more leadership roles have been perceived as power threats to men I was working with". Another wrote, "[A]s a woman, I have also experienced a great deal of sexism in the field. Our community continues to position men in power and perpetrate a patriarchal power structure". Another wrote, "[B]eing a male affords me freedom to perform various roles with ease and comfort", while another commented on their perception that "male dramatherapists have a much higher chance of working in positions of responsibility in the profession and probably get paid more than women".

Research showed that high levels of female employment and family-friendly policies can reduce gender equality in the workforce due to defensive employer practices and produce what has been referred to as a *glass ceiling* (Hakim, 2007). In connection with this, Frydman and Segall (2016) researched the *glass elevator effect* in dramatherapy wherein "within female-dominated professions, men still advance up the career ladder at a faster rate than do their female counterparts" (Williams cited in Frydman & Segall, 2016, p. 26). Their quantitative findings indicated a lack of gender bias, but their qualitative findings, while limited, suggested that registered drama therapists experienced a glass escalator effect with "gendered impediments to professional advancement; perceptions of disempowerment from both personal and professional perspectives; and financial inequity in the workplace" (Frydman & Segall, 2016, p. 35). In dramatherapy professional associations, it could be interesting to look at the gender make-up of committee members, trainers and supervisors. Is this female-dominated profession represented equitably in positions of decision-making power and when it comes to salary?

In the US and the UK, women are still paid less than men (Blau & Kahn, 2017), and transgender employees face greater wage inequity due to gender identity discrimination and a lack of protective labour laws (Davidson, 2016). As Davidson (2016) writes, "[T]ransgender women tend to have worse employment experiences than nonbinary transgender people and transgender men, the latter two tending to have similar outcomes" (n.p.). Gender discrimination gets in the way of finding and keeping a job, and when gender is brought into consideration with race, age and ability, pay discrepancy is even wider with women of colour and Indigenous women in particular (Bleiweis, 2020). The impact of the pandemic, and increasing online work, has also increased the pay gap intersecting gender, race and socio-economic status with those who were already in a position of inequality paying the highest price with unpaid caring responsibilities left to and consequently disadvantaging women again (Blundell et al., 2020; Litman et al., 2020; The Equality Trust, 2016), whilst the challenges faced by women remain largely unaddressed by support interventions (The Fawcett Society, 2021).

One of the factors to be considered when examining pay equity is work-life preferences and the impact of how people want to combine work and family (Schleutker, 2016). Too often, the reality of unpaid care work and its impact on wage and labour outcomes are not taken into consideration (Ferrant et al., 2014). When asked about their family composition, six respondents indicated coming from or being in a single-parent family where, in the words of one respondent, they were the "sole breadwinner". Another four dramatherapists identified as coming from blended or intergenerational families. The invisibility of care work has been a significant feature of the feminist movement and should be considered in relation to how the dramatherapy profession is (de) valued, as well as the impact of this on leadership, salaries and advancement. Research on the impact of patriarchal norms on women's work-life balance is scarce; its links to social sustainability are highlighted in some studies (Mushfiqur et al., 2018). We return to this in Chapter 9 when thinking about the impact of socio-economic status and class.

Ongoing education and awareness

Respondents wrote about the need for ongoing education about gender in dramatherapy because it permits insight, in the words of one respondent, into the "intersectional roles I play and how gender and expression function to meet separate needs". Some respondents wrote about becoming conscious of their own biases and being stretched to think beyond them. As one respondent wrote,

> I am learning to shift my thinking on gender identity. As a feminist I have been hugely aware of working with oppression as a woman and expected norms, but gender fluidity and expressions is new territory for me I am really enjoying learning and being challenged on.

Another wrote about the embodied impressions of gender socialisation and the ways in which encounters with people who identify differently along a gender spectrum have supported ongoing learning:

> My personal drama therapy work with individuals who are nonbinary, gender nonconforming, transitioning, etc has developed my own understanding of the power of gender narratives and imagery within my own cis male queer experience. In particular it has helped me confront ways in which my experiences have been codified in my body, language, and stories which has helped me look for ways to soften and shift these deep rigidities when working around other forms of difference.

Respondents commented on the value of having spaces to consider the role that gender plays in dramatherapy. As with our opening vignette, it is not always obvious how perceptions and behaviours are linked to internalised biases and associations pertaining to gender and other intersecting identities. As one respondent wrote,

> I have a limited understanding of gender myself, so it sometimes takes me a bit longer to understand when a client expresses associating particular behaviours with their gender, and I have to be more actively aware of the ways in which it can influence. I am aware of societal and historical attitudes and beliefs, but I don't always understand what behaviours, feelings, etc. are connected to gender or how.

These comments are tied to the raison d'être of this book, and we will return to them in Chapters 13 and 15 concerning training and practices.

Gender norms within and outside of one's cultural context

Consistent with our assumption that every interpersonal interaction may be cast as an intercultural encounter, we also noticed comments pertaining to working within and outside of one's own cultural context. As stated earlier and exemplified in our opening vignette, gender expectations will vary greatly in relation to other aspects of identity such as religious and ethnic norms.

As one respondent wrote, "In Thai culture, men are superior to women. The father and the oldest son are given an essential role in the family". They continued to comment on how both gender and age interact to create specific challenges in dramatherapy, especially as an insider to the community. They wrote, "[W]orking with a male client who is much older than me is always a big challenge at the beginning. It takes time to build up a balanced relationship that does not normally happen in Thai society".

In some cases, respondents wrote about the experience of being an outsider in a community with ideas about gender that may differ from their own. One respondent wrote,

> Most of my clients are either children or young adults with complex needs. I am very aware that I am a woman in my sessions...locally there is a predominantly patriarchal society with terrible statistics around the area for domestic violence. I sometimes challenge and explore with clients when they say they are better than me because they are male. I tend to play with these assumptions in my sessions.

The previous passage should also be considered in relation to the opening vignette in terms of how entire cultures may be 'othered' or blamed for violence despite its prevalence across cultural groups (see Narayan, 1997). Another respondent commented on being a dramatherapist working in South Africa, outside their own cultural context. They remarked that they have "had to learn – and continue to do so – that different cultures in South

Africa view gender roles differently and these do not align with my beliefs...
it takes reflection to meet the person in their belief system".

Gender stereotypes and challenging assumptions

Finally, responses also revealed the presence of gender stereotypes and the
desire to challenge assumptions about gender in our field. One respondent
wrote about the need to "joyfully disrupt" gender roles in dramatherapy. It
would be interesting to engage in more dialogue about the underlying value
systems here in our professional community and how they influence one's
practice in dramatherapy.

Dramatherapist reflections on practice

The need for reflection when therapists are working with clients across a range
of belief systems concerning sex and gender is noticeable in dramatherapists'
reflections on their practice. In this section, we present two vignettes written
from two different settings: a continuation of the opening vignette example
with a child and her foster carer, and a second example addressing the explicit
impact of patriarchy on women's lives in the context of incarceration. Each
has their way of working on trying to bridge different assumptions about
gender intersecting with other aspects of identity. The first offers an example of where these themes are worked with implicitly, whereas the second
involves a more explicit exploration.

Vignette I

Joan Moore, the dramatherapist who offered the opening vignette, provided
further reflections on her practice that illuminate the potential to explore
intersections of gender and ethnicity through dramatherapy.

> In play with Polly Pocket sets (miniature dolls), Zoe enacted a story in
> which the "children" are caught cheating in lessons. The main charac-
> ter was a girl called "Kayley" (the name Zoe's mum had wanted for her,
> "Zoe" being her father's choice). In the story, Kayley is up late, excited at
> the prospect of having her friend, Molly, for a sleepover. The next day she
> gets chocolate on her schoolbook and in her hair. The teacher tells her
> off, then her mother decrees that Molly is no longer allowed to stay that
> night but Kayley smuggles her in. A day later, the girls are searching for
> missing treasure. Zoe has imposters pose as Kayley and Molly, to outwit
> the mother, who initially realises that she is being duped. Then the two
> imposters come for dinner and she fails to notice they are not the real
> Kayley and Molly. These guests are given Indian food and the imposter
> of Kayley gets sick from it. Zoe explains that this is because Kayley
> "really hates Indian food". Kayley and Molly find the missing gem stolen
> by the impostors but have to escape a monster that tries to kidnap them.

The dramatherapist felt that the story projected Zoe's rejection of the culture she inherited from her father. The use of 'impostors' was a means of distancing, adding further layers to a story displaying Zoe's impatience with feelings about her ethnicity and identity. Zoe's remark that the impostors had come to see what else was worth stealing also suggested that she might be worried about how many of her things she would be allowed to keep when she moved on to a new placement. The dramatherapist worked implicitly to address the foster carer's stereotyped gender expectation intersected with culture, religion and ethnicity and the impact of that on Zoe.

Again, it can be interesting to note what is foregrounded, what is silenced. We will come back to these in Chapters 7 and 11 when discussing age and borders.

Vignette 2

A more explicit example of working on gender-based oppression comes from Zeina Daccache (2016). Daccache worked with women who were imprisoned in Baabda, a women's prison in Lebanon, to create a therapeutic performance and film to directly address the patriarchal conditions that had resulted in their confinement. She wrote about the therapeutic value of the group working dramatically with each of their stories and the political implications of their efforts, thereby locating healing as both a psychological and social process:

> The women inmates lived in the same conditions as the men: overcrowded prisons, long detention periods, etc. However, their reasons for being behind bars were totally different: most of these women were there because of the patriarchal society in which we live. Nine out of the 25 who joined the drama therapy sessions had killed their husbands, as there was no law to protect them from domestic violence; six were there for adultery, which is regarded as a crime in Lebanon. (Although the law applies for both men and women, no man has ever been incarcerated for committing adultery.) The rest were there for drugs, stealing, etc. Early marriage was a common experience for almost 90 per cent of them. Some had been forced to marry at the age of 12 or 14. They had a deep desire to communicate their stories to the outside world, in order to make sense of the lives they had led. As one of them puts it, "Perhaps our stories would serve to raise awareness to other girls outside, and who knows, maybe our play would help to finally generate laws to protect women…" Each of the women who had murdered her husband told her story, reflected on it, and listened to the other inmates' stories, thus feeling less lonely in their suffering. In the end, when all the bits and pieces of the stories were dramaturgically embroidered into one text, the group chose one or two persons to say the text in front of the audience. So the monologue would hold the stories of nine women, as if it was a single

story. ... I remember one woman who knew that her son who would be in the audience, and wouldn't accept her saying that finally, in prison, she feels at home, as she had never had a proper home outside. After discussing the matter in the group, it was decided she would not be on stage out of courtesy to the family member who thought she was the happiest mother on earth. Indeed, the effect of seeing her text on stage enacted by someone else was as cathartic for her and the audience as if she had enacted it herself. ... The women, just like the male inmates, showed their play for two months in 2012 inside prison to a wide audience of policy makers, media, their families, human rights activists, general public, etc.; and the award winning documentaries depicting both experiences (12 Angry Lebanese – The Documentary and Scheherazade's Diary) toured the world, carrying the inmates' messages even farther. Finally, in April 2014, after a succession of publicised cases of domestic violence, years of Lebanese civil activism by many NGOs, and many screenings of the play Scheherazade in Baabda and of the documentary Scheherazade's Diary, a bill for the Protection of Women and Family Members from Domestic Violence was passed by the Lebanese Parliament.

Other discussions of practice that explore gender expansive and other intersections of gender identity come from the wider field of arts therapies such as Gallo-Jermyn's exploration of the use of dance movement therapy with a transgender adolescent (Macwilliam et al., 2019) and Martin's (2020) use of photography as a means for older women to create self-portraits that challenge images of older women, asking participants to create self-portraits using re-enactments. These and other ways of working discussed in Chapter 15 on practices may enable dramatherapists to take this forward.

Conclusion

The title of this chapter was inspired by the writing of Judith Butler whose book *Gender Trouble* (1990) called attention to the performed and performative social construct of gender. As a construct, it continues to expand and change, as do the material consequences of exploring the space between sex and gender identity and expression. Gender has also been an influential force in dramatherapy, both in terms of practice and the development of the field. Dramatherapists have used embodied, metaphoric and performance-oriented approaches challenging gender stereotypes and internalised sexism and transphobia, but, as responses to our survey attest, there is room to grow. There are cultural shifts concerning popular understandings of sex and gender, which of course vary tremendously wherever we are in the world. Many of us still consciously or unconsciously reference and have internalised a gender binary of male and female, and this is made evident in daily interactions, in the structural foundations of the organisations we work with and within and in our literature where, despite our efforts, we were unable to locate direct accounts of dramatherapy practice with people who identify as transgender or nonbinary. Gender can also be considered in relation to racialisation, age, ability and religion amongst other important markers of differences, as is illustrated in some of the vignette material. It will be useful for us to better get at the nuances of meaning attached to gender as it is expressed in the intercultural encounter of dramatherapy.

Questions for further reflection

- What considerations regarding gender are illuminated in the two vignettes from practice? How do/might you address this in your own practice?
- What were the gender expectations that you grew up with and what has changed in your lifetime?
- (How) do you share authority with your clients, and (how) does gender identity feature in that?
- (How) do you challenge toxic gender assumptions, and how do you determine when and how to do so? Have you drawn on dramatherapy skills to explore or address gender-based assumptions?

Chapter 6

Stigma and desire

Sexual orientation in dramatherapy

When, in 1984, I was successful in gaining a full time job as a dramatherapist in adult mental health I came out to colleagues and never suffered any prejudice or discrimination. In retrospect then it seems a little odd that I was not out to clients. The theory was, and may still be, that it was important to leave clients guessing, to be an ambivalent figure, so as to receive their projections and not foreclose any fantasies or feelings they might have. My first gay client was a young man whom I felt warm towards and with whom I did some useful therapeutic work: he was discharged having recovered from his paranoia. Crucial to his recovery was a trial scene in which he created and played the defence lawyer who countered negative and homophobic attacks. A couple of years later I met him in a gay pub. He expressed astonishment: what was I doing in this place? I told him I was gay and he replied that he had known from the first day we met. That meant both of us had been discreet and avoided mentioning it!... In my own therapy I worked with straight therapists but on one occasion I deliberately chose to go for some counselling at the Manchester LGBT Foundation. I accepted their offer to work with a trainee therapist: the only thing I did not disclose was that I was a therapist myself as I did not want my senior status to get in the way of an effective therapeutic relationship. At the end of our sessions I told him it was important to me that he had been gay. I was then stunned when he told me that he was straight. I had presumed that all counsellors, including trainees, at the LGBT Foundation would have been gay. I felt betrayed and complained to the organisation, saying clients should be given a choice when they presented for help at a centre that identified itself as for gay people. Ultimately the sexuality of this counsellor had not mattered: but my perception that he was gay had made it feel safe to disclose matters I would have been cautious to speak about had I known he was straight (Casson, 2018, p. 181–182).

John Casson, Dramatherapist, UK

In this vignette, John Casson reflects back on his career and on starting as an 'out' dramatherapist in 1984. We recognise that the choice of this vignette privileges a white, gay, male narrative, a perspective that is dominant in gay communities. Indeed, as dramatherapists Snow et al. (2017) and Beauregard et al. (2016) remind us, the sexual lives of women, people of

DOI: 10.4324/9780429431593-8

colour, transgender people, people with varied abilities, older adults, undocumented youth and people in particular religious communities are not as prevalent in the literature. Thinking about the therapist/client match and asking questions about identity may mean different things at different stages of treatment. Representation is often very important and a specific requirement for someone when looking for a 'good fit', and finding a queer therapist may provide permission to start sessions and open up about their own identity. On the other hand, interest in a therapist's sexual identity over the course of treatment can suggest transference or a developmental milestone (K. Long, personal communication, March 17, 2021). Casson's story also offers a hopeful counter-narrative – of being able to come out to one's colleagues without undue consequences while still working through the nuances of disclosure and safety in the context of therapy. This chapter illuminates intercultural dynamics as they relate to sexual orientation and the stress of sexual stigmatisation as expressed in the context of dramatherapy.

The diversity of desire: Sexual orientation, stigma and mental health

Sexual orientation "refers to the sex of whom one is sexually and romantically attracted" (Moleiro & Pinto, 2015, n.p.). The diversity of desire has a long history with archaeological proof of a spectrum of sexual orientation dating back to the San people (circa 8000 BCE) near current-day Zimbabwe where rock paintings depicting same-sex relationships were found (Mehra et al., 2019; Shorter, 2005). In the US, the Kinsey et al. (1948, 1954) experiments, while largely predicated on a white college-educated sample, revealed a broad range of sexual preferences and experiences contrary to prevailing conservative leanings. Similar studies also revealed that adults in the US were up to three times as likely to indicate that they had same-sex attraction than they were to adopt any particular term to describe themselves (Gates, 2011).

The terms used to describe the diversity of sexual attraction have changed over time. There are continuously emerging questions around identity and the reasons for the labels people choose or are given. Some may use terms like *gay*, *lesbian* or *queer* to refer to same-sex attraction and/or *bisexual* or *pansexual* to refer to people who experience attraction to two or more genders. Dramatherapist Bayley discussed the term queer as indicating "an ontological challenge to the dominant labelling philosophies, especially the medicalisation of the subject implied by the word 'homosexual', as well as a challenge to discreet gender categories" (Meyer cited in Bayley, 1999, p. 3). The term 'LGBTQIA+' refers to lesbian, gay, bisexual, transgender, queer, intersexual, asexual and more. Gender is sometimes conflated with sexual orientation; like one's gender identity, sexual orientation can be regarded as fluid and changeable over time.

Despite evidence of normal variation in human sexual orientation, desire has long been stigmatised, regulated and pathologised (Drescher, 2015; Porter,

2000). In 1885, the Criminal Law Amendment act made homosexual acts between men illegal in the UK, and by 1954, the number of men imprisoned for homosexual acts had risen to over 1,000 per year. The *Wolfenden Report* by the UK Parliament (1957) recommended that homosexual acts between two consenting adults should no longer be a criminal offence, but this was not implemented by Parliament until the 1967 Sexual Offences Act, which only offered partial decriminalisation. Scotland and N. Ireland did not follow until the 1980s, whilst clause 28, introduced in 1984 by the Thatcher government in the UK, outlawed the 'promotion of homosexuality' in schools. Policing in the 1980s and 1990s was very homophobic and wrapped up in a growing fear of AIDS. Arrests for 'gross indecency' increased, for example, after decriminalisation between 1966 and 1974, by more than 300% (Cant & Hemmings, 1988). This was the context for Casson's opening vignette.

In 1973, the American Psychiatric Association declassified homosexuality as a mental disorder, and it was no longer included in the *Diagnostic and Statistical Manual of Mental Disorders* (Conger, 1975). However, it took until 1998 for the American Psychological Association (APA) to state its opposition to reparative and conversion therapy (APA, 1998). It was only in 2000 that the APA asserted that "same-sex sexual and romantic attractions, feelings, and behaviors are normal and positive variations of human sexuality regardless of sexual orientation identity" (APA, 2009), and in 2012, guidelines were issued concerning therapy with lesbian, gay and bisexual clients (APA, 2012). It was only in 2017 that the British Association of Counselling and Psychotherapy (BACP) and the United Kingdom Conference of Psychotherapists (UKCP) issued a joint memorandum of understanding with Stonewall to support the outlawing of gay conversion therapy (Turner, 2021). Similarly, these shifts in understanding emerged in writing within the arts therapies (Bayley, 1999; Beauregard et al., 2016; Carr, 2016; Casson, 2018; Kawano et al., 2018; Trottier, 2019; Whitehead-Pleaux et al., 2013) and were made explicit in our professional organisations (Beauregard et al., 2016; Bilodeau et al., 2016).

Over the last 25 years, being gay has increasingly been decriminalised, become more visible and subject to legal protection (Cameron & Johnson, 2015). Today, we are finding ourselves in a world where, in certain countries, concepts of sexual and gender identity are openly discussed and expanded as they are in the aforementioned terms (MacWilliam et al., 2019), whilst in other countries, homosexuality is illegal and punishable by imprisonment or death (Ward, 2018). Even in countries where LGBTQIA+ individuals have equal rights, intersections with others aspects of identity may result in unequal and negative treatment which, in turn, contribute to negative health impacts for those within the community (Flanders et al., 2016).

Being sexually stigmatised, a process of being overtly or covertly 'othered,' marginalised as different from a socially acceptable heterosexual norm, results in poor physical and mental health outcomes (Jones, 2009b; Matsick et al., 2020). There continue to be significant stressors related to discrimination in schools, in the workplace and in families (Bachmann & Gooch, 2018; Meyer, 2015; Pew Research Center, 2013) that, like Covid-19, have had an unequal impact on people of colour, undocumented and otherwise marginalised communities (Beauregard et al., 2016; Frost et al., 2013). The introductory vignettes in both Chapters 1 and 7 show that invisibility and medicalisation can be problematic, with experiences of discrimination and bullying contributing to this. At the same time, how therapists and clients in dramatherapy juggle a multiplicity of perspectives, including transparency about client/therapist sexual identity and different cultural and religious perceptions, remain important questions to be explored.

Dramatherapist perspectives

In this section, and as in other chapters, we present responses to our survey on the influence of culture and identity in dramatherapy in relation to examples of literature in the field beginning with demographics. What follows is a thematic organisation of the ways in which respondents observed the influence of sexual orientation in their experience of dramatherapy. The themes identified are judgement, self-disclosure, client-therapist match, internalised biases, the need for continuous professional development and considering dramatherapy as a queer practice. As with each chapter, we invite the reader to remain curious about the presence of these experiences in our field and to consider what is missing, what may have changed and where there remains work yet to do.

Demographics: Sexual identity

Twenty-seven of a total of 66 respondents identified sexual orientation as important to their practice but did not self-identify. Of the respondents who did self-identify, 40 % identified as heterosexual/straight, 23% as gay/queer, 21% bisexual and 15% other (pansexual, asexual, other). One commented, "[I]t is the spirit that I connect to, not the organs". This variation is somewhat higher than what was reported in findings from surveys of the membership of the British Association of Dramatherapists (BADth) (Carr et al., 2015; Dokter & Hughes, 2007a) and North American dramatherapists (Beauregard et al., 2016). These studies revealed that at least 25% of members in BADth and approximately 30% of respondents to the Beauregard et al. (2016) study identify as other than heterosexual.

Judgement

The fear of being judged for one's sexual orientation was raised by several survey respondents. As one respondent wrote, "Being very likely asexual, I tend to be concerned about being judged even by other LGBTQA+ members, but in practice, I try not to make assumptions or use heterosexist language in working with my clients". Others wrote about the complex ways in which judgement is internalised resulting in ongoing suppression. As one respondent wrote,

> I hope to be open and affirming in my practice. I work with teenagers and young adults mostly. If asked I will discuss my sexual orientation. But in my youth having had many sexual partners across gender and identities I was marginalized for not choosing a team to play on. That stigma (along with internalized oppression) remains with me. I am aware that because of this I will answer when asked but not always locate myself as directly on this topic as I might on others.

Similar themes may be found in writing by dramatherapists. Dramatherapist Southern (2018) reflected on the fear of judgement, rejection and misinterpretation in her reflections on practice as a bisexual dramatherapist. The pressure to conform to a label can be hard for someone identifying as bisexual, a label that we as authors share with Southern. She reflected on how fear can lead to secrecy and suppression, which she sees as a repeating pattern in the LGBTQI+ community and particularly in ethnic and faith communities in which sexual diversity is discouraged. She wrote,

> I recall how a former client experienced a similar journey to mine with her ethnicity, faith and profession. During a group session for a team of health professionals, a Muslim client shared her experiences of her sexuality when the group were exploring and disclosing "secrets" they did not know about each other. She reflected on a secret lesbian relationship…and was open with her colleagues about her difficulties in negotiating her sexuality alongside her family, her faith, and the conflicts that arose from this. I remember the risk she took in disclosing this information to fellow Muslim colleagues, which has since encouraged me to take that leap of faith.
>
> (Southern, 2018, p. 184)

What is particularly compelling about this passage for us is the way in which Southern and so many in the LGBQAI+ community draw strength from others, including our clients. Indeed, social buffering, a sense of belonging, has long been understood to be an important mitigator of stress, inoculating us against its worst impacts (Thorsteinsson et al., 1998). One of our respondents spoke about countering judgement and wrote that "modelling a positive attitude about sexuality in dramatherapy has been most effective in affording adolescents and young adults space to explore themes involving sex and sexuality".

Self-disclosure

Contrary to and in spite of the experience of judgement, some dramatherapists reflected on the benefits and challenges associated with self-disclosure in their practice and when, if, how this benefitted treatment. Long (personal communication, March 17, 2021) queries the nature of verbal and non-verbal disclosure and how client projections concerning sexuality may inform treatment:

> Given the privilege of verbal language, we often think of disclosing as only through spoken words…we can't not disclose – how we dress, our facial expressions, etc. all bring our subjective experiences into drama therapy spaces. There is also a range of disclosure. I am out to some patients, but not others who still project 'straightness' onto me in ways that serve their treatment.

Others wrote about taking an unambiguous stance in their practice. As one respondent wrote,

> I have chosen to be a formally and officially "out" drama therapist and have (in my experience) benefited from that personally and professionally. I do find when differences around queer identity present challenges in my own experiences I am often a bit off-guard, that sense of "oh, I thought I was safe here".

Dramatherapist Dixon (2018) evaluated what therapist disclosure surrounding sexual orientation can mean for the client in the context of family therapy. He discussed the fact that having no children of his own also had an impact in the context of family therapy and offered a case vignette of a gay foster family with 8-year-old twins and a 4-year-old younger brother. While the female twin would speak openly about living with her two 'gay dads,' the male twin never discussed them with his peers and was aggressive towards his foster carers. Dixon described his impulse to work with the identity of the foster carers in relation to how the children perceived them. However, the foster parents, aware that he was gay, appeared to be more interested in whether Dixon had children. In his reflection, Dixon described initially understanding this as them looking for role models of gay parents but then began to understand them as looking to find agency within themselves. Dixon narrated that his supervision helped him to understand that sexual identity was secondary to other complex issues such as accepting support and establishing trust.

Jason Ward's (2018) work with LGBTQ asylum seekers is discussed in greater detail in our chapter on borders in the therapy room (Chapter 11). He highlights the internal and external conflicts when being asked to 'prove' one's sexual orientation (Home Office, 2016), especially when in one's country of origin one has been socialised against it and may be at great risk when disclosing. Asylum seekers also have to prove that their country views homosexuality negatively by legislation (homosexuality is still illegal in 72 countries) or punishable by imprisonment or death. Even if not illegal, people may be imprisoned, sometimes for other 'crimes' such as waving rainbow flags with a partner.

Finally, Campinho Valadas (2018) raises that his years of controlling his own emotions left him ill-equipped in social interactions with fellow gay men which informed his perspectives on self-disclosure. He describes how inner insecurities affected interaction noting that "there isn't any type of discrimination that the gay community cannot inflict on itself first" (2018, p. 165). Valadas states how during the dramatherapy group he facilitated he also began to feel more secure in his attachments to gay men professionally and personally but notes the ways in which HIV, the lack of an efficient non-shaming public response, resulted in internalised stigma and conditioning both within and outside the gay community:

> As a community which has seen sex and sexual liberation as its main avenue of expressivity, but with this expressivity used as a weapon against it, sex and intimacy are rarely easy topics to explore with gay men. Often used as a cure for loneliness, rather than an act of intimacy, what kind of wounding is done when gay men are told and learn to perceive their bodies and sexuality as deviant or damaged, or when there is a stigmatising illness such as HIV?"
>
> (Valadas, 2018, p. 169)

Shame complicates disclosure even when it may be of use in the clinical space. This is explored further in relation to client-therapist match in the next section.

Client-therapist match

Connected to self-disclosure are issues pertaining to client-therapist match which were also present in Casson's opening vignette. Some survey participants wrote about deliberately choosing a matching therapist based on their sexual orientation. As one respondent wrote,

> This was a long-standing issue for me in my personal drama therapy. I worked with a straight therapist for 6 years. There were several times when I felt like her (straight, female) experiences closed off some places that our therapy might otherwise have been able to go. At the time, there were no queer options for me, so it was not a deep experience of problems. But when I shifted to non-drama therapy, I was easily able to find a queer verbal therapist in my city.

Dramatherapist Sheppard (2018) conducted heuristic research on therapist self-disclosure of sexual orientation and offered insights related to client-therapist match. She highlighted the lack of dramatherapy literature in this area, but as growing in the arts and psychotherapies, with Bayley's (1999) article as an early forerunner drawing dramatherapists' attention to gay affirmative therapy (Davies, 1996). Sheppard described a psychodynamic orientation in dramatherapy in which reflective feedback could be used to help the client make life-drama connections without drawing attention to the therapist's own experiences. Here, Sheppard referred to Kahn (2001) in describing how therapist disclosure might reduce the space for a client to explore, as well as Kramer (2013) in arguing that teaching trainees how and when to disclose might help therapist authenticity. In connection with client-therapist match, Sheppard raised that older literature (Goldstein, 1994; Kaufman et al., 1997) indicated that client-therapist match was particularly preferred by lesbians and that a therapist's willingness to self-disclose their sexual orientation could be perceived as more important than their actual orientation. She also highlights that non-disclosure can be damaging if the therapist brings shame, guilt and fear into the therapy space, potentially exacerbating the client's internalised identical feelings.

Dramatherapist Trottier (2019) looked at the parallel journey of the queer therapist and straight clients in his work with adult clients in an acute psychiatric unit. He uses Goffman's concept of *passing* or covering, a way to refer to individuals who appear as if they do not possess the stigma in question and perform as 'normals' (Goffman, 1963, p. 5). Trottier discusses how he makes choices and can be more comfortable when interacting with straight women and queer clients. He cites literature advocating client-therapist match on sexual orientation (Kronner & Northcut, 2015; Liddle, 1996; Porter et al., 2015) and discusses how he regulates his queer performance given evidence of how clients are affected by a therapist's non-verbal physical and verbal exchanges. A therapist may choose to hide these markers in an effort to be seen differently or unintentionally pass as a member of the majority (Fuller et al., 2009).

Trottier documents how, as a queer therapist working with straight clients, there can be complications around acceptance (Satterly, 2006), such as heterosexism and negative comments from clients and projection of homophobia from the therapist onto the client. Trottier does not mention internalised homophobia, but given socialisation processes, this can be an additional consideration. Each of these may lead to alternative ways of self-disclosure and complicate the notion of client-therapist match: risk is one factor, intimacy another, whilst guilt at not disclosing may be a third. Different categories of self-disclosure can be philosophical (sharing of perspective or facts), countertransference, emotions conveyed in the session, relational, fantasy and historical (Kooden, 1991). The latter is the explicit information specific to the therapist's life. Trottier advocates an adaptive model for decision-making concerning therapist self-disclosure.

Internalised biases and the need for continuing professional development

Some survey responses revealed efforts to grapple with one's own biases, as well as the necessity for ongoing learning. As one respondent wrote,

> [Sexual orientation] influences my interactions with others and teaches me about my own biases. It is sometimes difficult and I need to brush up

on my understanding of different orientations. Generally I am open to being educated, but recognise this should not be the role of client. I will take responsibility for learning here.

Four respondents stated that sexual orientation did not matter or was culturally contested. One cannot tell if this effort to deny difference was intended to minimise the reality and impact of sexual orientation or perhaps more of a call to value what connects us.

> [Sexual orientation] does not [influence my experience of dramatherapy]…we can teach each other about life, expectations, and cultures but ultimately we are all humans.
>
> In my country, LGBT people still face discrimination in many areas (e.g. education and employment). There are various degrees of acceptance for people of different sexual orientations; LGBT appears to be the least that gets accepted. The LGBT clients who have grown up in a traditional family, usually feel badly ashamed and guilty as it has been claimed that they are destroying a family reputation.

As co-authors, we believe the social positions of the authors (i.e. whether they identify as LGBTQAI+) can change the meaning of the previous statements. Whether the universal values in the first response equate with a certain dismissal of the reality of the second statement is worth considering. We are all humans, but within those experiences are constructs which significantly affect individuals and communities, so that they feel pushed to the edge of belonging (Campinho Valladas, personal communication, 2021). Is there an equivalent to colour blindness where assumed heteronormativity makes these experiences invisible?

Dramatherapy as a queer practice

Both dramatherapists and clients wrote about the value of dramatherapy in aiding their own exploration of sexual orientation. In our survey, both reflected on the role of dramatherapy in leaving room to explore uncertainty and, in some instances, likened dramatherapy to a queer practice in how it embraces a relational process of becoming.

Queer theory is "a framework of ideas that suggest that identities are not stable or deterministic, particularly in regard to an individual's gender, sex, and/or sexuality" (Gieseking, 2008, p. 738). Queer theory is committed to problematising previous ways of theorising identity beginning with troubling heteronormativity, the assumption of expected, normative, and constant relationships between people who conform to a male/female gender binary. This theoretical lens affirms identity as fluid and multifaceted. Dramatherapist Tomczyk (2015, 2019) observed overlaps between queer theory and dramatherapy. He wrote,

> A drama therapy informed by queer theory, a queer drama therapy, can interrogate our implicit and taken for granted assumptions of heteronormativity and homophobia, and can indeed disrupt these harmful binaries and become an intervention for homophobic bullying and develop a catalyst for social change.
>
> (2015, n.p.)

This confluence between dramatherapy and queer theory is evident in some of the responses received. One respondent, who identified as a client, described themselves as 'heterosexual questioning' and wrote about the importance of "the capacity of the practitioner to sit with my unknown as a client". Another respondent, who also identified as a client, wrote, "This is still a figuring out process for me – something that drama therapy has helped open up for me to question and play with".

Dramatherapist Gaines (2021) situated aspects of his work with LGBTQ+ older adults within the realm of therapeutic drama rather than dramatherapy. He conducted a qualitative case study about creative arts classes offered at a Centre for Urban Seniors with pride in New York, specialising in serving the needs of older adults who identify as LGBTQ+. As we discuss in Chapter 7 about age and ageing, the older age population is increasing, and so is the impact of their marginalisation. LGBTQ older adults are a relative minority faced with intersecting forms of discrimination; their sexuality and gender are compounded by their marginalisation as elders. They also have fewer children, which is noteworthy because adult children can be an advantage for advocacy in a social care network (Institute of Medicine, 2011). As Choi and Meyer (2016) have documented in their research with queer older adults, encountering discrimination can perpetuate a cycle of increased avoidance of needed assistance potentially exacerbating illness. While these challenges exist, Gaines (2021) emphasises the value of creative expression in affirming the strengths, achievements and vitality of his participants in ways that illuminate, integrate and transcend stable notions of sexual orientation, gender and age.

Dramatherapist reflections on practice

In this section, we offer two vignettes from dramatherapy practice that illuminate aspects of desire and sexual orientation. These extend what survey respondents chose to comment on in the survey and include opportunities to think further about therapist self-disclosure and issues related to erotic transference. These are presented with an invitation to the reader to consider in relation to training and practice.

Vignette I

I had worked for two years with a client who had self-referred for loneliness and her reluctance to enter an intimate relationship. During therapy, she explored her sexuality and towards the end of the first year in therapy entered into a same-sex relationship. This relationship ended shortly before she said she would like to end her therapy with me and find a gay therapist to explore her identity further. I had not named my bisexuality and wondered whether this would have made a difference to her, helping or hindering. I had wondered about self-disclosure in the engagement stage, especially when she was wondering whether she was bisexual. Over time, she felt that identifying as bisexual was her denial of being gay. Would it have been helpful or hindering for her to know throughout our therapy how I identified? I will stay with my wondering. My thinking about the ending was that she needed at that stage a therapist whose sexual orientation was explicitly identified to continue her therapeutic journey. She herself was now also more explicit about her identity. I had discussed self-disclosure in supervision and decided not to take that route, especially in the light of her ambivalence about bisexuality. It had not stopped her exploring her sexuality within and outside therapy, but there may be particular phases in a person's development or within the therapy when a therapist being explicit about their sexual identity can be more beneficial. She did not ask me, and I did not volunteer; Trottier's philosophical, relational and emotional self-disclosure were present both verbally and non-verbally in our therapeutic relationship. Both my client and I came from religious backgrounds where homophobia was present; the differences in our ages meant that she had grown up in an environment that was more tolerant of diversity but had also experienced internalised homophobic attitudes and the fear of stigma, which we could explore between us in a 'not knowing' opening up atmosphere.

Vignette 2

I had been working, in private practice, with an Italian-Lebanese woman who had recently decided to divorce her husband following the unexpected loss of a child. Over the course of the next few months, she began to work through her grief and the cultural expectations that had led her to marry him. She also began to question her sexuality and spoke about her fears about how she might be seen in her family if she were to share her questions with them. We often used small projective objects to clarify the different forces she was grappling with. In one session, she placed two small figurines in a confrontational stance with a group of other objects, and, together, we began to animate the scene. The scene conveyed her fears that her excitement about the possibility of feeling desire again would be overshadowed by her family's judgements about her attraction to women and about considering her own desire so soon after a loss. She imagined them calling her selfish. She described coming out to her family as a way of taking back some sense of control in a time when roles as a wife and mother had been disrupted. I disclosed the fact that I had come out as bisexual to my family following a separation and that I could empathise with the complexity of working through cultural expectations. She appeared to be briefly comforted by this connection. However, over the next few sessions, I became aware of her growing curiosity about me, about lesbian relationships and her slight but noticeable delay in leaving my office after our sessions had ended. At the end of one session in particular, she approached me in such a way as to communicate wanting a hug but shifted into approaching me for a kiss, which I avoided. She didn't return for two weeks afterwards but did eventually come back. I wondered about whether returning would be tolerable and how to acknowledge what felt like an erotic transference. I wondered about how to work with her newfound desire without coupling it with any shame arising from her feelings towards me.

Conclusion

As with all themes taken up in this book, there remains much more to explore. Bayley's (1999) 22-year-old call for gay affirmative dramatherapy practice has been followed up by more recent publications, some of which point to a positive embrace of dramatherapy as a queer practice. Yet, more research remains necessary to illuminate how the promise of a queer dramatherapy might unfold in conditions where sexual diversity is highly stigmatised. We would also benefit from further studies of the experience of LGBTQ+ dramatherapists and participants of varied ages, abilities, socio-economic backgrounds, legal status and faiths. In addition to this, further research about the impact of sexual orientation on the therapeutic relationship can enable this to become more explorable within the therapy room (see Davies, 1996). As dramatherapist Porter (2000) reminds us, the issue of desire in the therapy room can be difficult but crucial to acknowledge as a life-giving impulse that does not need to be destructively or abusively enacted.

Questions for further reflection

- What considerations regarding sexual orientation are illuminated in the two vignettes from practice? How do/might you address this in your own practice?
- From your own experience and maybe some of the examples in this chapter, how do you think desire and sexual orientation is/can be valued in your practice and, structurally, in your places of work?
- Create a collage of images representing messages you received as a young person about sexuality and sexual orientation and compare these to how you consider sexuality and sexual orientation today.
- Reflect on instances where sexuality and sexual orientation arose in the therapeutic relationship, whether as client or therapist. What was helpful, what was not helpful and why?

Chapter 7

Co-creating our future selves

Age and ageism

When I was a young dramatherapist working on an acute mental health ward, I was often referred to as 'young lady.' I encouraged clients in an open dramatherapy group to choose a puppet from a selection lying in the middle of a circle of chairs. An older gentleman looked at me with outrage "I know I am in a madhouse, but you asking me to choose a toy I would give my grandchild to play with feels you add insult to injury. I may be mad, but I am not infantile!" Later, as a middle aged therapist, I was sitting in an elderly psychiatric ward with an older woman searching for words. She had been an interpreter in her working life, now in the middle stages of dementia losing her words. Constantly searching for words that were no longer there, trying to interpret her thoughts into a language that could be communicated to someone else. I sat with her trying to help with the search, but also trying to draw her attention to images and objects in front of her, stirring memories. She did not want to move, so my more usual way of interacting in movement was not available to us at that point. I empathised with her frustration, not being able to find words, not being able to find the right words, with someone for whom language had been a way of making a living, who had been able to use more than one language to help other people understand each other. I felt an unbearable sadness, both at her situation and the potential of facing something similar myself in older age. Not being able to communicate in understandable language was familiar to me as an English additional language speaker, but the sense that this was not a development towards more understanding, but a development to less and less understanding felt at that point unbearable to me.

Dramatherapist, UK

In this vignette, a dramatherapist describes working with older clients as a young therapist, addressing each other in the language used at the time, and later at a more experienced middle age. Asking older people to play was intended to be an effort at liberation. The dramatherapist did not take into account that this could be received as one of the indignities visited upon older people which, coupled with the experience of residential psychiatric care, could lead to feelings of being disrespected. A repetition of how elders may feel treated and perceived in a youth-oriented cultural context. Later, the countertransference of unbearable sadness felt by this dramatherapist at

DOI: 10.4324/9780429431593-9

progressively losing the ability to connect and communicate was part of a migrant awareness of becoming even more out of place in older age unless someone else was willing to learn a second language (Walsh & Nare, 2016). As with the opening vignettes in other chapters, we have partial information here but enough of a picture to begin to consider how we regard youth, getting older and the provision of care and opportunities for creativity as we age. The opening vignette refers to the experience of an older adult that experiences a significant decrease in functioning, but ageing is very heterogeneous and our dramatherapy practice takes place with diverse populations whose ageing experience is informed by their racial, ethnic, gender and other aspects of identity. As dramatherapists, we often work in age-segregated settings. There are innovative institutional or community-based forms of dramatherapy practice that interrupt such ageism and offer instead inter- or multigenerational dramatherapy practices that aim to resolve the personal, familial and community effects of 'elder' un-well-being. Since ageing is the future of all of us, the encounter with ageing stimulates unique and sometimes complex emotions and thoughts in the countertransference. In this chapter, we focus on older age though we recognise the importance of examining childhoods in relation to dramatherapy where issues of voice and agency are also critical concerns (see Jones 2009b, and Jones et al., 2020). Here, we explore intercultural dramatherapy from the lens of age and ageism and include a thematic analysis of responses from dramatherapists and dramatherapy clients concerning the role of age in the experience of dramatherapy, as well as vignettes from practice that account for a variety of institutional, intergenerational and other care settings.

Ageing, ageism and mental health

Two demographic trends are taking place worldwide (UN, 2013). Firstly, population ageing as a result of decreasing mortality and fertility, and secondly, the ageing of the older population itself with increasing numbers of people living past 80 years of age. Age is conceptualised here as a sociocultural construction that emerges in place (Bytheway, 1995; Wilson, 2000) and includes chronological, physiological and social dimensions (Arber, Davidson and Ginn, 2005). The World Health Organization indicated that 60 constitutes the threshold of older age, although there is a wide range of variability interculturally as to which chronological ages are seen as older age, "the proportion of the world's population over 60 years will nearly double from 12% to 22% between 2015–2050", with 80% of older people living in low to middle-income countries (WHO, 2015). Ageing is a natural developmental process reaching across the lifespan that affects every single being. However, the experience and expectations associated with ageing are subjective and culturally specific. When we consider ageing through an intersectional lens, older adults are not one homogeneous group (Applewhite, 2017). What we qualify as 'old', the terms we use (e.g. senior, elder, older adult) and the status accorded to elders will vary in relation to regional life expectancy, cultural context, racialisation, gender, religion and socio-economic status, dis/ability, legal and health status, family composition, prevalent attitudes about ageing, death and dying and resources available. This can also vary due to self-perceptions of ageing, which is considered to be a significant factor that influences the way people age. Dramatherapy has great potential to positively influence the various aspects of self-perceptions of ageing, such as *successful ageing*, referring to how well people perceive themselves to age (Pruchno et al., 2010) and *ageing satisfaction*, referring to the way one perceives changes that occur with increasing age, such as changes in energy level, feelings of usefulness and life quality (Kleinspehn-Ammerlahn et al., 2008). This can contrast with *ageing anxiety*, which refers to the concern and anticipation of adverse physical, mental and personal losses during the ageing process (Kafer et al., 1980).

While we may be living longer (WHO, 2015), a longer life does not necessarily mean a better quality of life. We internalise messages about ageing as part of our socialisation as we grow up, and these narratives and attitudes have psychological and political implications in that they are reflected in policies, programmes and decision-making concerning older adults (Kendig et al., 2019). For example, older adults are constrained by labour policies that limit their presence in the workforce (Quinn & Burkhauser, 1994). Women tend to bear the brunt of ageism in what has been referred to as the feminisation of ageing (Brownell, 2014), with older people from racialised groups facing a 'double jeopardy' of discrimination in the workplace (Centre for Better Ageing, 2020; Ford, 2020).

The extreme manifestation of negative biases may be elder abuse and active neglect, but its contrast is no less harmful: a complete absence of interest (Lee et al., 2003). In a study focused on promoting positive attitudes towards ageing, Goncalves (2009) asserts that negative attitudes towards ageing are behind the difficulty in recruiting students in health-related academic training programmes. She offers examples that are rooted in a socially prescribed *role repertoire* available to older adults:

> Older adults are usually depicted in popular media as falling into one of three prototypes: the grandmother (accepting, helpful, emotional, and neat), the elder statesman (conservative, active, and dignified) and the senior citizen (lonely, old-fashioned, and worried).
>
> (Goncalves, 2009, p. 203)

Indeed, attitudes toward ageing remain quite limiting and negative according to a review of the evidence, with older people seen as incompetent, unproductive, hostile or a burden on society (Palmore, 2015). Even policy frameworks such as the *successful ageing* movement can carry implicit ageist messages; to age successfully is to not age at all or at least not exhibit any signs of illness and decline (Bowling & Dieppe, 2005). This influences the people working in elder care but also elders' self-perception in their perspective on therapy, whether they feel 'too old' to go into therapy or too consumed with negative attitudes towards their own ageing (Bodner et al., 2018). The risk of highlighting negatives about older age is to forget the positives of extended family support, gaining wisdom over time and seeing the older stage of life as an opportunity for specific life stage development: mental decline is not the same as growing old, whilst the brain reorganises itself throughout life (Quinodoz, 2009).

Age discrimination, or ageism, according to Robert Butler (1975), the gerontologist who coined the term, "allows those of us who are younger to see old people as 'different'. We subtly cease to identify with them as human beings, which enables us to feel more comfortable about our neglect and dislike of them" (Butler cited in Reinstein, 2002, p. 10). Ageism is one of the strangest ways of othering as it is "a prejudice targeting our future selves" (Applewhite, 2017; Baum, 2018). The concept of "ageism" is changing over time. More recent theories of ageism argue that when we treat "old age" as one period of life, or "older adults" as one group, and we don't consider the heterogeneity of ageing, we use ageist attitudes (Ayalon & Tesch-Römer, 2018).

The degree to which ageing is seen as a burden will vary across societies; even cultural groups that may be seen as honouring and respectful of elders struggle with negative biases (Boduroglu et al., 2006). The Covid-19 pandemic has led to a general increase in the incidence of ageism (Ayalon et al., 2021), whilst the young struggle, currently and in future, with the economic and social impact of the pandemic: highlighting the need for an increased fostering of intergenerational solidarity.

Flipping the script on ageing towards equating getting older with possibility and creativity (Ayalon & Tesch-Römer, 2018; Bloom, 2014) rather than deficits and impairments (Abrams et al., 2015; DOH, 2009) enables us and those we work with to approach the future with interest rather than with apprehension and anxiety. Thankfully, this shift towards ageing as part of an ongoing journey of self-discovery has been gaining traction over the last two decades within the creative ageing movement (Bloom, 2014; Klimczuk, 2016; Thomas & Lyles, 2007; Quinodoz, 2009). A review on the impact of arts participation with older adults revealed benefits to general health, mood, medication use, increase in one's sense of mastery, decreases in anxiety and depression and increased balance leading to a decrease in the occurrence of falls (Castora-Binkley et al., 2010; Dunphy et al., 2019).

Of particular interest to dramatherapists may be the work of Dintino (2021) who has written about embracing ageing from midlife and beyond as part of a future-focused dramatherapy in non-institutional settings in which play offers a means of reviving and reinvigorating possibility. Keisari et al. (2018) studied the use of playback theatre with older adults in therapeutic settings and found that the playfulness of this approach enhanced flexibility, development, belonging and social engagement. Jaaniste (2011) reminds us of the importance of spirituality as a cultural intersection of care with older adults, and specifically adults with dementia, in dramatherapy. She considers dramatherapy a means to valuing the ageing process wherein "cultural questions and answers can assist with celebration, reminiscence, pleasure and grieving, and ultimately the transition to a dignified and spiritually meaningful death" (p. 16). The outcomes related to theatre-based training conducted by Noice and Noice (2006, 2009, 2013, 2021; Noice et al., 1999, 2004, 2014, 2015) evidenced improved cognitive skills in several populations of older adults. Fraser et al. (2015) undertook a scoping review of the arts in relation to ageing and quality of life, whilst Hanna et al. (2015) in the same year reviewed the impact of the arts on healthy ageing. Novy (2019) emphasises a performance-oriented approach to life story individual dramatherapy with a client with dementia. Redhouse (2014) also advocates life story work as part of end-of-life care. In this chapter, we do not focus on end-of-life care, although preparation for death is of course another aspect of our life cycle (Miller, 2000) at whatever age it comes.

Dramatherapists perspectives

As with other chapters, data from our intercultural survey are included here in relation to relevant literature in the field on ageing beginning with demographic data and then the results of our thematic analysis of responses. As with each chapter, we invite the reader to remain curious about the presence of these experiences in our field and to consider what is missing, what may have changed and where there remains work yet to do.

Demographics: Age

Respondents (n = 66) to the survey came from a range of ages, reasonably evenly spread with similar small-sized groups in the lower and higher age groups. The majority of respondents were between 25 and 55. Three were aged below 24; seven were between 25 and 34, including two clients; ten were between 35 and 44; seven were between 45 and 54; four were between 55 and 64. One self-identified as an older adult without indicating chronological age. Thirty-four respondents did not complete this survey question and one explained why not:

> I don't reveal my age although always asked, because I made a conscious decision to not let age limit the potential journey we take. I stand out by my appearance alone and it works to use this strategy for me.

The quote is an example of the anticipated effects of revealing one's age. The use of the word 'strategy' is also noteworthy; we develop ways of coping with the stigma associated with ageing. We reflected on this as co-authors, and Ditty noted that she seldom reveals her age when in the role of therapist but uses queries about age to ask clients about the meaning that age holds for them. She noted that her body indicates that her age is on the older rather than younger end of the spectrum. She recalled how, as a younger therapist, it could matter for the clients if they were older than her, as age was perceived as corresponding with experience. Nisha reflected on her own hesitation in revealing her age and having had to contend with limiting narratives about getting older since her early 20s, as women were considered 'on the shelf' if they remained unmarried after the age of 24. Similar tensions were present in the written responses offered by respondents which we have categorised in the following sections and discussed in relation to literature in the field.

A changing relationship to play

Several responses resonated with our opening vignette with regard to the place of play as we get older. Some respondents commented on how age changes perceptions of play stating that "age disrupts or raises the fear of play and how play happens". Reinstein (2002), quoting a famous poem, reminds us that we may choose to "wear purple…with a red hat that doesn't suit me" and feel less inhibited about approaching life from a place of playful discovery as we age. On the other hand, as surmised by the complaint from the gentleman in the opening vignette, one may feel wary of playing the fool (Casson, 2005).

Indeed, the writing of dramatherapists leans towards an agreement that play in older age is a valuable and enjoyable activity with psychological and social benefits (Jennings, 2005; Dintino, 2021). This is supported by the Bernard and Rickett (2017) literature review on older people's participation in theatre, as well as their participation in improvisational playback theatre (Keisari et al., 2020a, 2020b). Thirty years ago, Michaels (1981) stressed the aim to transform institutions into rehabilitative rather than debilitative environments and focused on how joyful, dramatic techniques facilitate memory recall and creativity. "Whether the members are sick, senile, disabled or severely deprived in some way through the ageing process, the leader attempts to construct situations which offer enjoyment, ego reinforcement and ultimately the opportunity to build a stronger self image" (Michaels, 1981, p. 175). In his writing about dramatherapy, and specifically the Developmental Method, with "the elderly," Johnson (1986) remarked that his playful approach facilitated "the unfolding of murky, ambiguous, shifting feelings of the group into more coherent, concrete group themes and issues" and encouraged a deeper investment in interpersonal relationships with each other which countered the risk of isolation. Rather than ignore potential feelings of infantilisation that might come with participating in such processes in residential care, Johnson writes about inviting these expressions into the process:

> The Developmental Method is particularly effective, however, in improving personal relationships by ameliorating personal fears of being incompetent, stupid, or awkward, feelings of humiliation and emptiness, and the projection of these feelings through antagonistic attitudes to others

("I am not like those ugly old people"). The result is greater tolerance for oneself and others, and relief from the anxieties generated by rigid interpersonal stances.

(p. 18)

Several other colleagues in our field have written about play in the context of ageing in institutional settings where older adults may feel protective of their past selves. Crimmens (1998) emphasised seeking 'adventure within' in contexts where there are minimal opportunities for external exploration. Lev-Aladgem (1999) focused on the value of playing in residential settings as a means of creating alternative realities.

Client perspectives of their therapist's age

In the survey, three respondents self-identified as dramatherapy clients. One client offered their perspective in which they emphasise the importance of being able to choose as possibly being more important than the age of the dramatherapist:

> As a client – as long as a practitioner is authentic, age should not be an issue…as a client. … I have the agency and empowerment to seek out the therapy and so I can make the choices I need for the work I need to do. Sometimes a younger practitioner is just right for the needs, and at other times an older practitioner. However, if I were in a position to be given dramatherapy again – rather than have a choice, I might find it difficult to engage with who I am given, as my right to choose would be much more limited by the situation I may be in to be assigned the practitioner.

This perspective is congruent with research indicating that age is an often unrecognised factor in psychotherapy which can influence the outcome (Karasu et al. 1979, Rosen et al., 2012). Perceptions of therapists' age have also been taken up in writing about dramatherapy with older adults. Johnson (1986) referring to the work of Meerloo (1955), wrote about *reverse transference* in work with elders as "the therapist is seen both as a parental figure, who is responsible for the organisation, leadership, and safety of the group and, as a child due to his/her younger age" (p. 21). It has long been recognised that a primary source of the felt difference in working with older clients is the changed nature of transference and countertransference (Genevay & Katz, 1990, Knight, 2004).

Projections about competency experienced by dramatherapists who identify as being young

Turning now to experiences of dramatherapists, several respondents self-identified as young and wrote about the benefits and challenges associated with starting out in the field. In particular, they noted scepticism about their competency and their own propensity to identify with clients their own age. For example, one person wrote,

> As a person who looks younger than my age – I remember feeling that at the beginning of my practice, particularly as a student, some clients would express concern about my possible lack of life experience. This makes sense to me, and it was a topic for us to speak about as we were building trust.

Another wrote,

> As a young therapist working with young adults feelings of competency and identification tended to be mixed; connection / being understood was perceived as a positive, whilst being inexperienced a negative.

Some respondents wrote about youth as a privilege:

> I think that depending on the age of the client I am seeing some may see me as too young to understand their experiences, but in general I face mostly privileges from this experience.
>   I experience drama therapy through the lens of a young able bodied person with recent experience in theatre. I am privileged because of my youth.

Finally, the experience of being a young person was raised in connection with experiences of training in dramatherapy. One respondent wrote, "I think sometimes it is assumed that I don't understand things because I'm a bit young and I look younger than I actually am, but overall, I feel that my concerns are heard". Age and how it influences the group dynamics of a cohort are important to make note of here. We will return to this in the chapter on training (Chapter 13).

Projections about competency experienced by dramatherapists who identify as being older

Assumptions about competency were also an issue taken up by dramatherapists in the survey who identified as older, or involved with the profession of dramatherapy for a longer time. While, as one respondent put it, they "would not trust too young a therapist", they remained uneasy about the conflation of competency and age:

> As an older therapist I am aware of projections of competency which do not necessarily match my felt experience, insecurities can still surface and can be usefully worked with in the therapeutic relationship. The role of "expert" is unhelpful and does not enable empowerment.

This tension shows up again in this reflection from a dramatherapist who observed that they are often assumed to know more than they feel warranted:

> As someone who has been in the field for about 25 years now, it is certain that time has afforded me a level of wisdom. I am also acutely aware that there is a lot I am not as familiar about, as it relates to the field, and often people do assume that I am competent about.

In contrast, others felt like they might be discriminated against because, as one practitioner put it, "age may lead others to assume my practice is dated." Similarly, another dramatherapist wrote about the benefits of ageing yet the awareness that they may be seen as irrelevant:

> I feel my age contributes to my capacity for honesty and integrity and ability to sit more humbly in the work and in the world. There is a professional threshold, however, that I am aware of where advanced age can contribute to a decreased perception of relevance.

Generational differences as potential sources of tension in sites of training and practice

In addition to projections relating to competency and age, several respondents commented about how age and generational differences between trainer and trainees and between colleagues can be more explicit and where ageism can come into play. Is a trainer or older colleague seen as a model, an 'expert' or an embarrassment? Can we have an equal exchange between generations where 'established ways of practising' can be challenged and debated? Some of these potential difficulties are articulated in the following quote:

> I try my best but when working with people with dementia inside a broken medical model system, it is a challenge to determine what can be addressed or changed, considering my patient's brains are in the process of dying and their short term memories are extremely limited. I have to do small things such as use gender neutral language and rephrase the things my patients say in more acceptable terms. I have advocated and organised staff trainings to address the inherent ableism among staff but am often met with disinterest, apathy, and flat out denial of resources by both staff and corporate administration.

It is interesting to note that the dramatherapist does not mention the possibility of embodied communication with her clients, a really important shift in dementia studies (Kontos & Martin, 2013) and an important core process in dramatherapy. The dramatherapist expresses frustration at the perceived limitations of the clients and the care system. From an intersectional perspective, the oppressive care context needs challenging, but a moral high ground challenge can lead to disinterest and cutting off. Nicky Morris writes about some of the unconscious dynamics that may be at play here. She identified key themes of fear, stigma, anger and identity in her heuristic study about staff working with people with moderate dementia. The work highlights that staff, including the dramatherapist, find that they are "confronted by a paradox of emotions, forced to confront personal fears and limitations" (Morris, 2011, p. 144). We wonder if a shared acknowledgement of the difficulties around facing limitations may potentially enable more collaboration, whilst further research on the impact of comorbid health problems for elders with mental health problems is a recommended addition to current dramatherapy research (Scott, 2019). Focusing on possibilities through drama and theatre-based community projects in dementia care can involve staff and family members (Basting, 2009) and holds the potential of drama and theatre to gather the community and to better communicate.

Adapting the physical demands of practice

Following from the intergenerational differences described in the previous section, several dramatherapists shared insights into the process of ageing and their experience of practising dramatherapy with an emphasis on the physical aspects of our profession and the dynamics of a changing cultural landscape. One respondent wrote,

> I have been practising dramatherapy for over 30 years so am one of the older practitioners at my place of work. I try to compensate for any loss of energy or physical resilience with wisdom and professional experience. The benefits of being an older practitioner is that one learns to integrate different theoretical ideas and perspectives and trust one's own knowledge and experience.

Another two respondents wrote,

> While I try and pace myself, when I work with a group of children with ADHD and autism and it is very physical I feel old. My body aches and I wonder if I am too old for children with such high energy levels. I also sometimes am blown away when I work with teenagers and they give me a long list of gender identities or talk about APPS and jargon that to me seems from another planet. I deal with it by asking the client and learning from them. I think this helps the power dynamic. I am not this omnipotent person, I know nothing sometimes too and that is okay.
>
> As I'm older, I'm able to understand some situations which my clients are dealing with. From the other side I'm also losing connection with teens in some way. So it brings me to stay awake for all thoughts and feelings that my clients have.

On one hand, these practitioners aim to work from a place of cultural humility (Tervalon & Murray-García, 1998) in which the dramatherapist decentres themselves to remain alive to what is culturally salient to the other. Research investigating whether client-therapist age impacted on therapy outcome showed little impact of age but that therapist experience did affect outcome (Barber & Muenz, 1996). Previous research had shown that it can be easier for adolescent and young adult clients to engage with a therapist who is closer to them in age (Dembo et al., 1983), whilst therapists who are younger than their clients obtained poorer outcomes (Beck, 1988). The latter may be connected to therapist experience and/or ageist assumptions. This research needs updating for dramatherapy client-therapist match, but it is useful to remember the client quote emphasising the importance of client choice, which of course is impacted by resources to make that choice available.

Experiences of ageing and ageism within the professional community of dramatherapy

Respondents offered contrasting experiences of how ageing is perceived within the dramatherapy community. One wrote about their experience of ageism towards older dramatherapists:

> I have spoken to colleagues who are in their late 50s, 60s and 70s and they have shared about ageism in our NADTA community and how the dramatherapy community invisibilizes their experiences, respecting them less and creating less opportunities for their involvement.

Others wrote about how age came with greater respect within professional circles while acknowledging the gaps in technologies of working:

> I am now 63 and am feeling more respected than before within the profession. In some ways more highly skilled (the wisdom of the crone!) in other ways deskilled around technology for example.

Cultural expectations related to age

It is important to remember that age holds different meanings in different cultural contexts (Reinstein, 2002). Different expectations around age in different continents are shown in this quote:

> In my Asian context the youngsters are expected to respect and follow the elders' advice. I found it challenging to work with clients who are much older than me. In the same way, I can see how some of my clients struggled to work with me when I was younger. On the other hand, trust and respect can be earned easier when I work with young clients.

Dramatherapist reflections on practice

We asked two dramatherapists to write a short vignette about their experience of working with older clients whilst they were ageing themselves and how this influenced their practice. Joanna Jaaniste (2022) offered the first and Alida Gersie (1989) offered the second vignette, which we present with an invitation to the reader to consider what aspects of age and ageing are important to consider in training and practice.

Vignette 1

As I write about my research on the later stages of human development and visit an elderly woman in her care home once a fortnight, I am made poignantly aware of my own ageing body, mind and soul. It is all very well to be writing about and offering dramatherapy to people with dementia, but there is very strong countertransference as well. In the literature, particularly in articles about the diagnosis of neuro-cognitive disorder as the *DSM-5* describes dementia, there is little about normal ageing and the common life stage features with dementia that are shared. Just a few such similarities are wanting to sit quietly, feeling the presence of those who have died, losing words and being drawn to the natural world.

The activities of writing about dramatherapy for this cohort of people and reading transcripts of our own Australian Royal Commission on Aged Care tell me it is not enough to talk about the 'quality of safety' as they do, rather than quality of life, in improving care homes. What of the dignity of risk? What of the soul element of longing – for aesthetic well-being, for example? These are matters which move me, and I know, because of what many with dementia have told me through movement and speech, that they are among their concerns. They are areas which are not brought to life through cognitive activity but are trained by reverent devotion and reflection which comes from the heart, even in dementia. A woman with moderate dementia, given a piece of rock seamed with crystal to hold said, "It's beautiful…we need to see beauty, because if we don't see it, something dies in us…you've got to search for the good stuff, it grows from that stuff (pointing to the brown stripe) to that stuff" (pointing out the sparkling amethyst).

Vignette 2

In the late 1970s, I facilitated a series of "meaning-creation through story-making" workshops for residents in a British nursing home. Nine men and women signed up to attend. The first session was called "Beginnings." After agreeing to the group's contract, I suggested that each person place a one-dot image on a large sheet of paper using finger paints. My session notes say that a woman called Audrey crossly queried why I, "a flaming Dutch red-head thirty-something", thought it appropriate that they would do so. She had come to listen to stories. Not to finger paint. That's what you did in nursery school. They were too old for that. And also how dare I suggest that they start something new. Everyone else just asked them to think about the good old times, which was nonsense anyway, and to prepare for the end. She added that this end couldn't come soon enough. Didn't I see that they were old and sick? My record includes my reply. I say that I was sorry to hear that, but that I believed that, irrespective of age, life was for the living, loving and learning. Three L's until life's inevitable end. That's why, I explained, I had chosen the theme of beginnings for that day. The other group members maintained a tremulous silence. I asked Audrey if she was willing to give the technique a go. Looking me straight in the eye she grumbled: "Gingers are bad, really bad." I raised my eyebrows and retorted, "Maybe that's good? Shall we start?" We smiled at each other and began the finger paintings. Every one of us.

On re-reading these notes now, nearly 40 years later, I recognise the 'meaning vs despair' theme that emerges so frequently in group work with people of all ages. The psychiatrist and philosopher Viktor Frankl postulates that life has meaning in a threefold way. First, through what we give to life; second, by what we take from the world; and third, through the stance that we choose towards a fate that we cannot or can no longer change. Frankl, a Holocaust survivor, suggests that suffering, mortality and fallibility are core features of human existence. I think that some other inescapable features of life also need mentioning. These are beauty, kindness and evolution. I believe that the generation of answers to life's big philosophical questions truly matters. The questions are: where do we come from, what is it all about and what does it mean to lead a 'good' life? In my experience, the very process of finding answers to these questions grants clients and change-professionals alike a lasting sense of wonder. I hoped to share this process with the residents in that nursing home.

Looking back on these notes and recalling my memory of that session, I realise that I remember it not because of the emergence of the 'meaning' theme but because of the role Audrey's words played in ending my relative tolerance of anti-redhead prejudice. At the time of facilitating this group, I already was a strong anti-racism and anti-sexism campaigner. I just hadn't thought of anti-redhead bullying in this context. But Audrey's words had stung. On the surface, I did little about this sting in the group, but I did take my feelings about it to my supervisor. She thought Audrey's comments were funny and advised me to take them on the chin. No harm meant, etc. I made my displeasure known and shortly after changed supervisors. In her awkward way, Audrey helped me to liberate my voice. I am grateful for that.

Conclusion

These perspectives offered by dramatherapists throughout this chapter illuminate how, in the words of one respondent, "as time goes by, the older one gets, the more experiences one is exposed to, provides a unique way of becoming". This embrace of becoming over the lifespan is something we, as co-authors, value in our own professional community while acknowledging the ongoing presence of ageism. This attitude of becoming is reflected in the final vignettes, a stance we hope to cultivate in partnership with those we work with. Finally, this becoming is present in the playful approaches that dramatherapists bring to elder care, in the yearning towards beauty, in the search for beginnings and in the dignity of endings.

Questions for further reflection

- What considerations regarding age are illuminated in the two vignettes from practice? How do/might you address this in your own practice?
- From your own experience and the examples in this chapter, how do you think the voices of those often subject to ageism (e.g. children, middle-aged adults, and older adults) can be valued in your life, practice and research?
- Can you recall instances in your life where age was used to express power or to disempower? Can you exchange with others ways to re-empower yourself and if and how these could be translated in practice?
- Write a dialogue between yourself now and your younger self or your older self and exchange it with a colleague or share it in supervision.

Chapter 8

Seeking a higher power

Religion and spirituality in dramatherapy

> My Christian client asked "What is your religion?" When I asked her how this was important to her she replied "I know you are not supposed to tell me but how do I know if you are coming from God or the devil if I talk to you about my faith?" Her medical and referral notes indicated her faith as a risk factor; when she was going into psychosis she would often become very preoccupied with the split between god and the devil and would see NHS staff as acting on behalf of the latter. She chose to go and see a Christian counsellor before returning to me half a year later, when she told me how the counsellor had helped her distinguish between "healthy and unhealthy faith", so that she now felt safer to explore her relationships, including that between faith, health and illness with me in dramatherapy.
>
> Dramatherapist, UK

How does faith, religion and spirituality play a role in dramatherapeutic practice? In this vignette, the client first communicates her curiosity about the therapist's religion in a context in which her religious beliefs had been understood to be a potential risk factor. The therapist responds with curiosity about the meaning invested in the client's query. What is also interesting to note is the fact that, by indicating that they were aware that the topic of religion was somehow out of bounds, they reveal just how enculturated we may be in keeping silent about matters of religious and spiritual belief in the context of therapy. Indeed, a report on religion and belief in British public life pointed out the dangers of ignoring spiritual aspects of human life and emphasised the need for increased religious and "belief literacy in every section of society" given the "potential for misunderstanding, stereotyping and oversimplification based on ignorance" (Butler-Sloss, 2015, p. 8).

Census research indicates that religious adherence in the UK may be diminishing in Caucasian populations but may be increasing in other communities (ONS, 2021). *Spiritual experience*, understood as spiritual awareness, practice and belief independent of particular faiths, is associated with subjective well-being and quality of life (Emmons, 2003), as well as marked physical and social benefits (Koenig, 2009). On the other hand, religion and fundamentalism are often associated in current discourse. In a world where health and care professionals are required, in some contexts, to report

DOI: 10.4324/9780429431593-10

'radicalisation' (NHS, 2017), is it possible to distinguish between radical fundamentalist beliefs; "healthy and unhealthy" beliefs such as those termed psychotic delusion, as in the opening vignette; and mentally supportive spirituality (Royal College of Psychiatrists, 2016). This chapter delineates some of the concepts and outlines some of the debates in their historical contexts. We will then highlight different dramatherapist perspectives from literature and our survey. The chapter concludes with reflections on practice and questions for further reflection.

Religion, spiritual beliefs and mental health

Widespread debate throughout the ages has attempted to describe what *religion* means and, of course, definitions themselves run the risk of oversimplifying rather than addressing complex and diverse perspectives (Pattison, 2007). For example, Smith (cited in King, 2010) wondered if religion itself is perhaps an 'imagined' category and wonders whether a network of complex traditions, belief systems and patterns of ritual behaviour exist instead, some of which are labelled religion while others are not. He charts the history of the term, exploring pre-Christian definitions which saw the word as deriving from the Latin re-legere – to trace or to re-read, with religion "retracing the lore of the ritual of one's ancestors" (p. 1063). This is consistent with how religion is positioned in current censuses in the UK and US. For example, the recent UK census uses the term *religious affiliation* with reference to "how respondents connect or identify with religion, irrespective of whether they actively practice it" (ONS, 2021).

Whichever definitions are used, within mental health professions, religion has long been frowned upon and seen as a sign of mental ill health by the men who have shaped the dominant narratives about the place of *spiritual beliefs* in psychotherapy. Albert Ellis claimed that psychotherapy "should have no truck whatever with any kind of miraculous cause or cure, any kind of god or devil, or any kind of sacredness", whilst Sigmund Freud considered religion to be a collective neurosis and held that religious dogmas and practices offered clients illusory protection against human frailty (Barnett & Johnson, 2011). In contrast, Jung's work on himself and his patients, together with his deep and lifelong study of Judaism, Christianity, Hinduism, Buddhism, Gnosticism, Taoism and other traditions, led him to place the journey of transformation, which he called individuation, at the mystical heart of all religions – a journey to meet the self and at the same time to meet the divine. He wrote about the mistake of confusing the intellect with the spirit and saw the spirit as something higher embracing intellect and feeling (Jacobi, 2014).

However, the alienation that existed between the mental health professions and religion for most of the 21st century has been changing in no small part to the influence of liberation theology and the efforts of American Black feminists who have placed faith, as a life-giving resource, at the centre of their activism (Graham, 2016). In Europe, liberation theology is also associated with Latin American priests such as Gustavo Gutierrez (1988) to liberate the land working class and with South Africa's liberation anti-apartheid struggle, especially important as some of the major White Christian churches had given their blessing to apartheid.

According to the Royal College of Psychiatrists (2016), "[A]ll health care tries to relieve pain and to cure – but good health care tries to do more. *Spirituality* emphasises the healing of the person, not just the disease. It views life as a journey, where good and bad experiences can help you to learn, develop and mature". This report of the Royal College of Psychiatrists (RCP) looks at the importance of spirituality in mental health care, especially because spirituality often becomes more important in times of distress, emotional stress, physical and mental illness, loss, bereavement and the approach of death.

The difference between *spirituality* and *religion*, according to the RCP, is that religious traditions include individual spirituality, which is universal. But each religion has its own distinct community-based worship, beliefs, sacred texts and traditions. Spirituality is not tied to any particular religious belief or tradition. Although culture and beliefs can play a part in spirituality, every person has their own unique experience of spirituality – it can be a personal experience for anyone, with or without a religious belief. Spirituality also highlights how connected we are to the world and other people.

While keeping in mind the complexity of definitions, a delineation of spirituality and religion is provided within a psychotherapeutic framework by Richards and Bergin in their handbook of psychotherapy and religious diversity (2014). They differentiate between *spiritual*, which they understand to be those experiences and beliefs and phenomena that pertain to the transcendent and existential aspects of life, and *religious*, which they understand to be a subset of spiritual to do with theistic practices, beliefs and feelings that are often, but not always, expressed institutionally and denominationally, as well as personally. They also distinguish between expression and experience. Religious expressions tend to be denominational, external, cognitive, behavioural, ritualistic and public. Spiritual experiences tend to be ecumenical, internal, affective, spontaneous and private. Therefore, they propose that it is possible to be religious without being spiritual and spiritual without being religious.

Introducing spiritual and religious elements can incorporate theistic features into psychotherapy, including features like prayer, moral values and scripture readings (Richards & Bergin, 2014). Others critique this, arguing that the naturalistic worldview of science is incompatible with theistic conceptions, even amongst those who embrace religion (Slife et al., 2010). However, the pathologising of religion, as in the previous vignette, raises questions about the naturalistic worldview. Isabel Clarke, a senior clinical psychologist within the NHS Psychiatric Rehabilitation Service, called for a paradigm shift towards greater spiritual literacy in her book *Psychosis and Spirituality: Consolidating the New Paradigm* (Clarke, 2010). This book was the result of her own concerns about the enduring place that spirituality has in human experience, and with which the scientific worldview has had some tensions, together with her own observations, as a Cognitive Behavioural Therapy practitioner, of how closely some patients' experiences of psychosis match much that is contained in spiritual literature. Similarly, Schreurs (2002), writing from an emic protestant Christian perspective, debates whether psychological trauma can be distinguished from spiritual trauma: What is a vision? What is a hallucination? Is depression spiritual darkness? However, it is also critical to remember that some religious orientations can also pathologise difference, as in 'conversion therapy' (see Chapter 6).

A growing number of studies suggest a positive connection between spirituality and various measures of psychological well-being (Rollins, 2009; Balboni, 2022), which raises important considerations for practice. For example, some faith orientations may advocate that a client who experiences mental health problems should only be seen by someone within their faith (Vlachos & Williams, 1994). Clients and therapists may experience conflicts between their religion and what emerges as a therapeutic worldview within the context of practice; this may need time to work out the contradictions between the two. It is important for therapists not to prejudge beliefs harshly and be flexible. This can be specifically difficult in the countertransference if the therapist themselves has struggled in their child- and/or adulthood with a particular religious belief system. Jackson-Cherry (2008) states that when a therapist does not believe what the client believes, it is important to understand why that belief is important to them. This may mean working together with a spiritual 'healer' from within the client's belief system, either in tandem or consecutively as in the opening vignette. Collaboration with local spiritual leaders may enable clients to feel safer about their work in therapy, whilst spiritual leaders are often in need of trusted resources for such cases. More than 20 years ago, McGoldrick et al. (1996) already advised family therapists to collaborate with spiritual practitioners. Current practice advocates this increasingly, although published examples of dramatherapy practice where this has taken place are still few and far between.

Another implication for practice pertains to self-disclosure, which is advised by some (Cashwell & Young, 2011). The counselling stance is more towards asking clients to be the expert on their own beliefs, for the therapist not to provide their own interpretation because of the risk of the therapist's values becoming dominant. As a therapist with a fundamentalist protestant heritage, I (Ditty) am weary of a client feeling that they have to espouse my values. Christian proselytising has a long history of power imbalances in its colonising practices, although it can be fascinating to see how the early missionary messages became a dialogue, showing that, for example, Christian Africa has impacted the shape of Christian beliefs from the beginning to the present day (Tonghou-Ngong, 2017).

The client in the opening vignette was not told the therapist's faith association but did say that she was sure from the therapy work together that the therapist's background was Christian. She could not imagine that a therapist would be familiar with the texts if that was not the case. Familiarity with religious texts from an emic-insider's perspective (Geertz, 1993) can be useful. The therapist mentioned that her feelings about the potential oppression of Christian beliefs meant engaging with her own countertransference in clinical supervision. Dramatherapy training in the UK includes awareness of the impact of one's own belief system on that of the clients, but working directly with sacred text within the continuum of a particular faith orientation (rather than across different ones) has not yet been found much in publications. Spirituality that is beyond texts, the unwritten, the non-religious also needs to be enabled and developed in dramatherapy practice.

Finally, in the UK, the requirement for all NHS and education staff to undergo PREVENT training (NHS, 2017) means that the link between radicalisation and religious faith is directly made. This has the potential to make clients even more wary about discussing faith issues in therapy; doubly pathologised by medical, judicial and social systems of understanding faith. Part of a referral form could ask a client whether their spirituality is important to them, in what way and whether they might like to discuss it in their therapy. For some clients, this may be a relief, having the door opened, for others, it may be a too early disclosure, whilst later they may be able to bring these issues to therapy.

Religious and spiritual experience in dramatherapy

Roger Grainger, a dramatherapist and Anglican priest, wrote various publications on dramatherapy, rites of passage, liturgy and religion. His book *The Glass of Heaven* (1995) was published more than 20 years ago and gave some indications of how to start addressing potential relationships between dramatherapy and religion. Grainger saw dramatherapy as inherently and implicitly spiritual in its mode of communication. He wrote,

> Dramatherapy is a spiritual therapy, because from time to time, it becomes an acted mysticism, as its movements take on the form of a meditation, the procession of bodies which are movements of soul, glimpses of personal truth.
>
> (1995, p. 21)

Grainger was interested in the fact that the 'healing', unlike symptom reduction or functional improvement, is difficult to prove scientifically, highlighting the naturalistic vs theistic concepts in psychotherapy. Embracing a stance of not knowing, Grainger saw dramatherapy uniting "the intuitive/expressive instinct of the artist, the precise and controlled skill of the therapist, and the ritualistic and spiritual yearning of the religious man" (Koltai cited in Grainger, 1995, p. 11). While acknowledging the gender bias in this statement, we emphasise here how dramatherapy is seen by Grainger as providing a structure with the potential to contain and integrate complex human material, as long as the therapist has the skill to facilitate the process. The term 'faith' is used by Grainger in several ways; faith as a religion, as well as faith in the dramatherapeutic process itself. He does not note tension between belief and practice. Rather, dramatherapy is presented as unequivocally faith *and* practice based. He cites Burns, who saw drama itself as "a frame for action" (1972, p. 17). He describes how drama can frame actions so that they can be observed and given special attention, echoing Boal's contention that theatre is the art of looking at ourselves (Boal, 1992). The separation from 'the ordinary' in drama can be viewed as a feature of ritual, one of the core processes of dramatherapy (Jones, 1996, 2007).

Whilst *The Glass of Heaven* is written from a Christian perspective, and dramatherapy is seen as aligned with spiritual practice, Grainger emphasises that this experience is accessible to all. He wrote,

> Thus it is open to people "of any religion or none"; prior belief is not necessary for this revelation. It is also open to those who are not religiously inclined – first and foremost it is a place and time of discovery, discovery about oneself and others.
>
> (1995, p. 21)

Nevertheless, it is perhaps worth noting the religious tone of the word 'revelation' and wondering if this may deter those who may not be 'religiously inclined'. Grainger's emphasis on mystery may also prove challenging to those on the more scientific side of the spectrum, as well as funding providers. Yet, his writing has given dramatherapists an early connection between religion and dramatherapy even if his writing could be seen as slightly too easy on the complexities of faith differences and similarities between clients and therapists.

Since the end of the 20th and start of the 21st century, a sizeable number of books and articles on religion and clinical practice have been published, including in dramatherapy. Grainger's (1995) research on dramatherapist values seemed to coincide with a bigger trend. Derived from religious practices, Jones (1996) identified ritual, in which participants consciously leave the ordinary world behind and create an arena of experimentation in which change or transformation is rendered possible, as a core process in dramatherapy. Professional organisations, including those in dramatherapy, started to acknowledge in their ethical guidelines that religion is one type of diversity that mental health professionals are obliged to respect (Richards & Bergin, 2000; Sajnani et al., 2016). Muslim dramatherapist Fatmah AlQuadfan (TED, 2018) and Sikh dramatherapist Eshmit Kaur (2021) spoke about the influence of their faith on dramatherapy insofar as it oriented them towards service and care. Stephen Legari and Navah Steiner (2019) wrote about Buddhist influences on their practice of dramatherapy.

Dramatherapists have also examined how a spiritual paradigm might feature in training. Dramatherapists such as Mary Smail (2016) developed 'psyche and soma' as part of the Sesame Institute training, whilst Bruce Howard Bayley (2022) developed dramatherapy and a new spiritual paradigm – which became 'Tribhuvan: Threefold Dramatherapy'. In the US, Saphira Linden (2013) and Gary Raucher (2011) espouse a transpersonal perspective on dramatherapy, which emphasises the relationship between spirituality, consciousness and health. Transpersonal Psychotherapy and Counselling is an "integrative approach with a holistic and spiritual dimension, giving the therapist a variety of treatment methods, aims at balancing mind, body and soul, allowing you to live your life consciously, a life crisis is seen as an opportunity for break-through and self-actualisation" (Centre for Transpersonal Psychology, 2014). Most of these integrative approaches emphasise spirituality and religion in the context of well-being.

Many therapists and clients have negative experiences with religions and religious communities and may have rejected this part of their history because of those negative experiences. One part of an intersectional identity may be in conflict with another, i.e. being gay and growing up in a more conservative religious tradition which rejects homosexuality. This can of course occur in both therapists' and clients' lives. It may then be difficult to experience religion in a more positive context and increase the risk of pathologising religion. The therapist's countertransference may lead them to be judgemental and dismissive, unconscious and/or coldly ignoring of the influence of religion in a client's life. In an increasingly secular and polarised society where people of faith may experience the proselytising of non- or anti-religious convictions as oppressive, being able to take positions of emic (within) and etic (from outside) perspectives (Geertz, 1993) will lead to the possibility of flexibly engaging with our clients whatever belief system they hold, being able to explore the meaning for them of healthy and unhealthy beliefs and how this impacts on their relationships with others within and outside their faith, values and belief systems.

Finally, some dramatherapists chose to fulfil part of their faith tradition's emphasis on benefiting the society they are a part of. This is clear in the work of Kaur (2021) and AlQadfan (cited in Cunningham-Younger, 2016). Some dramatherapists are also priests, sisters and religious leaders in various traditions. They can find the very secular dramatherapy training a challenge to their beliefs. Therapists of faith may be challenged by peers on their awareness of the potentially oppressive nature of some of their beliefs, whilst secular therapists may equally struggle to see beyond the oppression to the potential benefits. Being able to consider both the shadow and the benefit of religious and spiritual traditions may enable us as dramatherapists to develop greater role flexibility and accommodation of our clients' spiritual needs. Could spiritual competencies in training be useful as part of intercultural competencies as a whole? We will return to this in our chapter on practice.

Dramatherapist perspectives

The 2007 and 2015 British Association of Dramatherapists (BADth) cultural background survey showed that dramatherapists not adhering to any particular religious tradition increased from 28% to 35.3%. This may be indicative of a trend, but the picture as a whole is mixed. Christian adherence reduced by 1.2%, humanist identification went from 0% to 10.8%, pagan from 0% to 3% and spiritualist from 0% to 6.5%. At the time, there were no dramatherapists who responded to the survey who self-identified as either Hindu, Muslim or Sikh (Dokter, 2016) though we know that this has changed since with Ehmit Kaur (2021), for example, offering insight into how Sikhism informs her practice of dramatherapy, and dramatherapist Fatmah AlQadfan has spoken about the influence of Islam in her life (Cunningham-Younger, 2016).

Demographics: Religious and spiritual identities

The respondents in our survey who felt spirituality and religion influenced their practice was 60.4%, which left 40% considering it irrelevant. Those who did consider it relevant self-identified widely in descending order 28% spiritual, 17.5% atheist, 14% each Christian and without belief, 10.5% agnostic, 2% humanist and 3.5% Buddhist, Jewish and multifaith.

Those who adhered to no particular religious tradition (maybe here self-identified as atheist, agnostic or without belief) made up 42% of the sample, whilst those who self-identified as adhering to a spiritual or religious tradition (spiritual, Christian, Buddhist, Jewish, multifaith humanism) comprised 54.5%. There were a few comments in the survey that were interesting in this respect: "as long as an open mind is kept no problem", "aware of allowing clients to bring it in and respond accordingly" and "yes, they can feel quite exposing sometimes".

Considerations regarding self-disclosure of religious or spiritual identity

Participants and providers of dramatherapy both commented on whether this aspect of their identities remained hidden or was disclosed:

> Within the family it also can be quite hidden, my mother did not talk about her Jewish background. She had been drummed out of the faith for marrying a non Jew, but also she grew up as a child not to tell anyone. … My brother wanted to take up the faith, but she dissuaded him.

Another wrote of the complexities concerning self-disclosure:

> My Jewish identity is one that is a bit more tricky for me, because I'm nervous about how it will be perceived, about antisemitism. I'm nervous for some of my Palestinian or Muslim clients – I worry about our collective histories of oppression and whether I will be a safe person for them knowing that I'm Jewish. I don't feel good hiding that I am Jewish, because I want them to make an informed choice about whether they want to be with me in the therapy space.

How much is disclosed between clients and therapists and negotiating changes of belief over a lifetime in relation to practice were raised:

> My own fundamentalist background (now no longer adhered to) raises my awareness of working with clients who have a similar expression of religion. I...wish to work within their specific value systems whilst enabling greater reflection on the differences between assumptions, values and the possibility of change. Shame and guilt issues in religion and empowerment in relation to faith and values can in my opinion be quite an important aspect of mental health (whilst being aware that clients and therapists can be uncomfortable about bringing religion to therapy). Clients have wanted to find out my religious beliefs, which I do not tend to disclose because I am wary about being perceived to proselytise; on the other hand this creates inequality with my client if I invite them to explore.

Worries about rigid belief systems

Some respondents wrote about their concerns that rigid belief systems might interfere with care. As one respondent wrote,

> I think it is very important to acknowledge and understand a person's spiritual and religious belief. At times this can be limiting or rigid, which may prevent them gaining insight into a different way of seeing themselves or others. In healthcare settings we need to be aware that some staff may be quite rigid in their understanding of mental health and offending behaviour.

Another wrote,

> Religious and family issues are sensitive. I worked with a muslim teenager. Her family is quite religious, her belief is influenced by her mum. Her mum believed everything is tested by God so she expected her daughter to be patient. I questioned the daughter if she believes the same as her mother or if there was a difference in their belief. Once the mother knew I questioned the daughter she stopped the client from seeing me.

Others wrote about what they perceived to be extremist views, though one would need to question what is considered extreme and to whom. As one dramatherapist wrote,

> I have found it difficult when working with people with extremist views. These have mainly been far right, but also extreme religious beliefs. Dramatherapy can be a vehicle for someone to express these beliefs hiding behind the masks.

Another wrote,

> I would be quite affected if someone came across with extreme ideas. I am well aware of my position and would at least try to relate. It may be the case that I request a referral and explain why I have reached that position. Ultimately safety is foremost for my clients and myself as a practitioner.

Respondents only identified the clients as expressing these, although it is possible that both therapists and clients may perceive each other as having extreme views. Is it possible to enter a dialogue across and about differences in values and at what point does this become untenable? Dwight Turner (2021) discusses the risks of silencing alternative perspectives, especially those of the right, so that we just perpetuate othering the other by not seeing or hearing them, making them equally invisible to any other minority group.

Worries about being judged because of one's beliefs

Some dramatherapists wrote about their concerns related to being judged because of their beliefs.

> I do worry about being judged for being atheist, especially since many clients have expressed not trusting people who are not religious, I also fear what other therapists may think in that regard.

Others wrote about the judgement and betrayal that clients may feel in disclosing concerns about their beliefs to an outsider. As one respondent wrote,

> About religion…the client can feel they are disclosing and shaming the whole of their community…problematic is also my ignorance, but sharing is important even if it can feel a religious betrayal to share aspects and culture with someone not from that background.

Another offered a contrasting view concerning being an outsider to the faith community in which they were working,

> Sometimes – like when I work in an ultra orthodox community and they like that I am not from the community or live in the community or know anyone in the community – and that space feels safe to them.

Spiritual beliefs as a source of comfort

Finally, respondents wrote about how working across faith communities and drawing on their spiritual practice has been a source of comfort and possibly even pride. One of the following quotes also speaks about how their beliefs are expressed in practice.

I remember working with a Somali colleague, a very devout Muslim, highly respected. We were invited to go to Norway post Brexit...fate threw us together a devout Muslim male and a secular liberal Jewish woman.

Another wrote,

I bring mindfulness into my practice. Referring to Buddhism we also work with the concepts of compassion and paying gratitude. They are part of a religious belief that I brought into my dramatherapy work. ... For non Buddhists I would use different words, because they might have feelings about the religious words. Sometimes it is not about naming but about the way you communicate, I do not call it meditation when we do a breathing exercise.

Dramatherapist reflections on practice

In this section, we offer one vignette in which a dramatherapist reflected on the intersections between religion, gender, race and colonialism.

There is a lot of the white mother, I had a big belly. In the role of priest my client put his hands on my belly to pray for my baby and said you can give the baby my name. I thought this is a bridge, an "I am good enough and you are good enough" moment. There is more often an unspoken power relationship. ... Church plays such a powerful role in the arche-type of the white Jesus...there is a strong involvement in the school from the church, praying for and with the children, bringing snacks. A child will come and pray for a packet of chips, it feels distanced. All this thing about religion, praying for your sins, you are the bad one/trouble but I am white and pure. ... I had to let go of religion for my own sanity, it stopped serving me, because this served the us and them dynamic. I need to think about this a bit more.

Coming as a dramatherapist to a country to introduce dramatherapy, these intersections can become even more prominent. Dramatherapist Caroline Miller gives an example of her visits to Fiji to introduce dramatherapy in schools for children with special educational needs. Fiji is a small inde-pendent republic comprising a number of islands in the South Pacific. The country gained independence in 1974, after being a British colony. Fiji has a subsistence economy, which is supplemented by aid from other countries, and by tourism. Fiji's early history dates from before 1500 BC, with colonial history dating from the 19th century.

The dramatherapist worked as a volunteer in special schools in Fiji on three occasions. Education for those with special needs is provided through non-government organisations and the Ministry of Education in Fiji. The dramatherapist worked for one week in a special school in Fiji in 2007 and for two weeks in two special schools in 2009. Students in the schools represented two ethnic groups of Fijians. These were Fijian and Fijian Indian. There were three major religious groups represented, which were Christian (of various denominations), Hindu and Muslim. Most ethnic Fijians belong to a variety of Christian denominations, and school assemblies were conducted within a Christian framework. The students were aged between 5 and 19, and all had been identified as having special educational needs within the moderate to mild range. Some students were profoundly deaf. Most of the children came from poorer families within a largely subsistence economy. The dramatherapist identifies as a white New Zealander. She researched the context as follows.

The Ministry of Education has been responsible for education since 1916, but the schools are owned by local communities and other groups like church groups. In 2007, the population of Fiji was 837,271 with approximately 50% ethnic Fijian and 45% Fijian Indian (Fiji Islands Bureau of Statistics). There is a small population of people of Chinese, European and Polynesian descent and a small amount of intermarriage among all ethnic groups. One-third of the population was given as under the age of 20. Approximately half of the population resides in urban and half in rural settings. There is a literacy rate of 91%. Generally, around 85% of children attend school, which is free, and generally, schools are provided along Fijian (Christian), Hindu and Moslem lines. Special schools are not segregated and contain a mix of all ethnic and religious groups. Ethnic Fijians acknowledge membership of extended family groups and of a specific village, even if they live in urban centres. Indo-Fijians retain religious and cultural practices from their original countries, but with a reduction in caste identification and practices. Both of these major population groups are welcoming and hospitable to visitors. All groups actively practice religious observances, Fijians Christianity and Indians Hinduism or Islam.

Dramatherapy appears to be unknown in Fiji, although music and dancing and other forms of performance are part of traditional arts practice, and have a role in celebrations and formal events. The schools where I worked were integrated in terms of ethnic group culture and religion. All students had an identified intellectual disability and/or were profoundly deaf. All students had good receptive language in English and their own home language, and most had a smattering of either Fijian or Hindi depending on their main language. All could use sign language, and the deaf students could lip read. My offer to provide drama was seen within the context of the school curriculum. The school where I worked had identified drama as a specialist subject which they were unable to teach with their current staff resources. Formal education follows styles and curricula and teacher/learner relationships introduced by the colonising powers. Perhaps the most dominant effect of colonisation is the proliferation of Christian churches and the power of Christianity in the everyday life of ethnic Fijians. Following the ubiquitous Fijian greeting of 'Bula', the two immediate questions are "where are you from?", and "what church do you belong to, or what is your religion?" With the dominance of English language and colonial societal structures, there is some inevitable privileging of European structures, knowledge, customs and goods.

Prior to my visits, I had discussions with the school principal about what would be useful and appropriate. It was agreed that I would provide resources in terms of props, that I would teach/coach the students in some basic drama techniques, and that I would use stories as frameworks for the drama, in keeping with the storytelling traditions and the students' love of stories. I tried to identify some local cultural and ethnic stories familiar to the students, but found this difficult at first. The teachers assured me that the children were most familiar with English stories and that these generally contained universal themes which were also apparent in Fijian and Hindu stories. The storybooks in the school contained English stories or European fairy stories written in English, so I settled for this path. A few students had minimal experience with drama, and this had generally meant enacting Bible Stories. I avoided those stories so that the students had new experiences and so that non-Christian students were not alienated by the single religious context.

For a second visit, I had prepared by reading Fijian traditional stories and looking at other possible therapeutic themes for the dramatherapy work. Some themes were likely to be related to some of the manifestations of ongoing factors in the lives of the students and their families. These were related to political and economic instability, poverty and reduced opportunity, ethnic conflict and the impact of regularly recurring natural disasters like severe floods and cyclones. I took three traditional Fijian stories – "The Great Flood", "The Great Serpent of Nakauvadra" and "The Terrible Son of the Sky King" – which reflected the impact of flooding, interpersonal and intertribal conflict and the relationship with supernatural powers. I also took a traditional New Zealand Maori story, "Maui and the Fingers of Fire" – about the ability of humankind to make fire.

Further details of this vignette are discussed in Miller (2009). It is interesting to note how the dramatherapist takes into account the religious context of the communities she is working with, including avoiding stories from one religion in the context of a multifaith setting. Given the colonial heritage and the predominance of Christianity in that heritage and the transition from European fairy stories in the first visit to Fijian stories and a Maori story from her New Zealand background, the breadth of diversity seemed to be a way of metaphorically navigating sharing power.

Working with sacred texts in the secular context of therapy can be complex, whether therapists and clients share similar belief systems or not. With a colonial history of missionary oppression, this may need to be unpacked a bit more, as in the client of the opening vignette in a context of potentially oppressive pathologising. In the work with the client from the vignette, it was possible to look at Bible texts which for her were sacred and look at how her way of growing up had influenced her view and understanding of these texts. So was god the father a vengeful and judgemental figure akin to her human father? Looking at texts where god was described as loving and kind could be a revelation. Therapist understanding of different views of the deity in the Christian old and new testament was helpful. When working with a Muslim male client, the fact that the female non-believing therapist was an infidel needed careful thinking about together. With both clients acknowledging the importance of their faith, it was crucial that as therapist I (Ditty) tried to show respect and not pathologise. This took some overcoming of my own critical stance of what could be considered fundamentalist beliefs, having grown up and struggled with that approach to faith.

Conclusion

Religious and spiritual diversity is a cultural fact. Many religious and spiritual people, like the client in the opening vignette, have an unfavourable view of mainstream, secular health professionals and a distrust of the process of psychological therapy. This distrust is rooted in awareness that psychological therapy endorses naturalistic, hedonistic, relativistic and atheistic values conflicting with most religious communities (Richards & Bergin, 2014). It is not just therapists who might view religion with suspicion. There can be mutual distrust between religious communities and psychological therapies. However, recent research demonstrates the importance of spirituality as a protective health factor with positive implications for person and population health (Balboni et al., 2022). Further, a person's religious and spiritual beliefs may intersect with other intercultural factors such as race, age, gender, sexual orientation and ideas about dis/ability. Therefore, incorporating a curious stance about the role of religion and spirituality in one's own life, whether one is a provider or participant in dramatherapy (or any caring relationship), may facilitate therapeutic work (Bohart and Wade, 2013).

Questions for further reflection

- What considerations regarding religion and spirituality are illuminated in the two vignettes from practice? How do/might you address this in your own practice?
- Would you as a therapist disclose your religious / spiritual belief system? If so, when, how and why?
- What are for you the shadow aspects of incorporating religious and spiritual belief systems in dramatherapy?
- Do you have spiritual beliefs? Do you think dramatherapy is a spiritual practice?

Chapter 9

Found in translation

The role of language in dramatherapy

My new 16 year old unaccompanied minor client was sitting with his foster mother on the sofa, I on a chair opposite. His social worker had asked if I could meet them, because his foster mother was worried about his older brother and my client, whom she had taken in when they arrived in the UK. They had been travelling in flight for some time and could not talk together or with their foster mother about what had happened during flight or prior such as what had happened to their parents. The older brother had intimated that he had seen them being killed, but had not been able to talk about this with his younger brother, neither during flight, nor now they were in a safer environment. They seemed estranged from each other, unable to communicate; his brother had been invited but did not want to come and join our sessions. My client's use of English was limited, his foster mother nor I spoke his native tongue. He was reticent to enter into any dramatic play, as play was associated with "childish things" at a younger age. My client did not want an interpreter as "there were already too many people wanting to know [his] business." I understood the subtext of me as yet another nosey parker and suggested we create a dictionary together of words we might need to share stories in both his first and my second language. The fact that I was an English second language speaker piqued his interest and we could exchange about the difficulties of learning a new language. It took some time, but in the process of finding a shared language we reached a point where we could discuss why he thought we were meeting. He said that he thought it was about how not knowing what happened to his parents made it difficult to settle here. I asked if his brother knew, he said he did not know and that they did not want to burden each other. I understood that both had lost the language to speak to each other, as they were too worried about what speech might reveal. He said he had bad dreams and was trying not to think about what happened before he arrived in the UK, but that also made him lose the good memories of life before the war. He was not sure who he was any more and it made it difficult to concentrate at school, especially trying to learn a new language when he could not find the words in his mother tongue either.

Dramatherapist, UK

In this chapter, we take up the nuances of language in dramatherapy and offer both theoretical and practical perspectives from the field. As seen in this

DOI: 10.4324/9780429431593-11

vignette, non-verbal and verbal language are crucial parts of cultural identity (Skutbnabb-Kangas, 1981). Needing to learn a new language in order to share stories with strangers, to share memories about family can be especially challenging in the context of therapy and in light of recent and unresolved trauma. His foster mother, social worker, and the dramatherapist were aware that learning English would help him to integrate at school and would also strengthen his application to remain in the UK when he became 18; his brother was already in that situation. The requirement to speak English at a particular level is necessary to be able to apply for citizenship/naturalisation in the UK and often requires sitting for a citizenship exam. Within multilingual societies, the maintenance of the various ethnic and cultural groups is critical for the preservation of cultural heritage and identity. However, when your first language is not accepted by the host country you live in or, worse, negated through a process of colonisation, this can result in a sense of alienation, an unequal 'second hand' citizenship, and a deep sense of injustice. This can further complicate the acquisition of a host country's language. There are many examples but one which portrays this vividly is the play *Translations* by Brian Friel (1981) about the English language cultural imperialism in Ireland. The poem "Search for my Tongue" by Bhatt (cited in Carr, 2016) also captures this well: "I ask you, what would you do if you had two tongues in your mouth, and lost the first one, the mother tongue, and could not really know the other, the foreign tongue."

Learning yet another new language can be complicated for refugees like the one in the vignette who had already experienced denial and persecution of his minority language and culture in his birth country. This was one complicating factor for the 16-year-old client in the vignette who felt that in learning yet another language, he was losing his identity. Compounded by the trauma of his parents being killed and not being able to find the words to share this experience with his sibling, this precluded sharing other memories too: a double alienation.

The client did not want to explore non-verbal dramatic language, so the therapist and client had to work through the complexities of verbal language and the meanings that held for both. The dramatherapist could share the difficulties of communicating in a second or third language, a sense of not being able to find the words, to find the way to express so that alien adults could understand. The therapist had to be willing to not understand and go back to the point of learning anew. This meant mispronouncing and misunderstanding, finding alternative ways of expressing things, being in a place where there were no words for what was felt and finding, where possible, new forms of communication together.

Dramatherapy and language

Dramatherapy, and other arts therapies, are sometimes advocated as a therapy of choice for clients who struggle with language. The non-verbal processes enabled through arts and arts therapies represent a unique strength of these approaches (de Witte et al., 2021). Arts are seen to encourage expressive and receptive language skills through play and have also been seen by arts therapists as a language in itself in the context of semiotics (Karkou & Sanderson, 2006) or, as arts educators Berriz et al. (2019) put it, *a way of talking*. Arts therapists have advocated that a body-based approach can facilitate non-verbal adaptation, integration and bicultural social development to help overcome initial language and social difficulties amongst new immigrants (Cohn, 1997; Wengrower, 1994). The valuing of the non-verbal may not take into account prior experience of oppression regarding language and trauma and the power equation in the expectation to acculturate. Do dramatherapists value the non-verbal over the verbal in dramatherapy; how do they see the role of language in their sessions; are the arts an alternative language or, conversely, do dramatherapists need to acquire additional counselling skills for verbal practice and the capacity to work with interpreters when warranted?

The therapists' language is part of their cultural identity; what languages does a therapist draw on? I (Ditty) had an experience where a client sought me out, as she wanted a therapist who spoke Dutch, her native language. However, the interesting aspect was that the issue of within-group difference became very prominent throughout the therapy. The feeling of isolation was strong in my client, and having a therapist who "spoke her language" was not enough to bridge that sense of isolation, where she still felt misunderstood and alone. The fantasy that a shared first language would overcome the verbal obstacle can be a misnomer. It may be equally important, as in the work in the vignette, to work with difference in order to come to a more shared understanding. I (Nisha) have worked with many international students, some of whom reflect on the alienation they experience from not being able to represent themselves as fully as they would like or internalise what they are learning in their home language. Time taken to consider culturally specific understandings of dramatherapeutic processes can aid in this process, though this process often continues well beyond graduate training. In addition to this, clinical terms, while useful for communicating across multidisciplinary teams, constitute their own language that must also be examined from the perspective of power and the primary duty of care.

Carr (2016) researched the experience of a small sample of five bilingual dramatherapists who were working with bilingual clients whose home languages differed from that of the therapist and arrived at four main themes. Dramatherapists in her sample readily affirmed the arts as languages themselves, as well as the power and importance of spoken language. As evidenced in other literature in the field, in cases of potential traumatic stress, as in the opening vignette, non-verbal exploration in breath, movement, images and sounds facilitate processing and serve as a bridge to insight and organised verbal communication (Sajnani & Johnson, 2014). Dramatherapists, like other arts therapists, are at times enthusiastic in their claims that the arts can transcend verbal language, their view supported by dramatherapists who see verbal therapy as a western concept (Valikhani, 2000). However, non-verbal communication is as culturally specific as verbal communication (Dokter, 2000b) across the arts therapies. As two music therapists observed, using music does not require the need to speak each other's language, but that does not mean that language barriers do not play a role (Orth & Verburght, 1998).

Secondly, dramatherapists in Carr's sample, reinforced the ongoing process and importance of negotiating meanings.

Thirdly, the importance of being understood alongside the challenge of working with interpreters and, finally, issues related to power and disempowerment when working across language differences.

These considerations are taken up in the following section pertaining to dramatherapists' perspectives from the survey.

Dramatherapist perspectives

All respondents expressed that language was an important aspect of their identity which informed their practice.

Demographics: language

Of the survey respondents, 30 reported practising in one language, 17 participants identified as bilingual, 3 identified as trilingual and 1 reported speaking four languages. Among the languages reported were English, Bulgarian, Czech, Cantonese, Thai, Maltese, French, Dutch and Spanish. Language shared third place with religion, sexual orientation and age when dramatherapists rated aspects of their cultural identity that influenced their practice (after race and gender). However, there were very few comments about the meaning and emotional attachment to and experience of language in dramatherapy. That said, we have organised the few comments we received into the following themes.

Language preference

One respondent expressed an explicit preference for using their first language: "I'm only working in my mother language…so it is easy for me". It is not clear whether the clients all shared their therapist's home language.

Appreciation for a means of non-verbal communication

There were no comments about whether being able to use a range of languages was useful, whether it was seen as a strength. Several other respondents expressed a preference and an appreciation for having a non-verbal means of communication. As one respondent wrote, "Fortunately, through the puissance of creativity potential within dramatherapy, I have found ways to communicate when verbal is not an option". Another wrote, "Sometimes language can be a barrier in some aspects of the work. Fortunately dramatherapy offers a variety of non verbal ways of working and expression which can be utilised where necessary".

These dramatherapists do not give details as to why verbal is not an option nor do they mention client preferences. Symbol and metaphor are one of the core processes in dramatherapy (Jones, 2007), but in the previous quotes, there seems to be a valuing of the non-verbal over the verbal and a feeling that language is a barrier. Is this part of our professional value system; may this impede us in using language as an aspect of cultural identity?

The importance of shared meanings

One more direct quote stresses the importance of finding shared meaning between client and therapist and echoes some of the dynamics in the opening vignette. This respondent wrote,

> Looking for a shared language is important in any therapy, but where there are language differences this takes longer. Dramatherapy is in part verbal so how to bridge the verbal and non verbal needs to be negotiated; be it via an interpreter or by creating a shared "dictionary" of both symbols and words.

The verbal aspects of dramatherapy and the use of a range of languages may be important aspects of further dramatherapy research. We will also consider this in the training chapter. The emphasis on the non-verbal seems in contrast to dramatherapy's link to theatre. A recent survey undertaken amongst 11 international MA dramatherapy lecturers rated what was most important to their training role: psychotherapy 21%, psychology 14%, counselling 11%, theatre 21%, drama 23% and psychiatry 10% (Holmwood, 2016). These disciplines are firmly rooted in language. Carr's (2016) interviewees stressed the importance of exploring shared meaning, not assuming it is there even if the client and therapist speak the same language. Power issues between therapist and client were highlighted when working in a second language; therapists felt disempowered if clients spoke the dominant language better than them and corrected their language; they felt deskilled clinically when lacking confidence in the majority language. Could this also be an issue when dramatherapists talk about language as a barrier? Seebohm and Holloway balance the emphasis that with our roots in theatre, we bring our understanding of physicality into the clinical space, our own and that of our clients, but that we also understand the power of language through image and the language of ideas (connected to the use of image and metaphor in talking therapies (i.e. Cox & Theilgaard, 1987). The dramatic metaphor is ultimately an embodied experience (Holloway & Seebohm, 2011), but language is part of our professional identity as dramatherapists whether we draw on theatre/drama or psychological therapy elements in our practice. (How) can we incorporate the range of languages available to therapists and clients?

Working with interpreters

The dramatherapists who gave their practice reflections both worked with interpreters. It is interesting that both refer to group work, whilst the fears from survey respondents and Carr's interviewees are more about individual therapy. In Carr's (2016) research about language and dramatherapy, the third theme was "the challenges of working with interpreters".

Like participants in Carr's (2016) research, one of our respondents referred to their concerns about working with interpreters. They wrote, "[I]t is tricky to have an interpreter, you lose the immediacy. I try to rely on using the art form. A third person between the therapist and the client may mean that issues disappear". Blackwell (2005) highlights that when working with an interpreter, it is a risk for the therapist to project their critical superego onto the interpreter, as they may be from the same country and community and may know the politics, culture and client's experiences better than the therapist may hope to. Interpreters may have seen other therapists at work and have a lot of experience to evaluate the therapist's performance. The interpreter may remain a threatening figure until a working relationship has become established and the interpreter can be drawn on as a creative and useful resource. There are suggested strategies (Carr, 2016; Dokter, 2000b):

- pre-briefing and debriefing post-sessions so as to prepare in partnership but also to check what material has been evoked for the interpreter;
- as an interpreter may be present with the client in a range of settings, it is important to check that the client is comfortable with the interpreter. This may include the role of the interpreter in the community for which they are translating in case existing relationships are compromised and confidentiality threatened;
- interpreters to translate meaning rather than words; the interpreter is also a translator of culture.

An art therapist highlighted that instead of the triangular relationship of client-therapist-arts form we have a four-way relationship where the interpreter is the fourth corner and a relationship of mutual trust and respect to incorporate this fourth corner needs to be established (McElroy, 2005).

Dramatherapist reflections on practice

Vignette 1

One of the interviewed dramatherapists, Adam Reynolds, spoke about his experience as a White, American dramatherapy trainer working in Taiwan and how the issues of culture, power and language interacted. His words portray the balancing act between embodiment, play, enactment and language, as well as the personal reflections within and about the interaction.

My students are tremendously powerful...and there's dynamics of influence and power that are actually resonating on these frequencies that I didn't have the ability to pick up at first. And so in particular, just like learning how status, how power, how choice, influence gets played out in a different culture has really helped me practice shifting ME to meet that...energetically and in role. Particularly speaking in the model of DvT.

He reflects on the issue of letting go of cultural assumptions about skill:

I came in with this intense "I'm an actor. I'm from a theatrical tradition". ... I'm trying to play worse and worse as time goes on. Let go of my own thoughts about what should happen – and then to be in a different cultural setting to realize it's not just being bad or good in the play. I don't have the building blocks that they have within the Taiwanese cultural conserve, within their bodies, within their history. It's not right to exercise authority in the way that I experience it in a place where I'm culturally more dominant (like the U.S.) and rather than sort of just blundering through and pretending it's not happening, I'm really struggling to try and discover these new places, to allow ourselves to be very rough and very uncertain, very ambiguous, and just create more mutual spaces that don't make any sense to maybe either of us so that we end up building together; we're really trying to dismantle history's territories in the playspace, at least partially.

When I go to a place, especially a place where my language isn't dominant. I experience all this disruption, this disorientation, this fear. And then I recognize I'm not in danger. I'm just not, you know, in control as much as I usually think I am. In teaching it's more important that I let the students play on their own, in their own language. I don't ask for constant translation, and especially now we have more advanced students and I don't always have a full time translator when I'm working with the advanced group.

I experienced this kind of existential loneliness. I, I feel like, oh, it's necessary. They have to play on their own. They have to play by themselves and they have to play in their cultural space. And I have to experience this exclusion. And I have to sort of rebuild what I'm seeing in the play from like building blocks of bodies, and I often find that my stamina to stay in the process like is much lower than I wish. I drift off, I start thinking about the next session. I'm making notes on that feeling, what it takes for me to stay in as the cultural outsider when no one is actively inviting me in or holding me. I find it's like a privilege moment "Why is no one taking care of me?", but also like a real discomfort. I think that I – am I not doing my job or am I not able to intervene – what will happen if I can't be an authority in this moment?

The interviewee then relates this experience to working back in the US in individual practice:

> Clinically, I've had several experiences where I'm working with someone where English is not their primary language. And I've asked if they want to consult with someone who speaks their language? … Many times people are like, "no, no, I won't." I had a Japanese client. Like, "no, no, I never would like to work with someone who is Japanese".

The interviewee recounts how the client may affirm they understand, but that the subtext is different and how this was anxiety provoking for the therapist:

> I have to let go of my own feelings about how it's [the play is] being experienced. Just tolerate that it could be violent. It could be shaming. It could be triggering. It could be anything. I don't get to choose that for the person, that's based on their experiences. It's based on their history, their triggers. And so…the playspace sort of allows me to really sit with, like, I may have really perpetrated. I may have really played out a harmful dynamic because I don't have that vulnerability in myself. So in real life I really don't notice my boots are just that big. I'm gonna step on something. The playspace sort of lets us really attenuate to like…how badly you can misstep. And it really, I think, gives a lot of freedom for the person to show me better what happened, whereas I think the rules of verbal therapy, especially since I most often conduct it in English, there's just a level of power and politeness that the language holds. There's only so much we could do in verbal play.

The interview also highlighted some useful additional strategies in working with interpreters. Namely, the value of playing with the interpreter as part of the dramatherapy:

> It has been different in Taiwan when I do therapy and we're working with a translator…it's just very humbling to sort of feel like…it's constantly all in that gap. I'm just spitting these words at a person who is then turning them into other words, that I can't decipher. Hopefully something happens. One of my most memorable sessions in Taiwan, the client killed the translator in the play. *laugh* The two of us (therapist and interpreter) are just looking at each other and I was like oh, this is very interesting. We are truly equal in this moment. I really screwed with her unintentionally a little bit in the play because I know three words in Mandarin. She clearly would ask me a question outside of just, "say yes or no," but I would answer her randomly with the little language I could speak. And she would look at me as if like, how do you – how do you understand what I said? I'm like: I don't. I don't understand at all. I'm

just pretending. ... That territory has really helped me a lot to say this is where we're really at. This sense that I can really get it right with all of my intense verbal skills and my cultural sensitivity is mostly just something I'm telling myself to feel better, you know? There's this existential divide that all of this stuff is flying across. Ohhh. And when you really acknowledge it, different things open up.

Vignette 2

This second vignette comes from Cathie Sprague. In a clinical practice example from the UK, a dramatherapist works with a group of refugees from the same African country. Concerns had been raised by mental health community development workers about the cultural suitability of care. The council for Improving Access to Psychological Therapies initiative seemed to focus on Cognitive Behaviour Therapy, which was only available in English and had a European cultural approach. The aim of the dramatherapy was to encourage and research other therapeutic approaches to mental health care, particularly the arts therapies, whether they might have the possibility of being able to offer a more culturally appropriate approach. It was decided to offer a series of 12 one-and-a-half-hour group dramatherapy sessions and to measure any impact using the Warwick Edinburgh scale pre- and post-group for mental well-being (Tennant et al., 2007).

The White dramatherapist worked alongside the Black minority ethnic mental health community development worker who was acting as advocate for this client group. This was particularly useful in terms of referrals for the group and for accessing appropriate follow on and support services. The basis of this dramatherapy work was centred on Alida Gersie's question-based story series. In the 1980s, Alida Gersie designed a series of story-evocation techniques to enable clients to develop their story-making (Gersie & King, 1989; Gersie, 1991, 1997a). The therapist and coworker had to argue to keep the group homogeneous in terms of nationality, which was a challenge as agencies often want mixed nationality groups. The dramatherapist wanted to work on the life story. She and her colleague had researched refugee stories from the country; young men were taken into the military and often experienced persecution on religious grounds by the military. They felt that consolidation of people in their own space would be important. The military had created divisions, not the people (sometimes mono-national groups can be problematic in case of civil war and persecution between different cultural groups). A case needed to be made for a mono-cultural group to re-establish cultural identity in exile.

The reasons that clients were referred to the group included social isolation, stress, low self-esteem and social skills, low mood and low confidence.

Twenty were referred and assessed; 15 attended the group on at least one occasion.

The average attendance was 6 clients per week over 12 weeks, but up until week 10, this had been 8 to 9 clients. Given that this client group has a very difficult relationship to endings, it was not surprising that the numbers dropped substantially. What is surprising is how many attended for so long. Only two women attended the group, at first sporadically but towards the middle, both came together and fully engaged with the work.

The case study is of **A**, who asked for his story to be written out for him in English. He had recently had his application for asylum refused and was in the process of putting together a fresh claim with his solicitor – he felt his solicitor wasn't quite getting his story, and he felt rushed, it was complicated. When he received his initial refusal, he also received notice to quit his accommodation. He didn't know what to do – as he had nowhere to go. A Refugee Service put him in touch with a charity specialising in housing people who were destitute; they found him accommodation. **A** talked about his fears of having nowhere to live – how he couldn't sleep on friends' floors, as he might jeopardise their accommodation. Through all of this, he kept a very friendly, respectful and smiley manner, never missing a session, happily building structures that he openly aspired to and placing his truck at the heart of the village to serve the community.

A was rehoused six kilometres away; during the course of a session, he disclosed that he had walked for over two hours in order to attend the session; at this point, we offered him his bus fare. The group seemed to parent A; he was the baby in the group; the only one without leave to stay; everyone was concerned about this charismatic young man. His only sense of power seemed to be within this group, and he grasped it and worked openly, giving permission to other group members to fully engage. There is something about becoming infantilised when all power and decision-making options are in the hands of others.

A appeared very contented in the group and engaged completely with the exercises. I believe the group was a strong container for him over a difficult transient period. An example from session 12:

After some warm-up ball games, the group created a landscape and dwelling where all individual stories might take place, using cloth, sticks, chairs, etc., as a physicalisation/embodiment of the first two to three sections of Alida Gersie's nine-part Story Question series).

As a therapist, I was taken on a tour; the dwellings were explained to me: food source of fish from the river, cattle protected from wildlife by a shepherd, S's hut was a traditional family one with family in it. A bridge allowed access across the river that ran through the centre of the space. K's hut was a temporary nomadic one, and he explained that they were there for one night only; then these ancient people would move on. K laughed, from his dwelling to A's is a big jump. A's dwelling is a concrete four-walled house, built with bricks, described as a 'posh house'.

I was moved by the love in this landscape and the group; pieces of cloth were tied in a bundle to be cattle; a large bin was covered with cloth to be a mountain in the distance. I asked the group to imagine a character in the landscape, to give characteristics and to write down some things about them. Everyone immediately engaged with this task.

A had needed a bridging interpreter to attend the group.

> When he was assessed he came with an older man who had taken him under his wing, who also became a group member. He soon got on with the other people, but initially did not know anyone and had been very isolated. The older man had acted as his interpreter to the world up to that time. Once in the group there was an interpreter who undertook simultaneous translation.

The importance of language was also related to trauma. The therapist felt that A's identity was traumatised by a lack of understanding about his story. When his leave was turned down, he asked the therapist to write his story because he felt no one could understand. The therapist stated her belief that "identity is compromised, when a life story cannot be communicated to self and others". There is an intertwining of linguistic and traumatic difficulties. Drama enabled A to communicate clearly; he was very good at embodied communication. Not being believed and understood undermined his sense of self. Dramatic and embodied communication enabled him to be witnessed and understood. This could then be represented to the solicitor and written down; using the six-part story, he structured how to communicate his life story.

The therapist emphasised that communication was a two-way process:

> They are in England, they are trying to understand the culture and the landscape and they try to provide that same insight about their country to me. When they describe I try to explain the equivalence in this country, when I was asked questions like do you have anything in this country like a…or where are your…comparing rivers, lakes, seas in the different landscapes. Also regarding dwellings and people, are there nomadic people in this country for example. Translating the language of landscape was important for this group and their therapist.
>
> Dwelling is big question for asylum seekers/refugees, not allowed or able to see much of the country. All were from rural settings and were now in big urban setting. There was an apparent love of landscape, A. was from a farming background. I am aware that my transference was important with this group who were isolated from their rural homeland and I recognized a parallel process in my own disconnection with a rural homeland. I did wonder at times if I was projecting my love of landscape and decided it was transferred back to and from me.

The UK dramatherapist also commented on the relationship between therapist, client and interpreter. "A was a very engaging, playful and smiley young man. Physical ball games were an effective way to connect. Regarding touch, at one point I wanted to touch him but he backed away. My countertransference image was him during flight in a container with masses of people where they had no choice but to touch all the time, smell of urine and body odours, etc. His sensory message towards the therapist was of a strong aftershave, not wanting to smell awful ever again, but also not wanting physical contact. He could manage playful touch in a ball game, but not emotional touch. He could be playful with the interpreter too. The interpreter was more serious/distant from the group but would have a good laugh with them before and after the session. A and the interpreter clicked; they had not known each other before the group. The interpreter joined in physical play; he joined in by choice and was a similar age to the group".

As authors, we also wondered whether gender may have played a role in taboos around touch; the therapist was a woman and the interpreter a man (Dokter, 2000b). Both dramatherapists stressed the importance of the ability to play, both by the therapist and the interpreter. Also that the therapist may be in the 'outsider' position, who does not understand; the client's language is the majority language and the therapist needs to negotiate from a position of vulnerability and not knowing.

Conclusion

The opening vignette showed the importance of being able to use words and using dramatherapy to help (re)find words. The survey findings related more to the interweaving of verbal and non-verbal communication in dramatherapy. The practice reflections highlighted issues of power in relation to language, the importance of having one's story witnessed and understood, the use of interpreters and being able to play with language.

The client in the opening vignette chose to focus on communicating with his foster brother and mother after a brief dramatherapy intervention. They created a life story book together and were able to create a memorial ritual for their parents (Zwart & Nieuwenhuis, 1998). The therapist's role as interpreter and culture broker can empower clients and carers to do the work that needs to be done. The therapist as outsider can be a profoundly helpful role for a therapist. Enabling clients to speak their own language and see a powerful other struggling to understand, find words, and give meaning provides greater equality in the relationship and models that these struggles can be played with and survived.

We have not addressed here the issue of the variations in a shared language that the interviewee raises. Variations in accent and dialect can intersect with assumptions about class, just like the issues of touch can intersect with gender. Some of this is further explored in chapters relating to socio-economic status and gender.

Questions for further reflection

- What considerations regarding language are illuminated in the two vignettes from practice? How do/might you address this in your own practice?
- What languages do you use in your practice?
- Can you recall instances in your life where language was used to express power or to disempower? Can you exchange with others ways to re-empower yourself and if/how these could be translated to client work?
- Practice a gibberish conversation with a peer; write up separately what you thought the text and subtext of the conversation were and compare notes. What was and was not able to be communicated without knowledge of each other's language?

Chapter 10

Money matters

The influence of social class in dramatherapy

Mia, a 10 year old girl in the final year of primary school, had been in indi-vidual dramatherapy for two years, attending weekly sessions with only two absences. A dizygotic twin, with two other siblings, the family live on state benefits, in conditions of overcrowding. She initially presented with low self-confidence, shyness and feelings of worthlessness. Yet in the dramather-apy space, her presentation was one in which non-verbal communication and articulation of need was noted as being strong, flowing and empowering. Mia spoke explicitly and demonstrated implicitly via her play choices and own-ership of the dramatherapy space, that she valued the time and focus alone in the room. She spoke little about her family, focusing on herself and her experiences in the present moment of being in the room.

Mia chose repeatedly to blow up balloons and store them in the room held by lengths of wool, fixed as high up as she could reach, whilst standing on a table. She would often go straight to the balloons and count them on arrival each week, noting any that had popped or collapsed over time due to lack of air. She was engaged in this self-appointed task, often accompanied by an excited declaration of balloon status. Despite her knowledge that the dramatherapy room was a shared space with other children, she managed to find a space where the balloons were out of easy reach from others – a space of her own in the shared room. Having captured a series of photographs of her dramatherapy process and, now at the point where she was aware that the celluloid film camera was about to be developed and images returned for viewing, Mia's narrative turned to family themes. She spoke about her mum:

MIA: *"I think I'd like to show my mum the photographs when they come back."*

DT: *"You'll have a complete set that will be your own."*

MIA: *"I'd like to show her the room and the things I do here and the balloons and the things I like. Can I invite her to come?"*

DT: *"If you would like to."*

When the time came for this session to be held, Mia toured her mother around the room, including her individual storage tray and its content. Whilst Mia often spoke little, this was an occasion where her dialogue flowed and

DOI: 10.4324/9780429431593-12

she spoke with ease and excitement to her mother. As mother and daughter had experienced some challenges in their relationship, once the news that her mother had agreed to attend the session had been confirmed, Mia seemed delighted to share her space with her all important visitor.

Dramatherapist, UK

This vignette does not name the class background of therapist or client, only the sentence "the family live on state benefits in conditions of overcrowding" indicates difficult material circumstances. As the title of this chapter states 'money matters'. A clear link exists between social and economic inequality and poor health, including mental health. Health disparities, including risk factors for common mental disorders, are heavily associated with social inequalities, whereby income and access to resources intersect with other social factors such as race, age, legal status and gender to produce differing levels of risk or precarity (WHO, 2014). Mia initially presented as shy, lacking confidence and feeling worthless. Later in this chapter, we will elucidate how this may connect to issues around class. The dramatherapist in the vignette aims to affirm and improve both the child's and the family's sense of agency. Research into education and class shows that cultural fit and identity compatibility in education settings constitute working-class disadvantages (Jay & Muldoon, 2018).

Poverty can be both a causal factor and a consequence of mental health concerns (Elliott, 2016; Liu, 2010). In this chapter, we will look at social class in relation to mental health in the context of dramatherapy. We will also discuss how dramatherapists perceive the impact of social class in relation to other aspects of identity in their own training and intercultural practice. We start by situating our own authors' stories in relation to class.

Situating ourselves in our lived experience

Coming from a working-class background, I (Ditty) was aware that the female ancestor mentioned in Chapter 5, when admitted to an asylum in the early 20th century, would have received more physiological than psychological treatment. Half a century later, her granddaughter was also regularly admitted to a psychiatric hospital, given ECT and medication, maybe the occasional discussion with a psychologist. Ongoing psychotherapy provided privately was expensive and not considered for those 'without education'. Freud (1905), who reflected the class consciousness and elitist mentality of his society, claimed that "those patients who do...not possess a reasonable amount of education...should be refused for psychoanalysis" (p. 263). The question of what characteristics render an individual amenable to psychological therapy and whether or not these are class related is one aspect of a complex relationship between social factors and mental health. These had been researched more by my aunt's time but had not much impacted on treatment yet in the Netherlands in the mid-20th century. Moving to the UK, a country with very persistent class divisions, increased my awareness of the impact of coming from a working-class background. In a family of plasterers and cigar makers, education stopped when you were between 12 and 15 years old, whenever the state stipulated you could leave school and start earning. I grew up in social housing, in the UK called council estates. Training as a dramatherapist meant a first degree, I was the first and only one of my generation to be university educated, which made me a class migrant. State grants and practical support from the extended family enabled me to study. Debt was frowned upon for religious and class reasons. Being able to train as a dramatherapist depends on that first degree; my later studies were funded by my National Health Service (NHS), social care and university employers. As a dramatherapist, I became aware of the performative aspect of class in terms of accent and language. For example, as a second language speaker, my class background is less noticeable in the UK, although in the Netherlands, I had also learnt to adapt my language. The fact that I do not speak dialect like the rest of my family (my mother having insisted that this batch of identity would provide me with fewer opportunities) reminds me of the performative aspects of queer identity discussed in Chapter 6; what we do or do not choose to reveal to those we are interacting with. Labov's (1966) research into New York pronunciation patterns established that language use correlates with class, gender and age. The older studies assumed that class hierarchies determined linguistic behaviour, whilst more recent approaches emphasise social practice and speaker agency (Snell, 2014). As a dramatherapist from a working-class background, I struggle with the fact that it can be considered purely in terms of economic deprivation. The strength of communal interdependence is rarely mentioned, although dramatherapists working with communities is common practice (Jennings, 2009). How communities provide themselves with agency by collaboration can be an important aspect of therapy considerations, especially the importance of identifying support networks. Ethnographers have examined the relationship between social class and parental/community involvement in schools (Lareau, 2011). The shadow side of my personal intersections of class and religion may have been one of social control and more rigid role expectations, but I am also aware that my attribution of poverty and wealth to contextual factors rather than talent reflects my class background.

As the daughter of immigrants with a history of displacement, I (Nisha) came from a family with a certain anxiety about maintaining a middle-class standing. My grandparents were very well established in Sindh, Pakistan, and, as the story goes, were *forced to leave everything behind* in an effort to survive the great Partition of India and Pakistan in 1947 (Sajnani, 2016a). A gendered division of labour was pronounced in my grandfather's tailoring shop, which he rebuilt in Malaysia and where his sons and male cousins in the family were employed. My parents moved to Canada, as it was seen as a *land of opportunity* for immigrants of colour. Yet, even as settlers in a comparatively stable country, we were concerned with what we could afford, a phenomenon theorised to be driven in part by the anxiety of our southern neighbours in the US whose healthcare and education costs continued to challenge middle-class means (Wente, 2014). Growing up in a single-parent family, I saw my mother manage stressful, and at times sexist and racist, work environments in order to secure and stretch her income to raise three daughters. She often relied on the support of extended family members; my grandmother paid for my initial application fees to college and for our trips to visit our cousins, aunts and uncles in Malaysia, Singapore and Brunei. Motivated by professional interests, I migrated to the US where the dominant narrative of opportunity and social mobility continues to circulate and is problematically tied up with notions of good moral character. As Sturm and Gibson note (2012), "[T]he main message is clear: If a person works hard enough and is 'of good character,' nothing should stop his or her socioeconomic ascent. Conversely, if people are not willing to work hard or are not 'of good character,' they and only they are responsible for their lot in life" (p. 17). These familial experiences combined with the inheritance of displacement and the desire to find a place within contradictory national narratives of socialist prosperity in Canada and extreme capitalism in the US. This tension is present in my role as a dramatherapy programme director at one of the most expensive universities in the world (Kurt, 2021), where a good portion of my time is devoted to raising funds for scholarships to expand access to training in this profession.

Social class, classism and mental health

According to the American Psychological Association (APA, 2017), *social class* encompasses both socio-economic status (SES) and subjective social status. In addition to subjective status distribution of wealth, social control, hegemonic practices and culture are interwoven through power relations. They encompass income, educational attainment, career prospects, financial security. The concept of *social class* in the context of economic health was advanced by Marx (1977) to describe a grouping of people in relation to their labour, which he regarded as central to the organisation or society which he characterised as an ongoing *class struggle* between two classes: the proletariat (low-income labouring class) and the bourgeoisie (high-income management). From a Marxist point of view, the bourgeoisie is invested in maintaining and advancing their position by exploiting the proletariat class whose only pathway to change lay in gaining control over the means of production, selling and governance or decision-making power (e.g. labour unions). This social division of classes has been, over time, reconfigured into a lower, middle and upper class and, more recently, into a more nuanced range from an elite (rich) to a 'precariat' class, a word referring to the experience of living without predictability or security to the extent that material and psychological welfare is impacted (Savage et al., 2013).

Classism "consists of a collection of behaviours, thoughts, attitudes, practices, and policies that work together to create and maintain a system of inequality that benefits those in a higher class while negatively impacting people of a lower class" (Williams, 2017, p. 1). Williams (2017) offers four categories of classism:

individual, institutional, cultural and internalised. Individual classism pertains to the negative stereotypes and beliefs we may hold about people from different social classes. Institutional classism refers to protection of wealthy classes through institutional laws and practices. This may appear as a lack of quality grocery stores or healthcare in lower income neighbourhoods or the practice of lending at higher interest rates to people below a certain income level. Cultural classism is the expression of classist attitudes and beliefs in the images and stories that surround us such as the glamorising of upper classes in magazines and other media. Finally, internalised classism is the internalisation of the negative projections associated with one's particular social class. Williams (2017: 1) writes,

> Internalized classism occurs when a person from a lower social class accepts or internalizes classism that is directed toward the social class to which the person belongs. In other words, people start to believe that the negative attitudes and thoughts about their social class are true. For example, a child who is put down by his teachers due to their bias because he lives in a disadvantaged neighbourhood may eventually come to accept these negative opinions as true, shaping his self-image as a failure, unworthy, or not as acceptable as other children. The result may be that his performance in school suffers significantly, and the lack of encouragement to pursue his dreams inhibits his drive to succeed. Likewise, an unemployed person who is constantly called lazy and a moocher may begin to internalize these opinions, which results in low self-esteem.

This definition offers a clear pathway to understanding how economic injustice may affect our physical and mental health as well as our relationships and behaviours. There is indisputable evidence that poverty impacts our overall health and well-being, including mental health (Burns, 2015; Kraus et al., 2011), and with the deterioration of social health, inequality intensifies (Wilkinson & Pickett, 2009). In the UK, children and adults living in households in the lowest 20% income bracket were found to be two to four times more likely to develop mental health problems as compared to those in the highest income brackets (Gutman et al., 2015; Marmot et al., 2010). Research has also demonstrated that those who are unemployed or economically inactive have higher rates of common mental health problems (Stanfeld et al., 2016). Lower SES is linked to a greater risk of cumulative stress, which is linked to greater rates of disorder and access to services, and, consequently, a marked difference in outcomes across the lifespan including end of life (Alegría et al., 2018; Rowley et al., 2021).

Social class affects one's quality of life, the opportunities and privileges people have in society and influences behaviour through cultural learning. Such learning includes socialisation processes within a family and social cognitive processes and habitual response processes pertaining to money and to the groups in which one experiences a sense of fit and belonging. For example, although there has been a decline of the "traditional working class" to 14%

(Savage et al., 2013), 60% in the UK still self-identify as working class, even if their occupational status suggests they are middle class. This self-identification is significantly associated with social attitudes (Manstead, 2018). Class is an aspect of culture that intersects with other forms to impact identity; working-class culture is often linked to greater interdependence and empathy. Class culture worldwide may intersect with regional variations in emphasis on honour and individualism, whilst religion may influence attribution and moral judgement (Cohen & Varnum, 2016). There is an ambivalence as to the location of class in the intersection of gender with other inequalities such as race (Walby et al., 2012). For example, while more US writing focuses on the intersections of social class, gender and race, there is still a great deal of denial in accounting for social class and mental illness (Hollingshead & Redlich, 2007). Social class is not a named inequality in European Union legislation, and the attempt to include socio-economic grounds in the UK Equality Act failed. Understanding the influence of social class on mental health is critical to quality care.

Dramatherapist perspectives

In this section, we offer themes arising from the responses about the influence of social class in dramatherapy. Thirty-four respondents indicated that social class had an influence on their experience of dramatherapy. Yet, at the same time, social class was understood to be a rarely discussed, invisible force. For example, very few respondents (n = 7) chose to offer further insight in contrast to other aspects of culture and identity. As one respondent wrote, "I am not able to see it in the environment where I work". Whether this comes from not wanting to acknowledge class or whether socio-economic inequalities are invisible to the therapist, the community, the clients or others is unclear but still indicates the possibility that class and economic inequality are rendered invisible. The rejection of social class as a meaningful category of identity is, as mentioned before, reflected in it being left out of human rights (Fagan, 2021) and equality legislation.

In a British Association of Dramatherapists survey, dramatherapists, when asked how they self-identified in relation to class, identified as working class (15.3%), lower middle class (21.7%), middle class (53.6%) and upper class (0.56%). It is interesting to note that the working and lower middle-class self-identification increased between the 2007 and 2015 surveys: working class by 5% and lower middle class by 14.7%. Self-definition can be problematic but debates about it unrecognised. Criteria for class identification is one of the factors that has made class an aspect of identity

The impact on the provision of care and access to dramatherapy

Dramatherapists wrote about the impact of resources on the provision of care and access to dramatherapy. One wrote from a US perspective,

I tend to experience this primarily in a social/national context where the U.S. has such a shitty and stratified question of access for people in health care. I experience "power" because I can often provide dramatherapy to people at a more reasonable cost because I am both a drama therapist and a social worker. But I'm very aware of the system's complex contra-dictions: why is it that my early-career client has a co-pay that's five times what this relatively wealthy mom is paying?

Others wrote about the need for subsidised care:

Often those in poverty are restricted in their ability to access therapy or to continue in it. Charitable funding is often short-term. It is unclear whether the socioeconomic status of my community clients has a mas-sive impact – they have absolutely no way to access drama or any other kind of psychotherapy, unless it's through a non-profit organisation that has funding to sponsor the work. Therefore, generally, the poor do not have access and the concepts or arts therapies are alien to most people in marginalised communities.

I have had clients who were unable to continue the therapy because they couldn't afford the fees. We have talked about creating a scholarship for the program, but I have not heard of it being implemented.

The socioeconomic status of my community clients has a massive impact – they have absolutely no way to access drama or any other kind of psycho-therapy, unless it's through an NPO who has funding to sponsor the work. Therefore, generally, the poor do not have access and the concepts or arts therapies are alien to most people in marginalized communities.

Funding is also a key factor for accessing the service. Government support for mental health treatment for Thai people is a severe deficit.

The setting impacts access for clients of dramatherapy

Respondents wrote about the influence of particular settings on access to dramatherapy differentiating between the perception of therapy in a private versus a public setting.

In the private sector, therapy could be seen as a privilege for those who can afford it. In the NHS (UK national health service), particularly in forensic mental health, all patients can access dramatherapy if they wish to. Many people do not understand what it can offer so we are having to publicise ourselves constantly. The best publicity, of course, comes from satisfied clients.

I work in schools which enables me to provide dramatherapy to a range of young people across the spectrum of socioeconomic influences.

I find that where I am taken seriously, it has been earned. However, in terms of employment in an area of extreme poverty this is an issue.

Social class informs help-seeking behaviour

The third survey theme was motivation for therapy as related to social class. As previously discussed, help-seeking behaviours in lower income communities are less studied overall but have an impact on engagement in therapy. One respondent observed differences in help-seeking behaviours amongst resource-poor people:

> From my experience, it is noticeable that the clients from different socio-economic status have a different degree of motivation and expectation in therapy. People who have a lower level of income and education are likely to not be as concerned about their mental health issues and treatment.

In this quote, we see an example of how clients' reasons for coming to therapy may only be considered in the personal realm without considering the systemic factors and stressors that play a role in limiting or obstructing care (Jones, 2010). By only focusing on intrapsychic factors and choosing not to ask or consider political and social exclusion factors that impede mental health care, we as therapists can be seen as "colluding with forces that work to oppress, marginalise and silence clients about (aspects of) their lives" (Jones, 2010, p. 25).

Access to training in dramatherapy and accessing therapy during training

Three respondents commented on social class as it related to training in dramatherapy. Two dramatherapists differently identified their socio-economic background and how it impacted on privilege and perceived status. One wrote,

> I am aware I wouldn't have been able to get a master's in drama therapy if I did not come from the wealthy, white background I come from, so my status does affect that it was accessible to me.

In contrast, another wrote,

> My background is working class. The profession I chose was new and as such unknown to my family, although they were familiar with mental health difficulties and related treatment. I was aware that dramatherapy was associated with privilege (as were other forms of psychological therapy), which meant more status, although the lack of access to and unfamiliarity with dramatherapy meant lower status.

The financial impact of dramatherapists needing to access dramatherapy during their training is also reflected in the following quote from a trainee:

"Finding the money to pay for it. Having access to drama therapy is costly, as a client and as a student, and lack of resources greatly extended my training".

The first respondent implied family wealth; the second does not identify how training was paid for. Different generations of dramatherapists may have received different types of access and support to do their training. Even if one is able to access a university education, the subject one studies may be influenced by which university one can afford; studying a performing arts subject is less open to people from less privileged backgrounds (Reidi, 2018). As Brook et al. (2018) write that with the exception of crafts, no creative occupation comes close to having less than a third of its workforce from working-class backgrounds. In fact, the percentage in 2018 was around 12.6%, and that was before the pandemic closed down much of the performing arts. In the training chapter, we will look at the impact of this in greater depth.

Identification with social class of family of origin

Many of the therapists identified on the basis of their family background. Samuels (2001, p. 29) comments on the relationship between class and a person's inner world. If they are, due to their education and occupation, in a different class than their parents, they will still identify with the class in which they are born. This is consistent with some of the responses received. For example, one respondent wrote,

> For most of my life I have experienced middle income privilege. This was not the case when my family first immigrated to Canada, for the first ten years of my life or so. Because my training and working professional years have been lived with socioeconomic status privilege – this is an area where I know I have many blind spots. I have to work hard to examine, unlearn and learn about different socioeconomic realities outside of my experience, and re-connect to some of the more financially unstable years I lived in my early childhood.

The impact of social class on employment

The previous respondent also offered insight into how financial debt influenced their work choices.

> I did incur substantial financial debt during my many years of post-graduate education and this has certainly influenced which jobs I have been able to take as a drama therapist. At the beginning of my career I had to make very difficult choices that were in part influenced by not being able to afford drama therapy internships as my monthly student loan payment was $600.00 per month. At the beginning of my drama therapy career I also had to work jobs outside the drama therapy field in order to continue paying my loan. Although I consider myself middle income now I still hold a debt of $40,000.

Overall, the responses received highlight how the system of health care in which a therapy is offered is part of a political landscape (Jones, 2010). That landscape is created by a government and its agencies (health, social and arts services, for example) and by non-governmental, private for-profit and non-profit agencies, and client representation groups set alongside or in opposition to those services. The actions and attitudes of a government affect areas such as the nature or extent of services; who can provide them, who can benefit from them, as well as those excluded or not considered in that provision. The accounts provided by respondents highlight issues of access to therapy, cost of training and treatment and whether the therapy is accessible to clients. What is not addressed is the issue of acceptability of therapy for clients (Steele et al., 2007) and any connection this may have to social class, which may be an interesting area for further research.

Dramatherapist reflections on practice

The opening vignette highlighted the importance of empowerment and involvement of the family. Children from a lower social class can experience higher stress levels, as do their parents, potentially resulting in a higher incidence of mental health problems. This appears to hold true across different cultural groups. A Korean study showed how cumulative work-family conflict can exacerbate mental health problems (Kim & Cho, 2020), for women often compounded by wider family care responsibilities (see gender chapter). People from more disadvantaged backgrounds experience greater rates of stress and anxiety. Families with a low socio-economic status suffer from a higher number of stressors related to finances, social relations, employment situations and health complaints than those with a high SES (Reiss et al., 2019). Dramatherapists identify special educational needs and parental mental health problems as influencing factors, not class (either their own or the client's), but identify the importance of empowerment and agency for the client and the importance of parental involvement and witnessing. Returning to the opening vignette, the dramatherapist stated the following:

Mia's therapist
  Identified as having special educational needs (SEN), Mia was assessed as having a verbal vocabulary below average for her age. Approximately half way through the dramatherapy term, Mia became involved as a co-researcher in a doctoral research study facilitated by the dramatherapist. Whilst framed around the existing dramatherapy structure, the additional research enabled her to record using cameras, via moving and static image, experiences of her dramatherapy process. In one session, Mia had invited the dramatherapist to join her in a den made of infant height classroom tables, various blankets and cushions. The den had been erected by a group of boy's a fortnight earlier, with instructions not to dismantle it,

but to allow other children to make use of it, should they wish to. In Mia's empowerment the role of audience and witness was crucial. Some of Mia's play may have been themes of escape in terms of identity exploration – the "avoidance of communicating", as a way of exploring play with just the sense of "other" rather than in a structured projected role of a real person. I was really concerned about the impact the mother would have on the therapeutic space, but on the day of this session – having prepared in clinical supervision for "what if's". As it turned out – she did come and it was a beautifully enjoyable and rare experience for me in my career to witness, as Mia became the "therapist of her own therapy" (I have written elsewhere in my notes) as that's what it felt like. She was the wise and knowledgeable experience of herself, as she toured mum around the room, telling her everything that she wanted to about being a co-researcher and being in dramatherapy.

Several factors intersect in the vignette; for us as authors, SES was a subtext, as neither clients, their families or the therapists (self) identify subjective class identity. As a subtext, the living on benefits in overcrowded conditions, mild learning difficulties and lack of confidence and agency indicate that socio-economic class may need to be considered as an intersectional factor in the work.

Looking at an example of therapist alongside client empowerment is a vignette of a dramatherapist working with working-class adult veterans diagnosed with posttraumatic stress disorder who are offered dramatherapy in the community via a charity. She identifies class and gender as intersecting variables for her as the therapist, particularly in relation to owning her own power, potentially in a different way than her clients assume power:

Being a female, working with males there can be projections. I am often seen as a white middle class woman; I would not self-disclose but work with the assumptions. Working with the military, people will check on backgrounds partly on the informal grapevine and partly on the internet, so clients will check out what they can. It is important for me not to be immovable, but to have a sense of my power too, not to be timid. I may have to prove myself more as I am not one of "them" by showing I can tolerate what goes on in the sessions and am willing to be tough at times as well. ... If things become destructive in the session, it is about the body going solid. Often when that happens the person feels out of control. Safety is important; never raising my voice, becoming quieter is much more effective.

The vignette about Mia also raises the impact of class on education. Research on the impact of socio-economic deprivation and class on educational attainment shows that help for those who have special educational needs tends to be behind that of young people from middle-class backgrounds (Holt et al., 2018). In rural areas, under-recognition may be even greater, as there tends to be an assumption of a rural middle class due to migration of middle classes from the city to rural areas, whilst working-class migration has gone in the opposite direction for economic /employment opportunities (Hoggart, 1997). Both migration routes have been exacerbated by the pandemic. Access to university for rural poor working-class students is 18% in rural areas in comparison to 48% of city-based students (Todman, 2020). Medication for treating mental health problems is significantly more common for clients with lower SES, but counselling being offered and taken up is increasing (Giebel et al., 2020). Access to psychological therapies, including arts therapies, in rural areas remains problematic, although increased online therapy provides opportunity if families are able to access the internet (another issue highlighted in the pandemic). Given the acceptability barriers of mental health interventions, dramatherapy community interventions which do not pathologise the individual on the basis of socio-economic stressors are crucial. We will return to this in the practice chapter.

Conclusion

Why is it important to consider social class in dramatherapy? It is part of the consideration of context on a person's opportunities and difficulties. Mental health and many common mental disorders are shaped to a great extent by the social, economic and physical environments in which people live. Certain population subgroups are at higher risk of mental disorders because of greater exposure and vulnerability to unfavourable social, economic and environmental circumstances, interrelated with gender. Class intersects in complex ways with all inequalities (Hills, 2010).

Most perniciously, it is an issue of addressing shame that has turned against the self and where we are from. Turner (2021) studies the shame related to othering and being othered. For those who do not benefit from the current system as a result of their social class, gender, racialisation, etc., encounters with hatred and shame are common. In the context of social class, shame can be related to unconscious complicity. De la Boetie (2015) suggests that the class other is aware of being complicit. Shame acts as a "glue to bind the other to the subject" (Turner, 2021, p. 53), yet struggles to move beyond the co-dependent position of compliance. What is shame in this context, is it "the reaction to an important other's unexpected refusal to co-create an attachment bond that allows for the dyadic regulation of emotions?" (Schore, 1998, p. 65). Dyadic regulation of emotions is based in the unconscious belief that relationships are co-created spaces. If the therapist is aware of the importance of co-creation, then shame can be transformed into pride in the authentic self. The shame of one's authentic experience amidst one's intersections can be expressed in how we speak and how we walk, which can be signals of class that are likely to be subject to politically driven assimilation. Shame can be a powerful weapon because it can lead the 'other' to see its authentic, cultural, spiritual, gendered or other identities as shameful, its name, its sexuality, its behavioural norms, even its language. To fit in, to be accepted, one has to lose that which makes one other (Bradshaw, 1988). This psychological lens on othering and shame clarifies why agency and empowerment are so crucial for both Mia and others; class and ability intersect for their families' experience of being other and less than.

The fact that interdependence is emphasised in working-class community backgrounds can facilitate a greater ability to read others' emotions (Graziano et al., 2007; Kraus et al., 2011), a very useful dramatherapeutic skill. It is important to recognise the strengths of certain class communities and that privilege in wealth may not equal emotional privilege. Class and education in the UK, and those parts of the world where the colonial legacy of British education is structurally embedded, can equal attachment trauma through the impact of private education and boarding schools. Privilege can equal emotional deprivation and very rigid expectations about lifestyle and life patterns (Schaverien, 2011; Turner, 2021). More dialogue about how dramatherapists navigate and negotiate class differences in their practice may enable us to work more effectively with both our own and others' backgrounds.

Questions for further reflection

- What considerations regarding social class are illuminated in the two vignettes from practice? How do/might you address this in your own practice?
- How do you relate to money? How do you perceive your social class, and is it the same or different from the family you grew up with? What impact does that have on you?
- Where does responsibility lie for people who are underprivileged?
- If you as a dramatherapist hold greater or less economic privilege than your clients, (how) do you engage with that in the therapeutic relationship?

Chapter 11

Borders in the therapy room? Nationality, migration and refugee experiences

T, a 12 year old son of an Iraqi asylum seeker, came to see me as a private client after his father's latest bid to apply for asylum had failed. An initial claim had been rejected and an appeal had also failed. Documents had then been submitted in support of a fresh claim but this attempt had also met with rejection. His father had since started the process via another solicitor of again seeking to make a fresh claim, this time under Article 8 of the European Convention on Human Rights, and hence the family was protected against the prospect of sudden repatriation. Nevertheless, that failure of the previous application had seemingly sent a shock wave through the once affluent family which had by now been in the UK for nearly five years living in severely reduced circumstances. Moreover, one of the father's opening remarks to me was "I've always believed in the dream... the American Dream, you know." This conveyed a heavy sense of identification with Western society and its values. It also became clear that this man, a fluent English speaker who had previously studied for five years in England, had worked in an interpreting role for coalition forces as well as his business having supplied them. All of this served to bolster both disbelief and a sense of injustice at the UK's rejection of his asylum claim. The failure of the asylum claim had also heralded distress in T's older sister who was 18, expressed suicidal ideation, and was being seen by a local mental health charity. T had reportedly become very withdrawn, subdued, and was suffering frequent sleep disturbance. His father told me that his son "lives in fear."

Charlie Moritz, Dramatherapist, UK

Moritz, the dramatherapist working with the son (T) in this vignette, wondered what he might be holding and enacting on behalf of his parents and what at a deeper level, beyond present anxiety and upset, might have been re-stimulated from the past for their son. Descriptions of how his parents tended to be day to day also suggested that, whilst they had fallen into states of hypo-arousal, he by contrast was unconsciously invited to carry and enact their distress. An avenue for dramatherapeutic exploration arose near the end of a session. Looking at him, the therapist saw how oppressed he looked and said "T, you look like you have to do it all on your own".

DOI: 10.4324/9780429431593-13

"Yes", he responded with an increased energy, "it's like a big heavy bag on my back which I can never put down".

The therapist reflected later,

> A resonant symbol of the threatened enforced journey to come, that imagined bag allowed for some powerfully transformative experiences. Offering to take care of it between sessions movingly deepened and cemented the therapeutic alliance. Unpacking it and eventually destroying it together produced relief and engendered energetic agency in T. and formed the culmination of work which required careful, respectful identification and patrolling of invisible borders: between helpful and unhelpful aspects of the father's involvement – he prematurely pressuring to extract a psychological report; and promotion of a healthy border to undo the immobilizing, merged entity parents and child had unconsciously fallen into in response to their collective plight.

In this chapter, we examine the influence of nationality, chosen and forced migration in the context of intercultural practice. This opening vignette offers insight into the experience of internal and external border crossings including the mental and social strains of in/voluntary migration, issues around loss and oppression for migrants, interactions with the legal system and the 'host' society, post-traumatic stress and post-traumatic growth. What are dramatherapists' perspectives and experiences in this area? What are their thoughts about trans/national identity?

Migration: Rights, trauma and opportunity

The right to freedom of movement was established in the 1948 Universal Declaration of Human Rights (UDHR). Article 13 of the UDHR refers to the "right to freedom of movement and residence within the borders of each State" and the "right to leave any country, including his own, and the return to his country" (UDHR, United Nations). Paradoxically, the history of migration, which is a long one, is a history of controls on the movement of all but a wealthy elite (Trilling, 2018). Many countries have long histories of migration, be it out or in. Countries like Britain, that do not think of themselves as having been settled by migrants, have a deep-rooted history of immigration (Winder, 2004), forced migration in the form of indentured labour and slavery (Taylor, 2020) and emigration beyond the history of colonisation. Although there is a perception that international migration has increased, the proportion of international migrants has stayed relatively stable over the last 50 years, roughly 3% since 1960 (de Haas et al., 2020), whilst at the same time, the formulation and content of foreign policy in both the US and European Union (EU) have had a significant impact with, for example, legal immigration falling by 49% as a result of changes to policies under former president Trump (Anderson, 2020).

Increasingly hostile immigration policies in recent years in the US, EU and UK have paralleled a rise in xenophobia, prejudice and right-wing populism (Helbling et al., 2010; Kende & Kreko, 2020). It is well documented that environmental racism contributes to an increase in migration (Rigaud et al., 2018) yet meets a challenge in a shifting political preference towards nationalism rather than globalisation (Fukuyama, 2018). Coinciding with this shift has been the emergence of the interpellation of citizens as individuals rather than as part of a community within which one has a responsibility to care for others, including minorities, migrants and refugees (Ceobanu & Escandell, 2010). Recent UK policy changes such as Britain leaving the EU (Brexit) and the "hostile environment to immigration" pursued since 2015 by British Tory governments, produced amongst others the Windrush scandal and difficulties for EU citizens in the UK (Remigi, 2017). The forced migration of refugees from war and climate change–impacted countries, often with colonial histories exacerbating the current difficulties, are well described as "victims of politics" (Kalmanovitz & Lloyd, 2005). Environmental racism (Lazarus, 2000) means that certain parts of the world are disproportionately affected, increasing migration within and across borders. The countries engaged in these politics often deny that connection when it comes to migration policies and asylum applications. Shifting the blame to criminals (and criminalised) exploiting the nationalist policies and inequities does not acknowledge responsibility for the past and present inequities created. The UK Windrush scandal where children migrated with their parents and then as adults lacked the paperwork to 'prove' their citizenship is akin to the US hostile immigration policy impact on 'dreamers,' a term used to describe young undocumented immigrants who were brought to the US as children (Wood, 2018). Intergenerational trauma, where trauma from one generation is passed on to the next, can escalate the psychological, physical and social impact of current policies.

These examples should not be interpreted as suggesting that people have no agency in their journeys or that every migration was dictated by a host country (Cowan, 2021). Positioning migrants as outsiders without connection to their host is ahistorical. The 1948 docking of the HMS Windrush at Tilbury, Britain, marked the first significant wave of immigration from the Caribbean as British citizens. The 1948 citizenship act granted full citizenship to people living in British colonies. England colonised Jamaica in 1655 and held power until its independence in 1962, whilst during the 17th and 18th centuries, enslaved peoples were transported by Britain in a forced migration from West Africa to Jamaica. The hostile immigration policies alienate citizens from a sense of belonging and continue to deny the contributions of migrants to the UK. Migration has historically affected Britain's concept of national identity. The first legislation to restrict migration was introduced in 1905, whilst the 1948 Nationality Act divided British subjects from Commonwealth citizens (inhabitants of the ex-colonies), not incorporating a uniform set of rights. It is interesting to note that this occurred in the same year that the declaration of universal human rights was signed.

Insecurities about being able/having a right to stay can create discrimination and exploitation in housing (Crisis, 2021), employment (exploitation/trafficking), health and education, whilst dual citizens/multinationals are viewed with suspicion and can (be threatened with having) have their citizenship revoked. Migration takes effort; for many migrants, the poor social conditions and loss of status/cultural identity take a toll on their psychological health. Dokter (1998b, p.146) wrote 20 years ago and regretfully retains, "It is not simply a matter of geographical and cultural dislocation, the adjustment and inevitable stresses of migration. An important issue is the ongoing response of and to the white host society, its values and institutions". Migration can be both trauma and opportunity; post-traumatic growth, as well as post-traumatic stress, needs to be considered in the work with migrant clients (Chan et al., 2016).

Both authors of this book are transnationals. Ditty migrated as a young adult from the Netherlands to the UK, initially having to register with the aliens department at the local police station, which stopped when she was granted leave to remain after marrying a UK citizen. After the Schengen agreement enabled freedom of movement between EU countries, this "leave to remain" became obsolete. When Brexit was implemented, one's settled status needed again to be applied for, as did British citizenship. Both were granted after a lengthy, stressful and expensive process, which nevertheless was a position of privilege restored. Nisha was born to first-generation immigrants to Canada and then migrated as an adult to the US. Navigating the application process for work visas, and permanent residency were similarly taxing and expensive processes, with the privilege of dual citizenship being the final hurdle. Negotiating this process while attending to other realities such as employment, homeownership, marriage and family obligations contributes to stress.

Marotta (2014) describes a transnational as in-between cultures. He argues that a transnational is situated within the cross-cultural encounter rather than dwelling above it. The discourse of the in-between cultural subject can be silent on how unequal power relations impact one's experience of in-betweenness. Belonging and attachment are complex for intercultural/transnational subjects. There is an assumption that you do not belong if you are black in a white context, as a migrant there can be an issue of being able to pass on 'skin colour', as long as silence is maintained. Invisibility can be a form of assimilation, denying difference, assuming sameness, a pressure to integrate. Belonging is as much in the individual as it is within the communal context. Blackwell (2005) in his work with refugees discusses the importance of addressing the political, cultural, interpersonal and intrapsychic level of both the client and the therapist's experience in therapy. His understanding of working with the unconscious in therapy provides an interesting perspective on "same and other" (2005, p. 17).

If we take seriously our professed belief in the unconscious…, we are always, in some important sense "other" to ourselves. Thus, whenever we talk about "us" and "them" we are always more "other" to each other than we like to imagine, and "they" are always another collection of others, not only more "other" to each other, but also more like ourselves than we are prepared to concede.

Research into the psychosocial effects and stresses on immigrants and minority groups highlights both the psychological opportunities (Beltsiou, 2016) and the risks of alienation (Dokter, 2008). This is true for both therapists and clients, as Nisha shows in her Chapter 4 opening vignette. The response of the surrounding community to these opportunities and stresses makes a great difference to a sense of belonging or not belonging (Dokter, 2008).

Social, political, cultural and historical contexts shape the psychological experience of migration and with it the encounter and interaction between clients and therapists and the possibility of intergenerational trauma being re-enacted between the therapist and client (Layton, 2017). Layton elaborates on a concept called "normative unconscious processes": the psychological consequences of living in a culture, many of whose norms serve the dominant ideological purpose of maintaining the status quo. Racial, class, gender and sexual hierarchies confer power and tend to idealise certain positions whilst devaluing others. Being assigned those positions causes wounds that organise the desire to belong to one group, not the other. In the clinical space (and our lives outside it) we enact conflicts between those unconscious processes, the "normative unconscious processes" that seek to maintain splits and those that seek to heal them. It is in interaction that these processes are enacted. We can only begin to understand the workings of complicity if we explore how our identities are constructed in relation to each other and how our histories have been impacted by the intergenerational transmission of trauma. "Every psychological category we contemplate is rife with hauntings from the past – and how our engagements across difference actualise those hauntings" (Layton, 2017, p. 162).

Dramatherapy and migration

Much dramatherapy literature on working with migrants focuses on migrant clients, the migrant identity of the therapist may or may not be explicit in the encounter. Several early articles and chapters (see Dokter, 1998b) advocated the use of dramatherapy to help in the process of acculturation, but more recent literature discusses the importance of being able to share stories as an aspect of empowerment with, for example, newly arrived refugee women (Landis, 2014). Landis raises the difficulties of settlement, which also figure in the opening vignette. A previous opening vignette in Chapter 9 about language echoes this too. One aspect of the difficulty is the process of being given refugee status, an extremely precarious process. This can be even more precarious for LGBTQ refugees who have to 'prove' that firstly their country is an unsafe place to be because homosexuality is either illegal (as it still is in 72 countries worldwide), punishable by death (Home Office, 2016) or that LGBTQ people have been treated badly (Duncan, 2017). This comes after proving country of origin, not easy when trafficked or having had to flee without documentation. Dramatherapist Ward (2018) highlights how in this asylum process the participant has to be open, bare themselves to the judge, relive previous rejections and shame and convince a stranger about a part of them that they themselves still have to come to terms with. Until status is granted a person is never truly 'safe'. Ward shows how adult flight and asylum trauma comes on top of the childhood trauma of being shamed for who you are: often hearing that homosexuality is wrong, evil and against nature. This complex amalgamation of trauma and shame makes building a trusting relationship extremely difficult. Dramatherapists working with refugee clients are very aware of this, although they can experience the same helplessness and fury at a traumatising and dehumanising system. Shame for one's own country is not unique to the client but shared by both therapist and client.

Scott-Danter, a migrant dramatherapist (Scott-Danter, 1998), showed in her community-oriented participatory theatre work that recovery can be a collective activity where people seek to re-establish the social and spiritual bases of their lives after displacement through war. She reflects on the impact of herself as an outsider, where a co-facilitator from Mozambique might have been useful as a bridge. As a reader, it is interesting that she is a female outsider witnessing/facilitating a piece of theatre where gender tensions are enacted, highlighting community tensions in this area.

Around the same time, Gersie (1997b) wrote about her work with a young migrant woman who, like herself, migrated between countries and languages. The client experienced anxiety attacks and alienation. She reported hearing her own voice as if there was a large space between herself and what she said. Gersie works with the reason for migration, the challenge to develop emotional access to early memories in a new language and the impact of both work and marital stress. Through storytelling, the client realised "she had treated the story of her unfolding life as a series of recent anecdotes without history or tradition" (p. 119). Gersie reflected on the importance of "good enough storying" in a similar way to Scott-Danter's collective storytelling, the need to step back a little to help major life transitions.

Migration is a life transition. Carr (2012) looked at how this is combined with adolescent life transition, where the adolescent is also a migrant. Carr highlights how working with a play text can help to develop resilience in the face of school bullying, Dooman (2007) discussed the effect of bullying on a young adolescent refugee and how, at his request, a re-enactment of his story was witnessed by his classmates which enabled a much-wished-for-by-him acceptance by his peers. In our chapter on gender, we also discuss dramatherapy work around female migrant empowerment and resilience in the face of trauma.

Some of these authors refer to their own identities as migrants, but this stays mostly in the background. If the therapist is a multi-national, (how) does this affect them in the countertransference; how do the dynamics of sameness and difference play out in the therapeutic relationship? This will be further discussed in the dramatherapist practice reflections, after analysing therapist perspectives on how nationality and migration impact their identity and practice.

Dramatherapist perspectives

In the survey, 34 out of 66 (51%) therapists and clients identified nationality as important and named their nationality, but only a few commented on how or why this was important to them. The nationality of the respondents who named this aspect of their identity as important were as follows: ten self-identified as American, seven British, three mixed, two Spanish and the remaining five were individuals who identified as being Asian or from another European country.

As researchers, we asked what country people practised in but not where they trained or whether their country of residence was different from their country of birth, and we did not inquire about their citizenship status. Maybe this aspect of identity becomes more important in the process of migration. Maybe migration enables a questioning of the concept of nationality.

Concerns related to national identity in relation to professional life

One of the respondents said nationality did not matter, as the therapist and clients all shared the same nationality. Two respondents mentioned that their political beliefs were currently causing them concern in their country of residence, whilst a third mentioned applying for citizenship because of their awareness of vulnerability in relation to their legal status, feeling marginalised. As one respondent wrote,

> "In the context of Brexit my upcoming lack of UK citizenship affects my personal and professional life, as does my ability to work in both my countries. The checking of passports for access to health care is and has been an impediment for my clients, especially those who are seeking asylum".

Pressure to comply with policies that criminalise nationality

Two respondents highlighted that the issue concerning national identity was particularly prevalent when working in forensic settings and when working across borders in different countries, that the legal requirements enabling the work could be experienced as restrictive.

> I was not able to refuse to undertake Prevent training, which undermines
> client-therapist trust and the notion of duty of care
>   It is present in every aspect of the work in forensic settings.

These last two quotes raise questions on potential criminalisation of nationality and citizenship issues; in the practice reflections, we will return to this. It is important to raise that

> ... globalisation is a highly unequal process. Although the proportion of migrants has not grown significantly, the origin and direction of migration has changed...people are leaving a much wider range of countries than ever before, and they are heading to a much narrower range of destinations than before. They are going to the places where power and wealth have become concentrated.
>
> (Trilling, 2018, p. 9)

Political conflicts and climate change are among the factors forcibly displacing people. Wealthier countries are increasing their efforts to keep people out, a significant number of whom are refugees; in 1990, 20 countries had border walls or fences; in 2016, there were approaching 70 (Jones, 2016); in 2021, more than 90 wall complexes existed or were in the process of being built. Dramatherapists who are migrants and those working with refugees and migrants reflect on the implications of that for their practice in the next section.

Dramatherapist reflections on practice

Two dramatherapists reflected on their migration history and that of their clients. The first dramatherapist works in forensics. When reflecting on how migration influences her practice, she discussed the impact on her clients more explicitly:

> In the area I work, forensic mental health, it can often seem to represent a microcosm of the wider world. People come from many different countries; immigrants, legal and illegal, ethnicities from all parts of the world, people with differing sexual identities including transgender; so many diverse groups, religions and cultures. That is what makes the world and the work so fascinating. I often think about how each person experiences finding themselves here (in the forensic setting)...feelings of alienation can exist in so many forms. Many have come through the courts and been judged as being an "alien" to society in one way or another, by virtue of their index offence. But many people, having been dislocated from family or their home country, also carry a feeling that they do not belong, a sense of being other, an outsider, victimised, alone and isolated. That sense of alienation may be experienced as a conflict

between the desire to belong and integrate on the one hand, and the need to retain a sense of individual identity on the other. Sometimes the conflicting positions seem polarised and are held in a paralysis of tension. Part of our work is recognising where the client is at, in terms of their individual identity and the lens they bring to the world, and trying to understand where they hope to be. At the same time, trying to encourage a sense of shared space, a feeling of commonality, community and the universality of experience.

The second dramatherapist works in different contexts. She discusses how she self-identifies in the work and some of the tensions she experiences in different aspects of her identity.

I work with a lot of clients who have stories of migration in their recent history – either in their lifetime or within their parents lifetime. Right away, I let my clients know that I am Latina and that I also have a story of migration. And I think this creates a touchpoint – even if our migration stories are completely different, maybe this person might understand some of what I have lived. I have a lot of clients where one part of the work is about living between two or more cultures and so letting them know that this is an experience that is part of my identity – being Latina is a part of my identity that is often pronounced especially when I'm working with radicalized clients or clients with a story of migration but it is also always just there. My Jewish identity is one that is a little more tricky for me because I'm nervous about how it will be perceived, about anti-semitism, I'm nervous for some of my Muslim or for some of my Palestinian clients – I worry about our collective histories of oppression and whether I will be a safe person for them with them knowing that I am Jewish

I don't feel good hiding that I'm Jewish because I want them to make an informed choice about whether they want to be in the relationship. My very first client – I worked with him for a long time and he was from Lebanon and had a war story – many war Stories – one was from Israel – but I don't have identification with Israel but people connect Judaism with Israel a lot. I had referred him and his partner to work with a couples therapist while he continued to work with me – his couples therapist was Israeli – he was processing what it was like for him to work as a Lebanese man with a couples therapist who was Israeli with me – and I was feeling a little bit dishonest not telling him that I was Jewish but then I was like – am I projecting that he will make a link here that other people have made – and maybe its fine – but I was also – he was a client I felt warm towards – and I didn't want to get hurt "Our alliance won't get hurt if he doesn't know and I won't get hurt if he doesn't know" but – I felt weird and bad about this. It didn't feel right, but I have a lot of physiological responses as I try to figure out how and when to naturally mention…so that is more of an invisiblized identity that I struggle with and my Latina identity is one where I have been more easily able to share join with clients.

The interaction between the clients' and therapist's stories is highlighted in dramatherapy work with a refugee client where the therapist, Ruth Goodman, reflects on the impact of the work on her.

> In the years that we worked together, slowly and painfully recovering the story that he had to tell, I too, shared each step of his journey. As his therapist I acted as witness to his testimony of suffering, the torture and abuse he and his family were subjected to at the hands of the rebel armies in his country, the brutal killing of his father and the rape of his mother and sister.

I listened as he told of his escape to a neighbouring country only to be held in the primitive conditions of a refugee camp and subject to the corrupt and prejudiced intimidation from the police before finally fleeing, on a false passport, to seek asylum.

I also became the safekeeper in which the feelings that were too hard for him to bear were held until such time he was able to carry them for himself. Gradually, over a long period of time, he was able to grieve for what he had lost, to express complex feelings of guilt at having left his family and anger towards his abusers. Finally, after much resistance, he was also able to acknowledge shame and remorse for the violent crime he had himself committed when suffering from paranoid psychosis, PTSD and severe mental illness.

This is one of the first stories my client told me during our work together.

> Mohammed had been meditating in a cave on Mount Hira in the desert for six months.
>
> That night a storm blew into the desert and into the cave where he was sleeping.
>
> He was in a deep trance when he heard a voice that cried out "Read!"
>
> Mohammed, shaking, replied "I cannot read" but the voice repeated to him twice more "Read!" "Read!"
>
> Mohammed answered "this must be a mistake for I cannot read" but the voice insisted;
>
> "Read in the name of your Lord, the Creator, Who created man from a clot of blood! Read! Your Lord is most merciful, For he has taught men by the pen and revealed the mysteries to them".
>
> Mohammed was given a scroll that he opened and read. When he awoke in the morning he remembered the words that were written on the scroll even though he had never been able to read before. The words said "as though written upon his heart". Mohammed was terrified and

ran out into the desert. He thought he might be possessed and thought about killing himself. Then he heard a voice that seemed to come from all directions at once. It said "Oh Mohammed! You are Allah's messenger and I am Gabriel!" He looked up and saw an angel in the sky. He tried to turn away but he saw the angel wherever he looked. Finally the angel disappeared and he ran back to his wife Khadija to tell her what had happened. She assured him all was well and that he had to accept his fate. He was now the prophet of Islam.

The story not only reflected my client's religious affinity, but also contains parallels to his disturbed mental condition at the time, that included his own attempt at suicide. It also provided a means of communication between us, one story generating more stories, that over time, indeed, would be "written upon the heart".

As his therapist I could no doubt fill many paragraphs describing the way we worked, a combination of creative and autobiographical writing, dramatherapy and working with story.

I could list the techniques we used and show how working with a variety of story structures eventually helped my client to find a way to tell his own painful story. I could analyse the processes, the sharing of fictional and sacred stories, the six-part story making technique, the writing exercises and poems, and the long process of writing and rewriting his actual life story from early childhood memories to the traumatic events of his adult life. I could describe how the dramatisations he engaged in helped him embody and express the feelings behind the words. Finally, I could describe the letter writing exercises that helped him to reconnect to family and friends he had lost and the letters he imagined he might receive in return with messages of love, support and forgiveness.

The last time I saw him was last summer in the car park of the hospital. He had come back for a visit some months after he had been discharged. He called out my name and came running over to greet me. He looked strong and handsome and smiled broadly as he told me how well he was doing at college and his plans for University. I felt so proud of him and proud of our work together. Some months later I heard that he has been recommended for deportation back to his country as part of the Government's policy of repatriation. I was told he was feeling shocked and depressed. He feared for his life if he was forced to return.

Elie Wiesel, a holocaust survivor, is quoted as saying

> Whoever listens to a witness becomes a witness, so those who hear us, those who read us must continue to bear witness with us.

As a witness and Jewish woman, I was strongly impacted by the resonances my client's story brought up for me. I was reminded of the anti-semitic persecution and trauma suffered by my own people: the progroms, the Holocaust as well as the complexities of guilt and grief carried by those who survived. I felt moved by the trauma and horror of my client's first hand experiences and recognised that, as a first hand witness, I also carried a moral responsibility.

The convergence of my client's story and my own story one day emerged in the form of a poem that I wrote to express and process some of the transferences of our work with one another.

Come forth witness!
Open your eyes!
Awake! Hear my voice!
Read!
This is your fate
There is no escape.
Know that from this day
My stories will be your stories forever
Written on your heart.

We have learned well
The rites of prayer
The ritual telling
Of ancient stories recited
Relayed and replayed
Year after year

So it is I
Who fled the land of Egypt
Exiled to the long years in the wilderness
Dreaming of the Promised Land

And it is I, Mohammed
The troubled spirit crying
"Not me!"
I did not want this fate
Do not ask it of me
Choose another!
Leave me be!

You look into my wild black eyes
A knowing recognition
The chosen ones
Lost tribes
Meeting again in a foreign land
To tell our familiar stories
Bear witness

These are my stories
My voices in the dark
My desert storms
My dreams and longings
My fears, my hopes
Bear witness

I called for help
But no one came
Only the men with weapons and torches
Burning our houses
Taking away our women till
I could not bear
The sound of their screaming
I begged them to take anything
But spare us
Spare us
But I had nothing but words
To their guns

They burned down our homes
Drove us out our humble shtetles
We chopped off the thumbs of our young sons
To save them from the army
I sold my shabbos candlesticks
And my wedding ring
Bribed the border guards to let us go
To let us in
I came carrying nothing but my baby
And praised God for sparing our lives.
I survived
Bear witness.

Bear witness
I held my father in my arms
And watched him die
And carried him to the grave
I saw the shadow of my future
And fled for my life
Leaving my tribe, my family, my homeland
Fleeing in fear, not brave
With nothing but hope and dreams
Of a better life somewhere

I changed my name
Spoke in a new tongue
Ate pork
Blended into the intelligentsia
The middle classes
Became a doctor, musician, teacher, writer
Married out
And still they came for me
Smoking me out
From the comfort of complacency
Branded like cattle
Taken away, caged
Gassed and tossed
Into shallow graves
There was no escape
Bear witness

I ran away
From the camps, away from
The stench of refugees
Packed shoulder to shoulder
Sweating in the dry wilderness
Waiting for life
Or death
I worked on the docks, the buses
Slept on the streets
Found a teacher, a friend
Forged papers to freedom
A ticket out of Africa
I escaped
Bear witness

Bear witness
They put me on a train
Waved goodbye
To my parents
Never to see them again
To the safety of a foreign land
To become an Englishman
They rescued my life
To father children of my own
And never again could I speak of my stories
Silenced by guilt, by shame
I survived
But I did not escape.

Come forth witness!
Open your eyes!
Awake! Hear my voice!
Read!
This is your fate
There is no escape.
Know that from this day
My stories will be your stories forever
Written on your heart.

The therapist reflected that they seemed to have been looking for a key to his "frozen story, the things we cannot talk about as injured people, the victim hood aspect of refugees and immigrants; people who may not be welcome. This work took place over 10 years ago, but is very relevant again in the current political context of the 'state of the nation' dynamic of 'splitting', polarisation, scapegoating". She highlighted the importance of therapy as bearing witness needed for the locked-away story of unfinished grief, be they first- or second-generation trauma/intergenerational trauma "often our own locked away stories and so it continues". She also made the connection to age: "[A]s older therapists we can see the lens coming round and round, meeting the same questions of identity and our own stories".

Conclusion

Working with socio-political trauma in the therapy room evokes both clients' and therapists' histories. The importance of therapy as witnessing, therapist as witness and client as witness is crucial to ensure "good enough storying" of the locked-away stories of unfinished grief across generations. It enables us to own our own histories as in past stories that are also inevitably gendered. Blackwell's reflections on othering, together with recognising both sameness and difference in the stories of clients and therapists may help us own the socio-political splits in our communities rather than projecting them on 'the other'. A discussion between dramatherapists internationally, owning the impact of politics on our therapeutic relationship, whether they are explicit or implicit, as well as the impact of the settings in the countries we work in has been evolving over time within national, cross-country and cross-continental professional networks and associations. The practice examples in this chapter show how dramatherapists weave between the intersections of nationality, language, gender, sexual orientation, race, age and religion.

To slightly paraphrase Beltsiou when she discusses seeking home in the foreign, otherness and migration, "[a]n immigrant client reaches out to an immigrant therapist; exploring, mapping, creating a place for us. As we encounter each other we move back and forth between our origin and our chosen home, back and forth between past and present" (Beltsiou, 2016, p. 89).

Questions for further reflection

- What considerations regarding national identity and migration are illuminated in the two vignettes from practice? How do/might you address this in your own practice?
- Where do you think therapist self-disclosure about national identity can help; where can it hinder? What about when asking about the client's national identity?
- How do you think the politics of your country/countries influence your practice with clients?
- If you are asked to undertake a government training programme to identify "those at risk of radicalisation" how might you respond?

Chapter 12

Beyond inclusion

Dramatherapy and dis/ability

> I do a lot of drama therapy group work which is like a rehearsal for what
> happens in the larger school system and for what happens at home and in
> the community. My students are working towards independence and young
> adulthood – drama therapy plays a role in that – how they identify them-
> selves and how they identify in relation to others. ... My students have disa-
> bilities and a lot of my work revolves around helping them understand what
> their disability is and how it performs in the world and also how it intersects
> with other aspects of their identity and how this performs in the world –
> and how do they use this as a source of empowerment. The word disability
> is often associated with shame and as being "less than" – the ability to rec-
> ognize that and work with students in a way that is honest and authentic...
> you know I call their abilities superpowers. ... They're going to go into work
> spaces and there's going to be people who don't share the same identity as
> it relates to disability – I want them to be able to go to them and say this is
> who I am and this how I present and this is what I need to be able to be suc-
> cessful here. Students that have learning disabilities present more "typical"
> than students who have more developmental disabilities and there's a bit of
> a hierarchy there and speaking to that in an honest way is important...it is
> a smaller version of what is going to occur in...their homes, communities,
> families, ...being able to recognize these dynamics is important.
>
> Adam Stevens, Dramatherapist, USA

This excerpt from an interview with a dramatherapist who self-identifies as
Black, cisgendered, queer male working in a school for students with specific needs offers insight into the social stigma surrounding disability and
the role of dramatherapy in providing a metaphor for different abilities (i.e.
superpowers) and a social microcosm within which to rehearse for potentially
challenging situations. Hodermarska et al. (2021) critiques dramatherapy as
follows:

> [D]rama therapy theory offers an insufficient structure from a disability
> activism perspective, as it presupposes a freedom for multiplicity which
> is unavailable to so many people living in marginalized identities...being
> human is experienced so differently by each of us, based upon the identity

DOI: 10.4324/9780429431593-14

parameters in which we live, and especially by those among us who live neuro-diverse lives. There is no single universal way to be human.

(p. 196)

Dramatherapists have a history of working with people with varied abilities, and the dramatherapy literature reflects the changing attitudes to what that has meant in relation to empowerment. Given this long history, we as authors were surprised that dis/ability came last in the rating of cultural factors influencing dramatherapist's practice in our survey. However, it may be precisely because of this long history that assumptions about ability are less examined. The subject of disability brings us as a profession into some deeply challenging questions about ableism in our practice and why limits on ability or not claiming disability may be the least considered identity parameter.

In this chapter, we present a brief review of literature pertaining to ability and dramatherapy and then present findings from our survey of practitioners. We also ask if there are disabling expectations inherent in dramatherapy practice that may hinder the potential of this work. If a sighted and visually impaired therapist-client dyad work together in art therapy, their respective visual and tactile cultures may highlight sensory, aesthetic and psychological differences (Hermann, 2016). What are the dramatherapy equivalent cultural differences of this? In the next section, we present perspectives from dramatherapists who responded with examples of how notions of dis/ability influence their experience of dramatherapy. We have elected to use the term dis/ability in some cases in order to simultaneously call attention to the presence of abilities in this discussion and to the variation in how disability is socially constructed across contexts as well as disability. Disability-first language, using the uppercase D (as in "Disabled person") has become increasingly popular among disability activists and within disability culture. Some embrace formerly derogatory terms, such as *gimps, crips* and *crazies*. Disability-first language embraces the shared identity of Disabled persons, community and culture (Mackelprang & Salsgiver, 2016; Dunn & Andrews, 2015). For example, person-first language (*person with a disability* rather than *disabled person*) challenged the narrative that defined people by their condition or diagnosis rather than by their humanity first (ADA, 2017). Over the last decade, dis/ability rights advocates and disabilities studies scholars have argued that person-first language does not go far enough and rejected any inherently shameful association to disability in favour of embracing disability as an expression of a diverse identity (e.g. neurodiversity). As autistic disability justice activist Lydia Brown writes,

It is impossible to affirm the value and worth of an Autistic person without recognizing his or her identity *as* an Autistic person. Referring to me as "a person with autism," or "an individual with ASD" demeans who I am because it denies who I am.

(2011, n.p.)

How people prefer to name themselves varies per location and over time; this is reflected in the next sections of this chapter.

Dis/ability, ableism and mental health

The definition of disability is multilayered and continuously changing. According to the World Health Organization (WHO), a disability is a normal and expected part of every person's life. However, difficulties arise primarily because of inflexible environmental conditions that limit the degree to which a person with a disability is able to participate in society, which, consequently, limits quality of life.

> Disability is part of being human. Almost everyone will temporarily or permanently experience disability at some point in their life. Over one billion people – about 15% of the global population – live with some form of disability and this number is increasing. Disability results from the interaction between individuals with a health condition such as cerebral palsy, down syndrome and depression as well as personal and environmental factors including negative attitudes, inaccessible transportation and public buildings, and limited social support. People with disability experience poorer health outcomes, have less access to education and work opportunities, and are more likely to live in poverty than those without a disability. Very often people with disability do not receive the healthcare services they need. Evidence shows that half of people with disability cannot afford healthcare. People with disability are also more than twice as likely to find healthcare providers' skills inadequate.
>
> (WHO, 2021)

Despite this definition, dis/ability has often been seen negatively through the lens of pathology with an emphasis on lost work productivity or welfare programme eligibility resulting from disability (Sinason 1992, 2010). Research has also suggested that professionals who work with people with disabilities may have underlying negative perceptions about disability of which they are unaware (Simplican et al., 2015). To mitigate this pathology-based approach and the negative effects of conflating disability with illness, many professionals and Disabled persons have advocated for changes in language and access throughout the last century. In the literature about disability rights, scholars separate impairment, the organic consequence of a condition, from disability, the result of a social context (Solomon et al., 2014). Here, Dis/ability refers to impairment rather than pathology (CDC, 2020; Shakespeare & Watson, 2001). The term "disability", in this context, is used to denote the interaction of people's internal characteristics within their social worlds and is "the loss or limitations of opportunities that prevent people from taking part in the community on an equal level" (French, 1994, p. 10). Here, the combination of external influences such as people's reactions, discrimination, architectural barriers and high health costs and impairments result in disability. As Wong writes, "[S]taying alive is a lot of work for a person with disabilities in an ableist society" (2020, p. xv).

The evolution of the disability rights movement has seen the return to Disability-first language and an identification with disability culture. In the context of mental health, a similar evolution may be seen from understanding disability as a medical disease requiring remediation towards an ableist norm towards a social model that acknowledges the impact of a disabling environment. The medical model characterises Disability in terms of deficits, loss and functional limitations because of some type of physical or mental impairment. From this perspective, Disabled persons must adapt to an environment that does not meet their needs. For example, people who are deaf must acclimatise to a hearing world rather than a more reciprocal arrangement. Their situation, within this paradigm, is often viewed as tragic, unfortunate and, in some instances, incurable. It is frequently assumed that grief and depression are an inevitable part of living with a disability (Artman & Daniels, 2010). Therefore, interventions tend to focus on coping and adjustment to disability (Olkin, 2002; Olkin & Pledger, 2003; Olkin & Taliaferro, 2006). Olkin (1999, 2007, 2017) emphasises that living with a disability forces a continued response; sometimes relegated to the background as one of many factors, sometimes very prominent, depending on circumstances and life stages. Sinason initially (1992) looked at therapy with people designated intellectually disabled, but in her revised edition (2010) broadens this to the ways all of us suffer from the limitations of our inner world. She addresses issues around loss and bereavement, abuse and its influence on thinking and meaning giving in our lives.

Dis/ability psychotherapy, as it has evolved, has focused on the emotional lives of people with disabilities (Frankish, 2015). Emphasis is placed on understanding the pain and distress of disability and how these may intersect with other past and present life stressors. However, the definitions of the problems that Disabled people encounter, and the appropriate solutions to them, are generally given insufficient weight in training therapists and other health and care professionals. These care professionals are asked by people with disabilities to broaden their perspective and to relinquish some of the power inherent in the medical model of disability. To this end, advocacy groups such as Disabled Peoples' International, a cross-disability organisation established in 1981 to take action on full and equal participation of people with disabilities (DPI, 2019), have emphasised the involvement of Disabled peoples' perspectives whenever decisions are made concerning their wellbeing. Over the last decades, service user involvement has become a required part of planning and delivering services in the UK, as well as more recently the training of care professionals. What service user involvement means has varied over time and settings despite the fact that papers written about this are rarely co-authored with a service user, especially in the field of mental health (Millar et al., 2015). In the next section, we give some examples from dramatherapy practice.

Despite some of these positive developments, many recent reports show that the aim of full and equal participation is still far from being reached. In a period of tightening resources, acquired rights may in fact be undermined. One recent UK example is the Personal Independence Payment, a newly introduced benefit that aims to help with the extra costs of a long-term health condition or disability. It was introduced as an

> "austerity" measure to save costs to the government. The claimant experience has been very difficult, many people have needed to appeal against "unfair assessment allocation", a lengthy process which on appeal tends to result in two thirds of appeals being upheld. The most common issue is inaccuracy in the PIP assessment reports (93%); the assessment is based on function (House of Commons debate pack, number CDP-2018-0020, 30 January 2018). This means that the emphasis is on what a person cannot do.

Disability support in the US is also based on functional assessments such as the Vineland scale (Sparrow et al., 2006). The power position of the assessor is obvious, the difficulties about bridging the different perspectives in an ableist society plays out to great detriment of the disabled or the 'assessed' one. Disability intersects with age and socio-economics in that people who qualify for and live on disability payments often live below the poverty level, and any earned income is deducted from the disability benefit (Joffe-Walt, 2013). This is just one example of how an ableist perspective can disempower.

Hodemarska highlights the contradiction and challenge that people must prove disability through annual traditional assessments and, at the same time, are encouraged to find their life paths based upon personal aspirations and wishes which are meaningless in terms of the system of diagnosis. The person with the disability is stuck in a system that pays lip service to a person-centred approach but privileges the medical model exclusively. She shows the impact on families in her performance on a storytelling program entitled 'The Moth' (https://themoth.org/stories/an-unexpected-alliance).

Psychological therapies are critiqued for their focus on psychosocial adjustment to disability, rather than strategies for better partnering with people with disabilities (Artman & Daniels, 2010). There is an evolving sense that people with lived experience need to be directly implicated in decisions that impact their lives. Declaring a disability is a statement and commitment, an outlook on disability that can be at odds with internalised ableism. This can feel very risky in an employment context. If it pertains to an invisible disability the act of disclosure brings the personal and private to the public. The decision whether to disclose or hide includes an act of self-preservation, information control, impression management and thus identity work (Brown & Leigh, 2018). However, not disclosing means that the voices of people with disabilities are not heard.

As a dramatherapist (Ditty) with an acquired disability, it took some time to self-identify as disabled. When a colleague advised me to register my mobility problems to improve my access, this process took some time. I realised that I came from an etic/outsider i.e. ableist perspective. Although I had worked for most of my professional life with clients with disabilities, I found that I automatically felt that I needed to adjust to my disability rather than question the social response to that disability. Thoughts about loss were prevalent, and emotions of anger and depression needed processing. Although critical of the medical model, I had been imbued with the meaning it gave to disability, especially as my disability was illness related (Dokter 2021).

Becoming solely identified as a person with a particular disability can mean that other health concerns become overlooked. The paradox is that Disabled people can have greater difficulties accessing health services for general health issues; someone with a mental disability is likely to be underdiagnosed for their physical health problems; someone with a physical disability may not be able to access general health screening (Sakellariou & Rotarou, 2017).

This has again been seen during the pandemic (Scope Disability Report, 2020). Covid-19 has shown the marginalisation of people with disabilities, including the impact on employment and health and social care. A recent report and study showed that almost two thirds of UK Covid deaths have been Disabled people due to changes in care, as well as higher vulnerability (Bosworth et al., 2021; Office of National Statistics, 2022). Similar findings have been documented in US and world reports which indicate that people with disabilities and autism have died at a significantly higher rate than the general population (Frost, 2020; Shapiro, 2020). The reality of long-term Covid presents a uniquely global opportunity and challenge to examine how we contend with disabling policies and programmes and how these inform practice in dramatherapy.

Dramatherapy and dis/ability

Dramatherapists in the UK have worked with people with disabilities from the beginning of the profession (Jennings, 1981, 1992; Landy, 1986; Lindkvist, 1981). The first dramatherapy volumes published (Schattner & Courtney, 1981) contained a section on 'special problems' that included several chapters on children with sensory, physical and learning disabilities. Whether this fitted into empowering or disempowering practice can be an interesting area for reflection. The language used in these early texts reflected the dominant paradigms and pejorative language regarding disability that was commonly accepted at the time with chapters referring to dramatherapy for the 'emotionally disturbed' and 'mentally retarded'.

The premise for engaging with people with dis/abilities seemed to be squarely rooted in the medical paradigm of the period wherein people with any kind of intellectual, developmental or acquired disability were seen as needing remedial care. For example, Jennings' (1974) book on remedial drama offered an influential perspective on developmental play with children with multiple disabilities. Her chapter on working with children with physical disabilities (Jennings, 1981) is an example of the impairment thinking of that period, although she also highlights the emotional impact of carers, teachers and institutionalisation on children in care. Jennings advocated for 'healthy' relationships with how one views one's body and relationships with others as an early form of empowerment in the field. Lindkvist (1981) considered autism as an illness, although she stressed the individuality of each child with 'the condition'. More recent books on working with people with learning disabilities are written for carers and professionals with an emphasis on connection, skills and play (Chesner, 1995; Booker, 2011), a similar approach to Chasen's skills and connection approach to clients on the autism spectrum (Chasen, 2011). Dramatherapy practice and research can focus on the ability to work through metaphor, an example is Jones' (1996) early work on story work with clients with autism and Chasen (2011) on the inability to play. This approach has been developed and researched in the UK by various dramatherapists (Haythorne & Seymour, 2016).

There are some interesting examples of dramatherapy practice that indicate a shift towards practices that seek to amplify the voices of people living with disabilities such as Snow et al. (2017) whose ethnodramatherapy practice at the Center for the Arts in Human Development offered a platform from which people with disabilities could speak directly to caregivers about their hopes, frustrations and desires. Bailey's (2010) Barrier-Free Theatre also seeks a greater degree of inclusion by creating opportunities. Here, " actors with and without disabilities, devise plays based on their ideas…for the purpose of breaking down stigma and enhancing inclusion" (Bailey et al., 2018, p. 2).

Finally, there are programmes that seek to fully partner with people with disabilities as full collaborators in the planning and execution of programmes which are, as such, examples of affirmative practice. One example is co-production in a mental health recovery college (Critchley et al., 2019). The practice-based research project demonstrates the collaborative creation and facilitation of a recovery college course between a dramatherapist and a person with experience of mental ill health, an 'expert by experience'. In this context, recovery is understood as a process by which individuals regain control over their lives (Center for Substance Abuse Treatment, 2009). Resilience, cultural and spiritual belief systems are prioritised over treatment and symptom management towards the development of fulfilling life. Beyond this emphasis on individual difference and resilience, recovery does recognise the impact of stigmatisation and discrimination and advocates the involvement of family and community to generate a greater sense of acceptance (Leamy et al., 2011; Mental Health Foundation, 2016). This is a substantial change from the earlier illness and impairment-based medical model. It recognises the need for community collaboration and combatting stigmatisation. Whether it goes far enough can be an interesting area for debate.

Another area that this discussion illuminates is that of authority, ownership and credit. James (1996) and Willemsen (2020) offer examples of involving a client in the writing of a chapter or article, though not completely fully co-authored. In the programme described by Critchley et al. (2019), the experts by experience were involved on an equal level in the design and delivery; one of the experts was also involved in the writing of the article. In a training context, Hodemarska worked with a dramatherapy trainee to ensure that training was adapted so that it was fully accessible to her and other people with divergent learning styles (Hodermarska & Filson, 2018). A chapter entitled "Disability Justice: Drama Therapy as Collective Liberation", by Hodermarska et al. (2021) was co-authored with experts with direct experience and brings dramatherapy into conversation with principles of disability justice, a movement "led by disabled queers and activists of color" (Sins Invalid, 2019, p. 16). Ethan Jones, a co-author with autism who reveals themself to be the son of dramatherapist Maria Hodermarska, writes,

> I define autism as a superpower that allows me to see certain things more sharply. Marvel and DC comic heroes are all really people living with disabilities. It's part of the metaphor. As an autistic, I have talents that neurotypical people don't. I have a creative way of solving problems. I am good at memorising details. And, I always bring joy to others. Neurotypical society wants to use me for these superpowers or at other times tries to take advantage of my vulnerabilities as someone living with difference.
>
> (Hodermarska et al., 2021, p. 187)

Ethan articulates the pleasure and risk they experience and, together with co-authors, charge the field of dramatherapy to move beyond what Benjamin (2018) has described as the paradigm of "the doer and done to" binary of care in which people with dis/abilties are only imagined to be on the receiving side of care rather than cultural producers, healers and partners in a process of change and discovery. They affirm the call for articulations of experience by Disabled people (Wong, 2020) and "a radical and participatory approach to centralising crip lives" along all intersections of identity and difference (Tovah, 2016).

Dramatherapist perspectives

It is interesting to note that dis/ability came last in the rating of cultural factors influencing dramatherapists' practice in our survey. This finding came from the question which therapist identity factors influenced their practice. It may say something about the respondents' thoughts and feelings about self-identification as abled or disabled, which may be a useful area of further research. What is dramatherapist diversity in this area, both those presenting for training and those practising? Approximately 55% (35/63) of survey respondents left the question blank. Those who did respond offer us a window into the diversity of practitioners that make up our field in the area of ability.

Demographics: Disability

Twenty-eight respondents to the survey (N = 63) reported how they identify in relation to ability. Eleven reported being 'able-bodied' or having no disability. The remaining 17 reported different forms of physical and psychological disabilities, including autoimmune disorders, chronic medical conditions or sensory conditions such as hearing loss and hearing impairment, mental health conditions such as depression, post-traumatic stress disorder and non-specific mental illness, and neurological conditions such as hyperactivity/attention deficit hyperactivity disorder and traumatic brain injury. Most of these responses used medical diagnostic categories.

Hidden dis/abilities

Three of these 17 dramatherapists also reported having a hidden disability that, in one respondent's words "alters what the physicality of dramatherapy looks and feels like". The aspect of 'hiddenness' raise the possible problematisation of making disability visible. One respondent wrote about their reasons for disclosing their dis/ability:

> My mobility and loss of hearing affects my practice, I share this with my clients at the start of therapy, the associated vulnerability needs to be worked with so clients do not feel they are responsible for my welfare more than I am for theirs (especially those with a history of caregiving can find this challenging), but on the other hand the undermining of "perfectionism" can be really helpful and can empower the client to own their vulnerability.

Here, the disclosure of dis/ability is thought to create an opportunity rather than create a liability:

> In my case living with an invisible disability is something that affects me overall. This can become useful but also could hinder my practice. Relating this situation to my clients I think it works the same way. Ultimately one works with what they can, providing and adapting... sometimes you could ask the person what to do next as even that can be "therapeutic".

Professional stigmatisation

Alongside comments about hidden dis/abilities, several respondents indicated feeling the need to hide the reality of disability in the field. One respondent wrote that dis/ability was "not discussed and held over [their] head by registered dramatherapists". Another wrote that knowledge of one's dis/ability "gets weaponised", indicating that the power differentials can become toxic in this area, which may also be why this aspect of identity comes last and may remain hidden. Another reason may be that, in some cases, students of dramatherapy may be inadvertently encouraged to understand dis/ability as an undesirable form of otherness. As one respondent wrote, "in my drama-therapy training, we had a course called 'drama therapy with special popula-tions' which is a title that disturbed me because it was used as a euphemism for cognitive disability when I was growing up". This comment will be taken up further in the chapter on training. However, the notion of disability as 'special', may reinforce ableism, which may then contribute to the reluctance of dramatherapists to reveal their own disabilities within their professional communities. Finally, while struggling with hiding dis/ability is a challenge, for some, it has also resulted in an expanded sense of empathy:

> There have been times when I have concealed the fact that I am consid-ered a TBI patient because I did not want to be assumed as incapable. However, this has also influenced my treatment of my clients with disa-bilities as I try to remember the ways in which I felt condescended to or where I felt heard so that I can better meet their needs.

The role of relatives with dis/abilities

Some of the responses point to the increased familiarity and comfort of dramatherapists in accepting and working with various abilities, as a result of having family members who have a dis/ability. As one respondent wrote, "I have a brother who is disabled so I am very comfortable around people with a disability and that culture." Another wrote from the role of "a parent of someone who identifies as living with difference" and how this has made them much more "aware of these issues [ableism] and how they present in the spaces that I work".

Adapting to varied abilities

Dramatherapists have also learned to vary their experience to meet a variety of abilities and needs. As one respondent wrote, "I am overjoyed when I am able to accommodate and get alongside people with disabilities. I have found it is often only myself that gets in the way!" Another wrote, "[Dis/ability] does not directly affect my experience of dramatherapy other than recognis-ing that clients vary in their ability to engage". Others wrote honestly about their simultaneous worry and desire to meet the needs of those in their care:

> I started work last week with a client with profound disability and I won-dered whether I should tell the centre that perhaps because of this client's limited mobility I would be more used to other clients. However I think I was just scared of failure and scared to think outside the box and try and find a way to engage the client. In the end we met and I will be assessing

them for 8 weeks. The work will be movement based, sensory and I will be using a creative expressive approach.

Preferences

Do dramatherapists have a hierarchical notion of which clients are 'interesting' to work with and which are less so? One respondent wrote,

> As a special educator I worked with all forms of disabilities. I would not do dramatherapy with people with mental retardation or mental disabilities. For me especially, that work is very slow. I prefer more action and energy in the work, that is why I work with people with behavioural disorders.

The quote raises the difficult balance between a dramatherapist being aware of their own strengths and weaknesses in client work, ableism in dramatherapy practice and the possibility of further marginalisation of certain clients in dramatherapy practice.

The need for greater accessibility

Finally, dramatherapists wrote about the need for greater accessibility to both dramatherapists and the places where they practice. A dramatherapy user commented critically about her experience as a carer:

> My aunt is wheelchair bound and quadriplegic and I have learned about the discrimination she faces when trying to work with a drama therapist or psychodramatist, many of whom told her they do not have the expertise to work with her... I have tried to advocate on her behalf to access services and have found much discrimination in this respect.

Wheelchair users are not only hindered by dramatherapy practitioners' lack of expertise. A dramatherapist wrote about the need for material accessibility as well as finding languages that are accessible to both therapist and client:

> Access can be a pain and buildings are not always as accessible as they legally should be. Regarding forms of theatre, I can facilitate forms whilst acting as witness or work together with my client on how to adapt forms so they are accessible to both of us. Working with a sign language interpreter has been part of my practice.

This comment regarding the use of language interpreters is taken up in the chapter on language as well.

The main themes arising from the analysis of responses about dis/ability are adjustments made for clients with disability so that the treatment suits client needs, difficulties of access, therapists' own experience of disability influencing how clients are received and treated and therapist preference for (not) working with particular dis/abilities feeling that dis/ability is not within their areas of expertise. We will come back to this in Chapter 15.

Dramatherapist reflections on practice

The interview data in the next section shows the old chestnut of disability vs impairment many therapists and clients grew up with. The dramatherapist from the chapter's opening vignette raised clients' disability identity in relation to intersectional identity aspects when working in school settings in the following way.

> All my different facets, certainly play a huge impact into my work as a clinician – some things that really stick out are my gender, race, and sexuality – and how, a lot of times that serves as a model for other students and as a vehicle for connection – students see themselves in me and I see myself in them – and this builds trust in the clinical space. And then also through differing identities – you know – this sparks curiosity – and through that we get to learn about each other – I do a lot of group work – and this becomes a rehearsal for what happens in the larger school system and this is a rehearsal for what happens at home and in the community. My students are working towards independence and young adulthood – this plays a role in that – how they identify themselves and how they identify in relation to others. … My students have disabilities and a lot of my work revolves around helping students understand what their disability is and how it performs in the world and also how it intersects with other aspects of their identity and how this performs in the world – and how do they use this as a source of empowerment.

In an interview where the researcher was aware of the therapist's invisible, disability the interviewer asked, "*Knowing you a bit, did you ever identify with disability culture?*"
The dramatherapist responded,

> Interesting, probably not. I came from a family with a lot of disabilities, but it was always associated with what someone could not do. Not associated with shame, but very private. My dramatherapy training helped me to identify it, got myself some help, but it is still a more hidden part of my identity. I do identify with it but it is a struggle and an area of great contradiction.

When discussing how in dramatherapy practice she worked with these themes, the dramatherapist mentioned Boal's image theatre (2002) and Gersie's story work (1989, 1991, 1997a), as well as Hill (2016) for working with conflicts between peer groups. She sees as common between them the practice of playing with self and other and that there is safety in playing with aspects in common. We will return to these sources in the practice chapter. When reflecting on whether it is safer to play with some people than others, especially if there are parts of identity you feel tender about, the dramatherapist commented,

> Yes, disability is countercultural, subcultural. … I can make "offensive" jokes with a colleague who shares my disability…maybe it is a way of appropriating back a term that was used in a disparaging way, I think that is how we use it, as a sort of empowerment. …I had not thought about it like that. But also working with difference. As an adult with a child client for example when they discuss a game and I do not know it in detail, the child can see me as an old fuddy duddy who does not understand. It can frustrate the client, you are just not at their level, you cannot possibly understand. As a therapist I can get caught in the frustration of not knowing enough rather than working with the difference.

Understanding of disability through different cultural lenses is highlighted by another interviewee who said,

> When we are talking about depression, of course the understanding of depression is culturally mitigated – what is my understanding of depression and what is their understanding of depression – how stigma plays into depression – everything – in every way.

How culture mitigates the understanding of dis/ability is reflected by another dramatherapist:

> I worked with a teenager who was very religious, as was her mother. Her mum believed everything is tested by God so she expected her daughter to be patient and accepting of everything that happened.

How to work with this in an empowering way, whilst recognising the individuality of each person *"The personal experience is always different from the book. I loved what one of my supervisees said yesterday: When you have met one autistic child, you have met one autistic child"*.

At the same time there is a recognition that Disabled people experience marginalisation and oppression in many societies and countries. The stigma of a dis/ability can lead to this being a hidden aspect of identity, which hinders empowerment and equalising of opportunities. The following vignette section continues to look at some of these contradictions.

The practice example is set in a European country; dramatherapy individual work is conducted with a client struggling in his secondary special school provision for adolescents with mental health issues. The dramatherapist Eva Boorsma's therapeutic stance is that all people will experience dis/ability at some time in their lives, some of them temporary, some ongoing and somewhere in the therapy the question is raised "to what extent will/can I adapt to society and to what extent do I want society to adapt to me?" All clients have different needs and wishes in this, and the therapeutic task is to build a playspace where therapist and client together can experiment, feel and explore what is desired and wished for.

Boorsma describes the work as follows[1]:

> Pepijn (pseudonym) is a 14 year old boy with a diagnosis of Autistic Spectrum Disorder (ASD) and a high IQ. He is in mainstream secondary education. The reason for referral was to learn to express his frustrations. Teachers indicate that he becomes upset when he cannot fulfill a task. He cannot express he does not understand something, withdraws and sometimes cries. He is physically restless in the class, regularly paces and works standing behind his desk. He makes sounds by knocking on the window. The PE teacher states he participates very little in team sport, he stays on the edge of the playing field and does not take any initiatives. During school breaks Pepijn plays with one other pupil, always in the same corner of the playground on his Ipad.
>
> Pepijn is active in interactive sensorimotor games. He does not initiate and shows little strength in his play when there is (in) direct contact with the therapist. Given his physical restlessness in class and lack of strength the dramatherapist decides to work with sensory integration first, before working on contact with the other. The dramatherapist works in the gym, running, pushing against walls and throwing pillows. After a few sessions the focus is more on indirect contact and especially tag games with a pool noodle become a favourite. In PE he starts to participate in basketball, but remains restless in class. The next phase focuses on making contact with the other. The therapist introduces DvT (developmental transformations, Johnson, 2014) especially the variation in reactions which the client may expect within the play.
>
> Game of tag: Pepijn bangs the pool noodle on the ground. The therapist plays she is frightened and jumps backwards. Pepijn comes closer and the therapist walks back as if frightened, when she can no longer go backwards he tags her on the arm "Oh no, I have been touched" she calls "One arm has come off, do you see that?" Pepijn grins. "Now I only have one arm and with that handicap will have to try and tag you" both hit the pool noodles rhythmically against each other. The tag game resumes. The therapist plays with the fear of the other and introduces the theme that arms can be hacked off. The grin of the client shows his interest in this development. The therapist articulates she has a handicap but still has to complete the task, hypothetically this may connect to Pepijns experience of the world. He was stimulated to explore new possibilities in the play, daily life dilemmas are introduced in the play, especially fear of failure and fear of unpredictable reactions in the contact.

Towards the summer holiday Pepijn indicates he wants to finish drama-therapy. The therapist indicates she would like to see him for three more sessions after the summer break (wanting to make some of the changes she has seen in his play more cognitive/conscious). The teacher reports Pepijn no longer is physically restless in class and that introducing regular breaks for him has also been helpful, 2 hours sitting is beyond him. When he does not understand something he will put up his hand and ask for help (the teacher even reported with great satisfaction that Pepijn corrected him in front of the whole class).

As authors, we wondered if the dramatherapist worked with the symptoms of the client's diagnosis and aimed to improve his adaptation to the school environment. The dramatherapist explained that she was working in a school system, which to a certain extent looked for adaptation from its students. Within the therapy space, the clients could take a leading role. She was not working on diagnostic symptoms: Pepijn was troubled by his anxiety to connect with others and did not feel free to express his thoughts and emotions. The therapist emphasised the use of DvT to make fear of contact playable. The therapeutic rationale was for a sensorimotor body-based intervention to support the development of social skills in autistic children (Gutman et al., 2012; Wilmer-Barbrook, 2013), so the initial dramatherapy intervention was diagnosis related. However, the dramatherapist clarified that she took ASD as a fact that might or might not have influenced his anxiety.

In therapy we try to offer the client expressive choices; do we give them tools to interact with the disabling environment and simultaneously as therapists work with that environment to provide adaptations to the clients' needs? I (Ditty), as a dis/abled dramatherapist, struggled with the therapist's statement that "the 'handicap' of the therapist connects to the client's world experience" because I was concerned that the 'dis' outweighed the 'ability' for Pepijn in the therapy and school environment. As a disabled therapist, I have had to engage with the disabling environment in requesting adaptations to provide me with accessibility. The dramatherapist (Eva) in reflection felt that her hypothesis of Pepijn's experience feeling handicapped was potentially framing and disempowering, but that her understanding of being 'handicapped' could relate to ASD, anxiety or something else. I (Ditty) wondered if my own anger at disabling environments had coloured my perspective of their interaction. The dramatherapist enabled Pepijn to engage with the school environment and as such empowered him.

Potential internal contradictions in our work are important to consider. Different cultural expectations and adaptations need to be a part of these considerations. Pepijn's 'stimming' behaviours from a neurodiverse perspective are a means of self-regulation, helping autistic people cope with overwhelming stimuli (Kapp et al., 2019). It would be interesting to think if liaison with the school might enable more acceptance of this.

In the practices chapter, we will return to the practice in this vignette, the dramatherapist's choices both of preparatory work and of developmental transformations, which Boorsma identified as the method that enabled her to follow the client; it gave them a lot of space to play with bias and prejudice, from client and therapist.

Conclusion

Reviewing some of the dramatherapy literature over the last 40 years changes are noticeable, recent literature such as Critchley and Hodermarska show how a greater awareness of the social model of dis/ability can improve access for Disabled people through collaboration. Advocacy is evolving from "acting for or on behalf of" to "nothing about us without us". Our research data showed that notions of impairment and the medical model of disability remain part of dramatherapy. We have not discussed mental illness as a dis/ability as part of dramatherapists' lives. Critchley's work may be a potential start for further developments in this area; can dramatherapists be experts by experience; how does this relate to training and practice? Cultural competencies for working with Disabled people are discussed in the wider psychological therapies (Artman & Daniels, 2010; Cornish et al., 2008; Olkin, 2002, 2008) and may be a useful area for further development in dramatherapy.

Questions for further reflection

- What concerns and possibilities are illuminated by the vignettes from practice?
- What messages were and are you surrounded by concerning ability and disability?
- How do assumptions about ability help and hinder you in your dramatherapy practice?
- What opportunities are there to enable greater collaboration and partnership surrounding disability dramatherapy?

Note

1   This case is discussed in further detail in Boorsma, E. (2015). In contact raken. *Tijdschrift voor vaktherapie 2*, 38–40.

Implications for training, supervision and practice

Part III

Implications for training,
supervision and practice

Chapter 13

Decolonising dramatherapy training within and across borders

I'm working with several clients...who are international clients. Some are international students. Some are people who are immigrants. I started to notice these boundary territories and I became much more sensitive to sort of what my shape is inside that territory. ... I noticed myself moving from a sort of colonial mindset where I was like, "oh, what an interesting thing to discover this person who is from another place" and "oh, now I'm more aware" to... "oh wait, there are two of us meeting here." I'm trying to experience [dramatherapy] more as the sense of two cultures are meeting in the space, and especially if I'm in the therapist role and I have this power over the space and over the encounter. I'm trying to engage in this dismantling of my own cultural habit as a way of being open to like thinking and feeling about things that wouldn't occur to me that aren't part of my cultural history – especially in my work now in Taiwan. ... I'm trying to experience it on a different level than stereotype, which is often how I found them to be communicated by a lot of other people who are my teachers in this arena, working with this population first. They would say these very stereotypical things about...the students in Asia, particularly like "They're so compliant. They don't ever argue with you. They just want to do what the teacher says." And I knew that was not right. I know that's not appropriate. But I did experience patterns of behaviour that could feed those stereotypes. And I've really tried to like, re-attune myself to a sense of what are the cultural signals that people are sending, but I'm not picking up at first. ... My students [in Taiwan] are tremendously powerful, tremendously resistant, and opinionated. And there's dynamics of influence and power that are actually resonating on these frequencies that I didn't have the ability to pick up at first.

Adam Reynolds, Dramatherapist, USA

This interview excerpt is from an American, white, gay, male dramatherapist who has been in practice for 20 years. We chose it for this chapter because it offers several points of entry into a conversation about decolonising pedagogy in dramatherapy. As we discussed in Chapter 2, cultural response/ability, our *ability to respond* to differences that present in the therapeutic encounter as well as an ethic of accountability, implies a *responsibility* to examine one's own implicit biases and relationship to systems that privilege

DOI: 10.4324/9780429431593-16

some groups over others (Sajnani, 2012a; Sajnani & Dokter, 2017). This is vital to ethical practice in one's own context, when sharing training standards and practices across borders and in the development of methods that are indigenous to one's own home communities. In particular, this excerpt reveals the intercultural exchange occurring in every encounter and the ways in which our embodied, projective practice involves an ongoing exchange of cultural information about past and present-day issues related to power, equity and difference. In this chapter, we consider a decolonial framework in the training and continuing education of dramatherapists. We offer these ideas from our perspective as educators who have taught a wide variety of students, including international students and on training courses in other countries.

What does it mean to decolonise pedagogy?

"Like many students, I grew up thinking that the most important books were written by white men" Dechavez (2018). This is the sentence that opens an opinion piece entitled "It's Time to Decolonize That Syllabus" printed in the *Los Angeles Times*. It is an indictment of the system of education in which the author was raised but she's certainly not alone. I (Nisha) grew up in one of two brown-skinned families in our neighbourhood school in Edmonton, Alberta, Canada. Parents of both families had immigrated from South Asian countries in the 1970s when Canada's immigration laws favoured migration that would align with its then new policy of multiculturalism (Plamondon, 2013). Unfortunately, the promise of that policy, heralded as an antidote to racism and white nationalism, seldom extended beyond food, fashion and festivals to structural equity in the form of shared decision-making power (Bissoondath, 1994). *Visible minorities*, an unpopular term used to describe people of colour in Canada, were encouraged to share these consumables of culture, thereby implicating ourselves in a complicated web of *cultural appropriation* where one's sense of belonging was linked to the mainstream circulation of signs and symbols of one's culture emptied of any historical context (i.e. yoga, henna, notions of shamanism). Textbooks in my French immersion primary school reflected a homogenised Indigenous history firmly located in the past rather than living, present-day communities. They privileged the stories and the logic of white, European colonial settlers and downplayed or outright omitted the contributions of people of colour. Only Christian holidays were officially observed. I did not question the impact of these dominant narratives in my education until much later. I have since wondered about the role of representation in the formation of one's sense of self and place across one's development. What does it take to undo the years of internalising "white as right" and how does this complicate or contribute to efforts to advance culturally responsible standards of training and care?

I (Ditty), as described in Chapters 2 and 9, grew up in a predominantly white working-class neighbourhood, with some Indonesian families mixed in the housing association flats/apartments in a family of Dutch and Indonesian origin. My Christian Dutch Reformed school (in the Bible Belt, schools tended to be segregated by religious orientations at that time) taught Dutch colonial history very minimally. There was some news about Moluccan migration to the Netherlands at the time of the train hijacks in the 1970s, but no history of Dutch colonialism beyond the establishment of the colonial empire in the 17th century, the trading wealth of the Golden Age and the spice trade generating this wealth. I was taught about the Vietnam and Korean Wars, but not about Indonesia's struggle for independence, which took place in the second half of the 1940s: between 1945 and 1965 around 300,000 Dutch, Moluccan and 'Indo People' (of mixed Dutch and Indonesian parents) left Indonesia for the Netherlands. I learnt about that history only when I visited Indonesia, just like I discovered in Derry the role of William of Orange in Northern Ireland and the role of the Dutch reformed church in apartheid in South Africa once I had migrated to the UK. My history teacher taught me that history was written and taught by certain groups of people, excluding other perspectives, but that was taught as a general historical academic concept rather than applied to the Dutch history curriculum. I have wondered in retrospect whether shame can be a powerful dynamic in what is and is not included in the curriculum. We were for example taught about Dutch resistance against the Nazis 20 years post-war, rather than Dutch collaboration, which took at least another 25 years to become acknowledged. The slavery monument in Amsterdam was commissioned in 2002, 139 years after the official abolishment of slavery in Surinam and the Dutch Antilles.

As authors, we assert that the systems of education and curricula have privileged ways of knowing that are and often continue to reflect colonising values. Values that are upheld as superior to Indigenous and other ways of knowing. Privileged ways of knowing include Eurocentric notions of knowledge (Denzin et al., 2008), science (Cajete, 2000; Ng-A-Fook, 2013) and culture (Donald et al., 2011). As Sandy Grande explains (2011), "[T]he curriculum is, by definition, a Western (linear, temporal, hierarchical) construct that can and should be continually reimagined to better serve democratic imperatives" (p. 42).

But what does it mean to decolonise the curriculum? As Morreira et al. (2020) explain, "decolonisation's contemporary manifestation in the academy…comes on the back of years of debate around the concept and its meaning, particularly within the Global South" (Morreira et al., 2020, p. 1). It is critical to recognise this point, as too often the roots of liberatory movements are erased as they gain mainstream momentum. Early writings about anti-colonial struggles (Césaire, 2000; Du Bois & Edwards, 2008; Fanon, 1961; Freire, 1971; Neeganagwedgin, 2013; Nkrumah, 1970; Nyerere, 1968; Said, 1994) laid historical and theoretical frameworks that, as Morreira and colleagues surmise, have yet to be effectively implemented; there remains a gap between theory and practice. To this end, they offer the following definition and framework:

We thus define decoloniality as it applies to curricula and pedagogy as an inherently plural set of practices that aim to interrupt the dominant power/knowledge matrix in educational practices in higher education. These practices affect both what knowledge is produced via research and then selected for a curriculum (what content is taught), and the ways in which teaching and learning and assessment occur (how curriculum knowledge is taught, including the social power relations at work in teaching and learning).

(p. 2)

Decolonisation has gained traction in institutions of higher education where it is continuously at risk of being diminished. Morreira et al. (2020) list three dangers of locating this movement in the academy:

• the danger of appropriating Indigenous knowledges for personal gain through publications and career advancement;
• the co-opting and subsequent diminishment of the revolutionary thrust of this movement to performative notions of 'diversity and inclusion' in an effort to please 'the customer'; and
• the hypocrisy of advancing notions of inequality within institutions that thrive off exclusivity and are increasingly financially inaccessible to the broad public.

Indeed, the project of decolonisation in higher education questions the value and prospect of the university as a public good. This applies equally to primary, secondary and post-graduate schooling. As these ideas have become increasingly instrumentalised, there has been increasing attention to what is authorised as knowledge, including how and what is considered research (Denzin et al., 2008), what knowledge is incorporated into syllabi and writing such as the citation challenge in which we are asked to consider whose voices are included and excluded in referencing practices (Ahmed, 2013; Tuck et al., 2015) and how learning happens. How schools fail black children (2005) and material from the 1980s Inner London Education authority already highlighted the need for inclusive strategies in education, whilst black history research like Staying power (Fryer, 1984) and others provided and continue to provide research material for those excluded voices to become included (Olusoga, 2016).

So, how do we decolonise dramatherapy education and/or better understand and work within its constraints? Based on the previous discussion, the process of decolonising the curriculum in dramatherapy concerns itself with how knowledge is created and circulated within curricular materials. What ideas about illness, health and care are embedded in our current literature? Seymour and Holloway (2019) assert the importance of supporting dramatherapy students in recognising "that all therapeutic practices carry ideological implications" and that "different types of ideas co-exist in all of us, some which hold us back, some which urge us forward". They point to the value of the embodied, metaphoric practices through which dramatherapy educators can support students as they "face their own vulnerabilities, develop and apply vocabulary of therapeutic and artistic skills, and importantly find ways to explain these experiences" in the relative safety of the classroom.

Decolonising the curriculum involves becoming cognizant of the ways in which biases such as racism or ableism may be inadvertently embedded in our teaching and evaluative practices. Dramatherapist and educator Maria Hodermarska and then graduate dramatherapy student Veronica Filson (2018) wrote about ableism in the context of dramatherapy training and the necessity of valuing multiple ways of demonstrating knowledge. The themes they raise are also considered in the previous chapter on dis/ability (Chapter 12).

> Graduate education in the creative arts therapies…still privileges the able body and mind. …It's the more difficult conversations, the ones we'd like to avoid having, that pose the greatest dangers. Educating clinicians living with mental illness, for example, requires conversations about how people are managing their own symptoms under the stress of clinical internship and coursework and future practice. Educating clinicians living with learning disabilities requires conversations and strategizing about how to manage EPIC note systems in hospitals when spelling or sequencing of ideas presents challenges. How do we support student's research or capstone projects when the form that research scholarship must take may prohibit the student with certain learning disabilities from completing the task at the standards set by the institution?

Finally, what happens when training developed and experienced in one context (i.e. US or UK) becomes exported to other countries? This is a question that has surfaced periodically in our field which deserves greater attention (see Chandrasegaram, 2009; Chang, 2009; Jennings, 1994; Landy, 1982; Lee Soon, 2016; Makanya, 2014). The ethics of international, intercultural exchange have also been taken up by our colleagues across the creative arts therapies:

> The art therapy literature about international work seldom addresses the ethics involved. Conducting ethical work outside one's home country requires continuous examination of cross cultural ramifications of power and privilege. When international work is framed as helping or empowering people, there are often overlooked implicit biases that: a) those requiring help have limited power, b) there is a radical division between "us" and "them," and c) those with more resources hold exclusive rights to empowerment, wellness, and fulfilment. While most art therapists would deny this colonial logic, research suggests that it may unconsciously hold sway. … A common assumption is that Western

psychology is implicitly more valid, developed, and valuable than folk or ethnic healing systems. In reality, Western psychotherapy is also culturally determined and exists among many other contemporary, relevant psychological healing practices across the globe.

(Potash et al., 2017, p. 74)

In addition to these ethical concerns, dramatherapist Couroucli-Robertson (1992) named, early on in the development of the profession in Greece, the potential professional pitfalls and benefits of having dramatherapy introduced by visiting colleagues from abroad in one's home country, as well as the need to develop and compare standards of training and practice.

> What I refer to as cultural differences in attitude toward drama therapy in Greece may have to do with the fact that it is a relatively new discipline. It has not yet been practised over an extended period of time, but mainly by visiting drama therapists from abroad. The result is that it is less accepted or understood by other professionals, who believe that drama therapy is a vehicle for clever techniques that, used over a short period of time, leave the client with no support for dealing with the new avenues that it opens up. ... Recognition of dramatherapy practice varies from country to country and it is not always clear at what scale professionally a drama therapist is placed. This is not only due to the novelty of the profession but also to the different educational standards that exist between and within these countries.

(p. 117)

The concerns raised in these passages pertain to the ethics of international, intercultural exchange, local perceptions and legislative recognition of the profession, the necessity for comparable standards of training and practice that respect cultural variation and the geo-political dynamics of power in which our small profession is embedded. Some of these questions were taken up in the first international handbook of dramatherapy (Jennings & Holmwood, 2016) which created a space for dramatherapists to write about the development of the profession in their own home countries. These concerns have also been central to conversations between members of the World Alliance of Dramatherapy (WADth), which, as of 2021, was composed of 14 professional associations representing over 3,400 members worldwide (worldallianceofdramatherapy.com). A consistent theme in these conversations has had to do with how to support Indigenous and endogenous training while contending with the reality and desire for recognition from professional bodies in the UK and the US in particular. As a representative from India to the WADth put it, "[W]e need a conversation about what a post-colonial dramatherapy looks like" (Gopalakrishna, personal communication, 2021).

Given our location as co-authors, we have also asked ourselves how we might support reflection in this area in the training programmes with which we are most familiar. This is where we turn our focus in the next section where we offer a theoretical framework for exploring dramatherapy as an intercultural encounter in the context of training.

A framework for training[1]

The inclusion of training pertaining to cultural diversity and social justice is not new in mental health programmes (Kareem & Littlewood, 1992; Ratts et al., 2015; Sue et al., 1992). However, the inclusion of competencies related to cultural diversity and social justice is a relatively recent phenomenon in the training of arts therapists (Emunah, 2016; Hadley, 2013a; Hahna, 2013; Powell, 2016; Sajnani, 2016b, Whitehead-Pleaux et al., 2013; Williams, 2016a). The Health and Care Professions Council, the registration body for UK dramatherapists, in its standards of proficiency (2013) stipulates the need for dramatherapists to understand the psychological and cultural background to health and to be aware of influences on the therapeutic relationship. Effective intercultural communication means being able to select, move between and use appropriate verbal and non-verbal communication and understand how these can be affected by factors such as age, ethnicity, culture, gender, socio-economic status and spiritual or religious beliefs. Recently, dramatherapists have begun to explore how "the projective, embodied and relational foundations of drama therapy" may be used "towards challenging bias and moving towards just practices" (Mullen-Williams, 2016, p. 9).

Experiential learning

The training of dramatherapists typically involves an understanding of dramatic reality, embodiment, dramatic projection, play, active witnessing, aesthetic distance and performance (Emunah, 1989; Jones, 1996, 2007; Landy, 1982; Landy et al., 2005; Pendzik, 2006). This understanding is usually cultivated through a balance of didactic and experiential learning (Kolb, 1984). Kolb's ideas have had a dramatic impact on the design and development of lifelong learning models and have also been critiqued since their inception more than 30 years ago (Greenaway, 2016). 'Experiential learning' can apply to *any* kind of learning through experience, though it is often used by trainers to refer to a structured learning sequence which is guided by a model of four stages in which one moves through a cycle of concrete experience, reflective observation, conceptual theorising and active experimentation.

It is important to note that experiential learning does not automatically connote a set of shared values beyond the assumption that reflection on the doing of something (such as having a conversation, drawing, participating in a movement or a role-play exercise) encourages learning. However, experiential learning can be used in concert with pedagogical approaches that support social justice through intentional framing and by encouraging shared authority. For example, the transformative experiential approach developed by

Paulo Freire (1971), in what he referred to as the *Pedagogy of the Oppressed*, has also been used by dramatherapists (Gersie, 1987; Mayor & Dotto, 2014; Sajnani & Johnson, 2014). This iterative approach begins with drawing out participants' lived experiences, moves toward identifying patterns and themes, then moves to the introduction of new content (theory, techniques, or tools) and ends with strategising, applying in practice and beginning the process of reflection anew. Central to this approach is the humility of educator(s), the respect for the lived experience and expertise of every member of the group, a commitment to collaborate on collectively defined social problems, learn from one another and see ideas through to active experimentation in life.

A conceptual framework

Consistent with current training guidelines for intercultural practice (Bilodeau et al., 2016; Dokter, 2000b; Kareem & Littlewood, 1992; Ratts et al., 2015; Sajnani, 2016b), we propose a conceptual framework that is equally a scaffold upon which to organise training and a thread to be woven through training curricula and ongoing professional development. The framework consists of four developmental and overlapping domains that contribute to cultural response/ability:

1)   therapist self-awareness
2)   client worldview
3)   therapeutic relationship
4)   advocacy

Each domain consists of key competencies comprising specific *attitudes and beliefs*, *knowledge*, *skills* and *actions*, which are underpinned by an awareness of the implications of diversity and working within the context of not knowing, but being willing to find out and explore rather than assume knowledge or take one's own assumptions for granted.

Cultural awareness

In this domain, trainees and professionals develop self-awareness about themselves as cultural beings informed by past, present and anticipated experience. People are not necessarily aware of their own cultural values and assumptions but rather "we see the world and each other through our own cultural filters" (Dokter, 1998a, p. 147). Therefore, the objective of this domain is to cultivate an *attitude* of openness to learning about one's own cultural background and how membership in particular or multiple social groups (e.g. groups such as cis-men, transgender women, dramatherapists, Christians, Muslims, people of colour, citizens, refugees) influences experience in ways that may result in social, economic or another form of advantage (privilege) or disadvantage (oppression).

Knowledge in this domain consists of acquiring a knowledge of social inequities, of past and present events that give rise to one's own social advantages
and disadvantages and an awareness of how one's status or privilege may
influence or limit one's worldview. It also consists of learning about theories
relating to cultural (racial, gender, religious, migrant) identity development
and intersectionality (Sajnani, 2013).

Skills in this domain refer to the capacity to interpret, evaluate and communicate how one's cultural background and social status influence personal
and professional relationships. Finally, one is encouraged to take *action* to
learn about their assumptions, values, beliefs, biases and culture as a member
of an advantaged or disadvantaged group in one's own context.

Client worldview

In this domain, the objective is to cultivate an *attitude* of openness concerning the worldview, values, beliefs and biases of other people – the clients and
participants – with whom we work. This involves de-centering oneself from
one's own assumptions and communication preferences in order to learn
about what is important to another.

It involves deepening *knowledge* of the historical events, current socio-
political issues and religious perspectives that may contribute to the client's
worldview. It also involves developing a knowledge of theories of culture and
identity development that may be relevant to the client as well as a knowledge
of one's own biases and prejudices against clients from particular social
groups.

Skills in this domain include language skills and the capacity to research,
locate and critically evaluate information pertaining to social inequities
affecting clients' lives. It also includes the skills necessary to work through the
discomfort that may come with learning about particular client groups.

Action, in this domain, includes seeking out opportunities to immerse oneself and learn about the experiences of different social groups, using acquired
theories of cultural identity development in writing, teaching or speaking
about various social groups, and collaborating with clients/participants to
identify individual, group and universal understandings of culture and
identity.

Therapeutic relationship

In this domain, the objective is to cultivate an *attitude* of cultural humility
which is the ability to maintain an interpersonal stance that is other-oriented
(or open to the other) in relation to aspects of cultural identity that are most
important to the [person] (Hook et al., 2013, p. 2). This involves acknowledging that the cultures, and particularly the assumptions, biases, values,
preferences and prejudices of both the therapist and the client influence the
therapeutic relationship.

Knowledge, in this domain, refers to knowledge of specific ways in which cultural identities, stereotypes, power, privilege and oppression strengthen or interfere with the therapeutic relationship.

Skills, in this domain, refers to interpersonal communication skills and the capacity to apply knowledge about specific groups in practice while following the lead of the client. It involves assessment skills to identify one's own limitations and strengths when working with particular groups and the capacity to ask questions to assess the degree to which historical and current social inequities contribute to presenting problems expressed in the context of therapy. This is also important insofar as avoidance of social and political realities in the context of therapy can result in individualising and pathologising the client further (Brouillent, 2016; Sajnani, 2016b; Sajnani & Nadeau, 2006).

Action, in this domain, includes initiating conversations amongst peers and with clients to determine how the worldviews, values, beliefs and biases held by arts therapists and clients influence the therapeutic relationship. Action also involves participating in supervision concerning work with specific client groups and the needs and issues that they present in therapy.

In the meeting of different cultural backgrounds and worldviews, the therapeutic relationship needs to be engaged with, formed, sustained, therapeutic ruptures repaired, evolved and ended. There are several case examples of intercultural practice in dramatherapy (Braithwaite, 1997; Dokter, 1998a, 2011; Gersie, 1997a; Jennings, 1994), as well as relevant collaborations between arts therapists (Dokter, 1998a; Finklestein & Dent-Brown, 2008). The value of examining cultural relevance in dance movement psychotherapy has been examined by Chang (2009). There are also relevant and instructive accounts in the vignette research offered by Colkett (2007), Dooman (2007) and Carr and Andersen-Warren (2012). Accounts of practice with internally displaced persons and refugees have also been provided by Colkett (2010), Dokter (1998a, 2000a, 2004) and Sajnani and Nadeau (2006). Finally, case accounts about supervising therapeutic encounters from a cross-cultural perspective may be found in Dokter and Khasnavis (2008).

Advocacy

In this domain, the objective is to encourage an *attitude* of engagement in which arts therapists acknowledge the value of intervening with and on behalf of clients and concerning the issues they bring to therapy.

Knowledge, in this domain, pertains to developing an understanding of how external factors influence clients' intrapsychic processes and knowledge of what advocacy strategies may be used with or on behalf of clients. For example, it is important to consider how living in a region that has a high unemployment rate or that promotes racial hatred or homophobia might contribute to personal expressions of anxiety or inform behaviour (Brouillent, 2016; Sajnani, 2016b). It is important to consider who has access to services if a service is not covered by insurance or when to offer sessions if clients cannot negotiate time off work in hourly paid employment. It is also important to consider how unpaid child care influences access, attendance and participation.

Skills, in this domain, refers to the skills necessary to advocate for change. This may include undertaking research to highlight inequities present in current literature and practices in order to advocate for systemic changes to the profession. For example, as head of a National Health Service arts therapies department in adult mental health, I (Ditty) initiated an audit of therapist and client cultural backgrounds that brought to light differential referral patterns to psychological therapies (Dokter & Khasnavis, 2008), which could then be addressed. As therapist to asylum seekers, I have written letters to the Immigration Department supporting claims for asylum (Dokter, 2004), as do many other therapists. Skills, in this domain, also refers to facilitating an awareness of how external influences may be influencing presenting issues. As coordinator of a domestic violence programme at an immigrant and refugee women's centre, I (Nisha) asked group members to identify the external influences that create additional pressure in the home environment. Participants named difficult encounters with systems of transport, education, healthcare and justice. Their perspectives were included in the therapeutic theatre performance created by the group and published in a paper that extended a popular conceptual wheel model for addressing domestic violence to account for systemic violence (Sajnani & Nadeau, 2006).

Action, in this domain, includes assisting clients in forming relationships with family, friends and peers from similar social groups and, where appropriate, connecting clients with opportunities for self or collective advocacy. Action may also include efforts to change public perception. For example, dramatherapists who work with therapeutic theatre often regard these opportunities as a means of challenging social stigma (Bailey, 2009; Emunah & Johnson, 1983; Grainger, 1996; Hodermarska, 2015; Jennings, 2009; Sajnani, 2013; Snow et al., 2003; Dokter & Gersie, 2016).

During training, students are made aware of the possibilities for advocacy but also asked to reflect on the potential disempowerment for clients through therapist messianic zeal. Clinical supervision plays an important role in ongoing monitoring and reflection (Dokter, 2008).

In the area of advocacy, we need to question, as therapists in training and in practice, the potential shadow aspects in the therapeutic relationship, such as creating dependency through rescuing dynamics in an asymmetric relationship between, for example, an immigrant therapist with leave to remain and an asylum-seeking client. Where are we empowering a client to exercise their rights, and where might we be disempowering through rescuing out of privileged guilt? I (Nisha) have sought out ways of working that involve sharing authority and responsibility with those I work with. This has meant challenging the notion that anxiety and distress must only be worked with behind closed doors and in private. Dramatherapists can use their skills to facilitate a sharing of lived experience in the space between two people (therapist and client) or as part of public health strategies designed to challenge the stigma associated with specific social groups. In the context of training, I have emphasised that dramatherapists need to consider a private-public continuum in practice while remaining accountable to the needs of those in their care first and foremost.

Conclusion

Nigerian writer, Chimanada Ngozi Adiche, reminds us of the danger of a single story (2009). This warning is at the heart of the movement towards decolonising pedagogy in its acknowledgement of the power dynamics that shape what we know and how we come to know it as well as in its encouragement of pluralism. In this chapter, we have laid out ideas relating to decolonising pedagogy and considered implications for dramatherapy. We also offered a framework for teaching cultural response/ability in the context of training within and across borders.

Questions for further reflection

- What attitudes, knowledge, skills and actions have helped or hindered you in intercultural encounters?
- What does ethical intercultural collaboration look like? Draw an image of this and discuss it with a colleague or peer group.
- In what ways can we continue to decolonise training, practice and research in dramatherapy?
- How does your role as a trainer facilitate or hinder empowerment? How does your role of trainee (dis)empower you? To both: are there any actions that may encourage further empowerment for both?

Note

1 A section of this chapter has been adapted from Sajnani, N. & Dokter, D. (2017). A conceptual framework and experiential approach to teaching cultural response/ability, in R. Hougham, S. Pitruzella, and S. Scoble (Eds.), *Cultural landscapes in the arts therapies*. University of Plymouth Press.

Chapter 14

Illuminating intercultural considerations through supervision

> Joy was a twelve-year-old boy with ADHD who entered group therapy in a day-center for children. The group consisted of 5 boys and 1 girl who were 11 to 13 years old. In the group, children were referred who were diagnosed with ADHD and socially disruptive behavior such as fighting against authority figures and throwing chairs. His mother noted, on Joy's intake interview form, that his anger would often be triggered at school and he was constantly in trouble with friends and teachers in school. The group therapy sessions took place in a large hall for physically active play. It encouraged expression of their feelings and emotions through the body.
>
> Tae Seung Lee, Dramatherapist

How might we begin to explore the cultural considerations in this opening vignette in the context of supervision? It is presented without context but conforms to the kind of case reporting one might use in a shared clinical team. In this case, the dramatherapist and client self-identified as being of a similar cultural background – namely, South Korean adolescent and middle-aged adult male. As discussed in several previous chapters, sharing cultural similarities may be a source of understanding or assumptions in that certain attitudes or behaviours may be taken for granted. The supervisor in this case, Ditty Dokter, self-identifies as an older woman from another cultural context in the UK/Netherlands. In this chapter, we will look specifically at the supervisory relationship as an intercultural space where the work might focus on acknowledging assumptions in order to elicit and address potentially salient cultural issues. We will review some of the supervision literature in our field, revisit and follow up on this vignette as a case study with excerpts of supervisory dialogue and compare/contrast this with responses from our survey. We discuss intercultural concerns and issues raised in previous chapters, drawing on both intersectional and intercultural perspectives on experiences of discrimination, privilege and match from the context of supervision. We conclude the chapter with a few scenarios from the British Association of Dramatherapists (BADth) intercultural good practice guidelines launch for readers to complete and/or enact with others.

DOI: 10.4324/9780429431593-17

Intercultural supervision in dramatherapy

Supervision is understood to be an important part of ethical clinical practice for students and professionals. Supervisors support the growth and insight of mental health care providers with a view towards safeguarding client well-being (Bernard & Goodyear, 2014). The supervisory relationship is inherently complex, as each person in the supervisory relationship brings their own identities, worldviews, goals, strengths and challenges into the dyad, triad or group. As with psychotherapy in general, the relationship, *alliance*, or bond has been found to be the greatest predictor of supervisee development (Ladany et al., 2013), satisfaction (Ladany et al., 1999), engagement (Weaks, 2002), willingness to share openly (Cook & Welfare, 2018) and client outcomes (Bambling et al., 2006). Cultivating a strong supervisory relationship is of paramount importance. The strength of the alliance is influenced by many things, including the social and cultural identities of the supervisor and supervisee involved (Beinart, 2014).

In the last 40 years, the impact of culture and identity on training and the supervisory relationship along with recommendations for effectiveness has been increasingly studied and integrated into ethical guidelines (Hawkins & Shohet, 1989; Jones et al., 2019). For example, in a content analysis of 78 articles pertaining to multiculturalism, diversity and social advocacy published between 1989 and 2005, Smith et al. (2008) indicated that publications focused on culture-specific groups but that the overwhelming majority of clinicians sampled in the studies surveyed identified as white, thus contributing to a skewed narrative wherein the white-identified helper works with 'diverse others'. In a later publication involving a content analysis of 184 supervision-related articles published between 2005 and 2014, Bernard and Luke (2015) highlighted 26 publications that examined the process of multicultural supervision and advocacy but did not specify if this trend towards assuming that the clinician was white-identified continued.

Jones et al. (2019) asserted the critical importance of acknowledging cultural differences towards encouraging safe-enough, open relationships between supervisors and supervisees and see the exploration of power as important to supporting ethical supervisor leadership. Sommers-Flanagan and Sommers-Flanagan (2015) offered questions to support the exploration of power that supervisors might undertake directly or in the context of the supervisor relationship. In their chapter on feminist ethics of care, they begin with the following questions:

> What is your experience with and attitude toward power? Have you seen individuals wield power in mostly positive ways or mostly negative ways? What is it like for you when you have power over others? What do you think is necessary so that power does not have a corrupting effect on people?

(p. 50)

Evidence has shown that, in the context of racial differences, supervisees of colour are less likely to introduce conversations about race and cultural differences with their supervisors, citing discomfort, fear of overemphasising race or supervisor disinterest as barriers (McKenzie Mavinga, 2019). When discussions about racialisation and ethnic differences are initiated by the supervisor, supervisees of colour have indicated a decrease in role ambiguity and discomfort and an increase in a sense of agency within the relationship (White-Davis et al., 2016). Inviting conversation about one's worldviews, assumptions about health, care and illness, as well as similarities and differences in sociocultural identities between supervisors and supervisees and, by extension, between supervisees and their clients may contribute to increasingly effective, culturally responsive and responsible care (Jones et al., 2019).

There have been several publications on supervision in the arts therapies, with a minority of these focusing on intercultural considerations in the supervisory relationship. One of the first publications in this area was led by two Black-identified art therapists Hiscox and Calisch (1998) who looked at multicultural issues in art therapy. Payne (2008) edited a collection in which contributors emphasised the importance of cultural context in dance movement therapy supervision, especially in relation to physical proximity, touch and gender from a psychodynamic perspective. In the last decade or so, we have seen an increase in literature attending to specific facets of identity in supervision in the arts therapies. Young (2009), Hadley (2013b) and Seung and Whitehead-Pleaux (2015) have focused on racism alongside intersecting issues and identities in music therapy supervision. Awais and Blausey (2021) offered in-depth examples of illuminating racial, ethnic and sociocultural differences across supervisor, supervisee and client relationships in art therapy supervision.

The literature concerning supervision in dramatherapy has, in the past, consisted of theoretical reflections (Landy, 1982), ways of conducting supervision (Chesner & Zografou, 2014; Jennings, 1999; Lahad, 2000) or case studies from the supervisors' perspective (Tselikas-Portmann, 1999). Jenkyns (1997) explored gender issues in the context of dramatherapy supervision through the character of Nora Helmer from Ibsen's play *A Doll's House*. She emphasised the need for therapists to continuously monitor and analyse their own experience in the therapeutic encounter through a gendered lens.

Jones and Dokter (2008) dedicated an edited volume to the subject of supervision in dramatherapy in which they shared research from a survey of UK dramatherapists which included questions about whether certain issues were discussed in their supervision. Twenty percent of the membership of BADth completed the questionnaire. The most frequently discussed, in order, were specific client responses to dramatherapy, the therapeutic relationship and the supervisee's professional development. Out of a checklist of 27 items in 4th and 5th place were issues around age and gender, in 10th and 11th place issues relating to race and cultural difference and in 18th place issues concerning disability. However, nearly 8% of supervisees indicated that gender and age were seldom discussed, 15% of respondents said that race and disability were never raised in their supervision, whilst 25% said sexual orientation had never been discussed. It would be interesting to conduct this survey again today to see if these issues are more readily explored in supervision and to possibly include other intersectional variables such as language, nationality/migration status, class and religion.

In that same edited volume, Dokter and Khasnavis (2008) authored the first chapter to directly explore intercultural concerns in the context of dramatherapy supervision. They describe intercultural supervision as being primarily concerned with "the therapist's awareness of their own ethnocentric perspectives" (p. 113). Blackman (2008), in the same volume, explored the role of supervision in supporting reflective functioning amongst dramatherapists about clients "with learning disabilities" (p. 185).

Finally, as described in Chapter 3, both the BADth and the North American Drama Therapy Association have issued intercultural good practice guidelines which reiterate the ethical imperative of examining issues pertaining to cultural identity in supervision.

Intercultural supervision in dramatherapy: A case study

Returning to the introductory vignette, (how) can supervision focus on the cultural context of practice, and how might this benefit the supervisee and the care provided?

The supervisee and supervisor had been working together for four years via online supervision. The supervision was requested after the supervisor was invited to teach in Seoul, and the supervisee acted as interpreter.[1] The supervisee had trained as an international student in the ritual model of dramatherapy in the UK (Mitchell, 2012, 2016) and then returned to practice in South Korea. Practitioners in South Korea developed their own dramatherapy training and have their own professional association (WADth, 2021). In her writing about the development of dramatherapy in South Korea, Miri Park, one of the major proponents of training in South Korea wrote,

> It has only been a decade since dramatherapy has been acknowledged as an academic specialty in Korea. It started spontaneously with two different groups. The first group included students who studied in the USA and the UK; the second group involved drama and psychodrama specialists in Korea.
>
> (Park, 2016, p. 3)

Park describes welfare centres in Korea for particular client groups and how dramatherapy is provided for both individuals and groups. Joy, in the opening vignette, is in such a dramatherapy group in a day centre. The dramatherapist offered two more examples of practice that took place in this setting:

Early in the sessions, during 6PSM/BASICPh,[2] Joy portrayed a hero for his own world. Thor, the main character, was a fighter who used a hammer as a weapon. He illustrated patterns of killing and fighting. Joy's dramatizations reflected his anger and fear respectively. In the middle of sessions, he brought some props (gun, sword, umbrella) for the purpose of preparing role-play. It would be important to say that with props, as a symbolic representation, Joy felt safe to play with them to project his emotions. I suggested that perhaps using embodiment might help him to think about his sabotage. We entered into the creative space by enactment from Joy's story making. He was able to project the aspects of himself as a protagonist. Moreover, the hero characterized his interactions with others. I tried to respect and understand his need for symbolic action as gathering members for fighting a monster. I initially supported the process by guiding the structure of imagination to enter this confrontation. A significant part of Joy's difficulty seemed to be a denial of physical pain in his life. He said, "I can stand anything for physical pain." I tried to create his sabotage as a cushion monster for playful fighting. My position was failing to defeat heroes. Joy was able to imagine more control through expressing his feelings through words that best represented possible courses of action in anger rather than denying his fear of attempting to ask others. I focused on establishing the foundation for the boundary during cushion monster by using a fully improvised play.

In other sessions, the group members responded to Joy's predicament, failing warming up games. After his turn at the play, Joy continued to express emotionally in words related to his situation. The projection of inner fears and anger into outer dramatic enactment gave an opportunity to gain access to freedom. Learning how to use emotional embodiment provides children with a more solid self-confidence. He can effectively express ideas and feelings. The role-play provided Joy with interventions that empowered affective self-monitoring and a better understanding of other friends. Through experience and exploration he was able to change his awareness and understanding of that part of peer relationships. Joy was able to make the space between real life and creative space by de-roling in the therapeutic space.

An excerpt of dialogue from supervision

The following exchange about the practice described in the previous vignette and excerpts is presented not as best practice but as an example of how the supervisor sought to call attention to areas that might benefit from further elaboration.

SUPERVISOR: *Joy is a 12-year-old boy in an adolescent group, including boys and one girl. In the UK, you might have that at a school; how does that work in a day centre setting?*

SUPERVISEE: *The government provides the community resource; a social worker checks the children for ADHD and advises the mothers to refer the children; the mother decides involvement in the group. The mothers do not attend the day centre.*

SUPERVISOR: *How is ADHD understood in that setting: medically, socially or other?*

SUPERVISEE: *In order to attend the day centre, they need a diagnosis from the hospital, so it is understood as a medical issue.*

SUPERVISOR: *Having worked with you for a period of time I am aware that, in practising DT, the link with the family is very important for both children and adults, especially if they have a disability.*

SUPERVISEE: *Usually the mother/family does not have disabilities; the children come from 'normal' family group. As dramatherapists, we do not have enough time to check about the children's backgrounds with the mothers; we just work with the children and explain the behaviour.*

(Short exchange about single and two-parent families and with whom the DT liaises. There is a high rate of divorce in Korea. Joy comes from a two-parent family, but the DT only has contact with the mother. This is a common pattern.)

In the supervisory work, some of the current stressors in Korean society and their impact on dramatherapy have been discussed, whilst eliciting how the diagnosis is given meaning within the family structure in that context. The dramatherapist usually only meets the mother in single and two-parent families.[3]

SUPERVISOR: *Is there a social model of disability in South Korea or is it more understood medically?*

SUPERVISEE: *For many children, there are relational and social problems in school and at home. The parents want to control the emotions.*

SUPERVISOR: *Especially around anger? (looking back at Joy in the vignette)*

SUPERVISEE: *Hmm, hmm, I think so, the children really find it hard to control the anger…*

SUPERVISOR: *…and that was the case for Joy too (response affirmative hmm, hmm). Is it possible, in terms of understanding anger, how is the emotion of anger seen culturally in South Korea?*

SUPERVISEE: *Physically, the students try to break tools, throw away some objects. Also shouting, the noise and punching others. It is kind of acting out through the body. (The supervisee understands the question as how anger is expressed)*

SUPERVISOR: *(Picking up on the emphasis from the supervisee on how anger is expressed) I am aware in terms of dramatherapy aims that was what you were trying to do, express through the body in dramatherapy. You say, if I understand right, it is a cultural taboo?*

SUPERVISEE: *In South Korea, I think so, partly culturally speaking we are focusing on others behaviour in a public space. For example, in a restaurant, do not speak loud as you may be interrupting, disturbing others. We like to keep calm in public areas, in schools too.*

The supervisor checked with the supervisee about cultural gender and ability meanings, but also about cultural understandings concerning emotions;[4] the role of gender is neither mentioned by the supervisor nor by the supervisee.

In supervision, some of the shadow aspects of the story are explored

SUPERVISOR: *What was Joy's six psm story?*
SUPERVISEE: *He tried to fight, use a weapon, a hammer and to kill others. It was quite grotesque.*
SUPERVISOR: *Did he want to kill others; what was he hoping to achieve?"*
SUPERVISEE: *He wants to kill everyone. My sense of his visual image (understood by supervisor as the metaphor) is that he wants to control the space and others*
SUPERVISOR: *Did he have a helper?*
SUPERVISEE: *The weapon was the helper.*
SUPERVISOR: *Did he succeed; how did the story end?*
SUPERVISEE: *He stands on the ground alone without anyone.*
SUPERVISOR: *How did the other children respond to the story?*
SUPERVISEE: *Some children were laughing...yes it was curious...one boy agreed I also want to fight and kill someone.*
SUPERVISOR: *Was the laughter embarrassed, worried laughter or laughter of recognition?*
SUPERVISEE: *Playful, not worried about the image; they just want to play with killing someone.*
SUPERVISOR: *It reminds me how, if people in this country work in forensics, there may be a worry that the clients will act out the destructive fantasies. If you talk about the social space and anger being quite a taboo, how do you make the life drama connection for the children? Do you become the agent of social control saying we can do it here in fantasy but not outside, or do you work with the parents what the child might be so angry about and whether he can get some more agency in his life, or do you work with the school about how frustrated he is about having to be calm?*
SUPERVISEE: *When I started to work with the group, I told them they can express anger here, but when you open to leave the door you have to control. Maybe teachers and parents would not understand the expression, but here it is safe to express.*

The supervisor and supervisee exchange here their ways of understanding how shadow aspects are worked with. The worldview congruence model (Calisch, 1996; Dokter & Khasnavis, 2008; Myers, 1992) is a framework used by the supervisor in discussion with the supervisee for this exploration. Worldview is defined as the way the person perceives their relationship with the world and their place in it. It is brought into supervision to exchange understandings of Joy's dilemma; as a conflict in terms of axiology/values, such as emotional restraint vs expressiveness; direct verbal expression vs indirect; and seeking help vs saving face where saving face is experienced as a moral and ethical responsibility within Korean families (Lee et al., 2015).

Although the literature review provides useful background material to the supervisory relationship as an intercultural space, it remains important to remember "each family culture is relative within one's ethnicity, demonstrating its own unique differences" (Song et al., 2009). In Korean society, the family culture shows a strong homogenous element, but the degree of adherence to societal expectations may be different for each family and each family member. Arts therapies literature focusing on migrant Korean families often mention the impact of religion and churches on family life, both spiritually and socially (Lee et al., 2015; McGoldrick et al., 2005; Park, 2016).

Checking back between supervisor and supervisee about an individual client and family in their uniqueness is part of regular practice, knowing the general context enables that too. Exploring the supervisory relationship as an intercultural space is part of this. The supervisor asks here a few questions about the impact of difference: Jones et al.'s (2019) concept of 'broaching' in supervision. "Broaching cultural similarities and differences with respectful inquisitiveness is an important supervisor intervention" (Jones et al., 2019, p. 1). It enables the power dimension of the supervisor's 'European white expert' to be questioned, especially as the supervisor as trainer offered training in Asia. This presents intercultural and intersectional issues in prompting questions about the historical and present-day dynamics that make it possible for practitioners from dominant groups and nations to circulate their perspectives (see footnote 1). The supervisee was an international student; his migration experience and whether/how the training enabled him to practice was a part of the exploration. The next discussion excerpt is an example of how this can come into the supervision through 'broaching' (Jones et al., 2019, we discuss this further in the next chapter (Chapter 15) on practices).

SUPERVISOR: *Can I ask a bit more about what is it like to have supervision from someone who does not speak your first language, the one in which you practice, who was involved in the UK training you trained at, but does not know the South Korean context?*

SUPERVISEE: *At the time we started, there was no training for supervision, there is now, just started. It was hard to discuss amongst DTs Although we had supervision it was different from the UK model, where I had supervision for two years. Felt more unsafe in supervision in South Korea. But these days the supervision group is quite settled, as more DTs understand the need for supervision to develop our skills.*

SUPERVISOR: *I was interested when I was asked to teach in South Korea about therapist self-care. I wondered if you see yourself as part of a community; would your understanding of self-care differ from my individually based*

*understanding? Would self-care be seen as part of the more Western indi-
vidual understanding of self-care?*

SUPERVISEE: *It is different, in South Korea and in Asian culture it is really
hard to explain your weakness to others, "I am well, fine", but in a supervision group, we sometimes try to explain our difficulties honestly. But I am
still struggling to express my feelings to others; this may be a cultural thing.
In the UK, we can discuss some topics freely with others, but in South
Korea, we try to explain what is the right answer, the right position. That is
why it is for me important to have a safe space to express my own feelings
and my situation.*

Our supervision has always been via Skype; the excerpts from the discussions
span supervision over several years, with an emphasis on verbal exchange.
With the onset of Covid, we explored more non-verbal ways of working
online, as both supervisor and supervisee were developing ways of facilitating dramatherapy online for training, practice and supervision purposes.
Whether emphasising verbal or non-verbal exploration, working in a second
language means that there is an awareness of checking meaning and understanding, finding different ways of framing and phrasing (see also Chapter 9
for the impact of language in the therapeutic relationship). Being able to use
a first language can be very important in gaining a sense of identity. As one
participant in a workshop for American Korean adoptees names it, "It felt
easier to relate to my mother tongue" (Kim & Ginther, 2019). The experience
of Zoom working for both of us has emphasised more dramatic and experiential ways of working in online supervision. This was important, as one of
the issues the supervisee brought to supervision was the struggle to translate
his UK training to his South Korean practice in relation to experiential learning and embodiment.

SUPERVISEE: *When I trained in the UK, we were focusing on drama and theatre and also experiential work, checking with myself emotionally and cog-
nitively. In South Korea, it was the opposite dimension, many DTs focus on
reading and books, psychological theory for example. As dramatherapists
in South Korea, we are using drama skills in therapy; theatre skills felt
difficult to translate, to explain, to understand fully in embodiment.*

Supervision training has now been established in Korea, the supervisee has
been active in its establishment. Our supervision has focused on client work
but also the training of dramatherapists and dramatherapy supervisors, professional development.

Looking at issues around transference and countertransference in supervision incorporates the dramatic form (Jenkyns, 1997) and what is enacted in
the supervisory relationship as a parallel process (Hawkins & Shohet, 2012).
This is absent in the vignette discussion, although it is present at other times.
It can be interesting to reflect on the other absences in the supervisory

intercultural space. There is no mention of race or gender in the supervisory discussion. Does this stem from an avoidant, isolating or incongruent broaching style (Jones et al., 2019)? One of the respondents to the survey said, "I describe myself as an Asian race. I seem to usually receive a good welcome and make a more natural connection with Asian clients. I understand that it is part of the collective culture that people value interpersonal relationships". Kim and Ginther (2019) highlight how racial minority status, discrimination and in the context of Covid an even more traumatising impact of racism on Asian Americans. The impact of a white older woman supervising a younger Asian man remains unexplored in the previous vignette discussion, (how) is it present in other supervision discussions? Intersectionally, the supervisor does not ask about the one girl in the group; the fact that ADHD is more diagnosed in boys; the girl in the group is in a minority of one with a male therapist. Could it be useful to ask more about the impact of gender and gender perspectives?

Relating the case study back to the intercultural good supervision guidelines actively seeking out knowledge, considering contexts that may impact on the asymmetry of the supervisory relationship and the differing values concerning experiential learning and embodiment are illustrated in the work. Power differentials and empowerment are continued areas for exploration, between supervisor, supervisee and client. The supervisory responsibility to point the supervisee to further training resources does not take away the supervisor's responsibility to also continue familiarisation with and research into the, in this case South Korean, context. Staying curious and being able to broach with respect, whilst being/becoming aware of assumptions that need to be questioned help to challenge cultural prejudice (Bilodeau et al., 2016)

Dramatherapist perspectives on clinical supervision

Throughout the chapters in Part II, dramatherapists regularly say about difficulties encountered, "I took this to supervision". Regretfully, that is where the discussion usually stops. These were often issues related to therapist self-disclosure and client-therapist experiences of privilege and discrimination. Occasionally, dramatherapists express the wish for client-therapist match, often from a client rather than therapist perspective. We have looked for quotes from our survey to try and elicit (how) this applies to the supervisory relationship and provide examples of other national contexts beyond the UK–South Korea dyad from the case study.

Therapist self-disclosure

Respondents reflected on the value and challenges associated with self-disclosing and discussing aspects of their visible and invisible racial and ethnic identities in dramatherapy. What is visible about us includes skin colour but also includes how we move, dress and speak. Literature in this area suggests that therapist self-disclosure is a skill and competency that is important to develop (Bitar et al., 2014; Henretty & Levitt, 2010). However, the racial composition of therapist and client dyads strongly influence client perceptions of whether therapeutic self-disclosure may be appropriate and under what circumstances (Simonds & Spokes, 2017). An interviewee in Chapter 4, said "I believe firmly in working transparently and I do not know if I was right in concealing that aspect of my identity, however I also acknowledge that this feels personally complicated. I have sought supervision in this respect".

In this example, the therapist sought out supervision to continue to reflect on the choices related to self-disclosure. The opening vignette in Chapter 4 illustrated the dramatherapist receiving racist comments from the client; she said that the supervision was "a space to reflect on that experience of racism and to plan a way forward". Questioning the competency of a therapist of colour can often have a subtext of racism, as illustrated by dramatherapists in Chapter 4. Another dimension can be a lack of trust in the practitioner. This is illustrated in this excerpt from an interview with a white dramatherapist from South Africa:

> I more often trip up in the silences through the power position as white person and therapist in farming communities...people are silent, more subtle...people are used to being compliant. But possibly even more so, people are silent when they do not trust the therapist. I think in the time it takes to work on rapport and building cohesion in any therapeutic setting, we as therapists also have to actively reflect on race and diversity and what's in the room, in order to form genuine connections. ... The dynamics just did not work until I brought in a male Xhosa drama practitioner. I stepped back and he did the work...that worked. Sometimes there is a need for the whiteness to step aside.

In this example, self-disclosure may be used as an intervention to build trust and attend to social and power imbalances (Constantine & Kwan, 2003; Henretty & Levitt, 2010). However, the dramatherapist is also aware of the limits of this approach and points to the value of representation and collaboration. The complexity of self-disclosure is present for therapists who pass as white as well. As one survey respondent wrote,

> I have heard much antisemitism from clients over the years. This has been difficult and is a steep learning curve that I am still learning to manage /experiment with. It also connects to my own senses of internalised anti Semitism and feeling on the margins of the Jewish community...as a bi-racial light skinned person who passes as white I have also had to examine unearned privilege and work across difference with racialised clients who did not see me as a racialised person...I have both shared my Sephardic, Mizrahi and Ashkenazi[5] background with Palestinian clients and I have also not revealed this aspect of my identity. I believe firmly in

working transparently and I do not know if I was right in concealing that aspect of my identity, however I also acknowledge that this feels personally complicated. I have sought supervision in this respect.

In this example, the therapist sought out supervision to continue to reflect on the choices related to self-disclosure.[6] Tuckwell's (2002) discussion of inter- and intra-ethnic (counter) transference issues can be a useful area for supervisory exploration in this context.

Client-therapist experiences of discrimination

Several vignettes in this book describe experiences of discrimination from the client to the therapist. The authors often mention that the experience of discrimination is taken to supervision to process (examples can be found in Chapters 4 and 9). How did our supervisors enable us to work with this experience of setting boundaries, but not retaliating? Which perspectives did our supervisors take? The supervisor for the Chapter 9 case encouraged authentic self-disclosure on the part of the therapist. Saying "the place I come from is not there any more" enabled the client to share her own experiences of alienation and share her 'passing' as white, projecting the unacceptable difference on the 'foreign' white therapist. For therapists of colour in cross-racial contexts, such as in the opening vignette in Chapter 4, where the dramatherapist was a self-identified person of colour working with a white woman, there may be additional challenges (Hays & Chang, 2003).

Supervisors of interracial therapeutic relationships may also find Tuckwell's interethnic transference and countertransference concepts useful (2002, p. 67). From the client, there may be an overcompliance and friendliness as a way of dealing with the power differential, a denial of ethnicity and culture to avoid racism (from self or other) also reflected in the therapist's countertransferential belief that all clients are or should be treated the same in therapy. This could lead to a mutual silencing, a trying to avoid the mistrust, suspicion and hostility as seen in the vignettes of both authors. Ambivalence may be present in the therapeutic relationship where clients in an interethnic dyad may struggle with negative feelings towards their therapists whilst simultaneously developing an attachment towards them. Parallel processes in the supervision relationship (Hawkins & Shohet, 1989, 2012) can alert the supervisor to the presence of these dynamics. Countertransferential guilt about non-disclosure can also be problematic, whether it is survivor's guilt or privilege guilt; we will come to this area next.

Client-therapist experiences of privilege

As mentioned, guilt can be stifling and silencing, both in the therapeutic and the supervisory relationship. A therapist may be aware of how they have benefitted from societal and political forces, which may dictate a lower status for other groups of people (Tuckwell, 2002). A sense of privilege, as well as oppression, is cultural. They are both as systemic as they are individual (Turner, 2021). In the previous section on discrimination, we looked particularly at interracial discrimination, but the dividing line for privilege is not always racial; measurement occurs in a variety of forms. Bhopal (2018) gives an example of traveller communities within the UK, viewed by the majority privileged community as the white outsider, a mirror to the experience of the Jewish community (Jacobs, 2003). Both white patriarchy and privilege have evolved, so they have become less rooted within the original racial and gender paradigm where they originated: the ongoing oppressiveness of whiteness has moved beyond skin colour to become more multi-gendered and racial, as seen in supporters of Donald Trump and Boris Johnson (Boffey, 2018).

Some of these invisible differences can also be reflected in experiences of invisibility around disability and sexual orientation (Samuels, 2003). Within each of us, there are layers of privileges. That construct of privilege is formed on the basis of culture or, for example, religion, changing over time and place. Much intersectional privilege is unconscious and may need both therapist and supervisor to become more conscious of the mechanisms of oppression. However, being or becoming conscious of privilege can evoke guilt in the therapist that they – through education, income or other means – have 'escaped' their origins or the guilt that one's privilege has been 'achieved' through the oppression of others. Guilt and aggression may alternate, because of ambivalent or negative reactions towards one's own or the client's background. All can lead to paralysis and a wish to not address these too painful areas. The alternating of need to control with fear of 'the other', enforced by cultural, religious, educational and political institutions. Supervisors can usefully incorporate an awareness of privilege in the triangular supervisor, therapist, client relationship. As power is intrinsic in the supervisory relationship and attending to power and diversity in the supervisory relationship leads to higher satisfaction for supervisees (Green & Dekkers, 2010; Soheillan et al., 2014), what type of power do we need to consider? Ryde (2000) identified role power (inherent power differential between supervisee and supervisor), cultural power (power specific to an identified ethnic grouping) and individual power (associated with the characteristics/personality of the supervisor).

The conscious realm of privilege can include aspects such as whiteness, patriarchy, gender differences, being able-bodied. The unconscious aspect is related to our gifts and whether we are able to express them. Gifts recognise the mutual interrelationship of self and other, a responsibility for the other (Levinas, 2006). In an individualistic culture, using gifts for the benefit of the other can seem countercultural, more collectively inclined cultures perceive this as more 'natural'; the readers of the vignette in South Korea could use it to examine their perspective of collective responsibility as enabling or suppressive. The dramatherapy emphasis on individual expression may need to be contextualised and from an intersectional as well as intercultural perspective problematised. From a transpersonal perspective, gifts are those qualities that we all have access to (Hamilton, 2014; Tyagi, 2008). How do we as therapists deal with our privilege? "Privilege often has a moral or cultural responsibility towards the other. In order to facilitate this responsibility, the one with privilege has therefore to build a relationship with the other, be they disadvantaged or just in need. This takes humility, an awareness that they are whole as they are and a recognition of the humanity of the other. Privilege… is not ripped from the other by force of will, it is earned, it is recognised and is held respectfully between the pair" (Turner, 2021, p. 31).

The quote can be read as an endorsement of 'well-meaning' intentions, 'for' rather than 'with' the client, potentially still perpetuating oppressive systems. Turner comes from a more Jungian perspective and is concerned that privilege and supremacy are often conflated with each other. Power is a core component. He links hubris (the conviction of superiority) with supremacy and narcissism. He quotes Jung, "an inflated consciousness is always egocentric and conscious of nothing but its own existence" (Jung, 1968, p. 563), and connects it to the British education system privileging of private boarding schools (Schaverien, 2004, 2011); the worldwide bedding in of a more than 2,000-year-old patriarchal system. Privilege becomes supremacy only when we reject the idea that the other is part of us. Whilst we need to be aware that feeling responsibility for or over another group or individual may perpetuate oppressive hierarchical systems, we hold both certain privileges and positions of otherness all the time. If privileges ebb and flow over time, so does our sense of otherness, i.e. from a position of youth through ageing to a position of older age: the interplay between powerless and powerful becomes thus more inclusive. Supervision and training of (drama) therapists can engage with the "complexities of the wealth of material about ourselves hidden within our interactions with the other, should we venture beyond our own cultural shore on the island of safety" (Turner, 2021, p. 41).

Client-therapist match

Some respondents wrote about this in relation to how it supports the therapeutic alliance and creates openings in therapy. One respondent wrote,

> I feel that being Latinx has helped me to connect to other racialised clients…at the very least I let clients know that our multiple identities are important to who we are, how we see the world and that there is space to explore these things together.

As this suggests, sharing points of similarities may help us to connect. Clients indicated a moderately strong preference for a therapist of their own race/ethnicity and had a tendency to perceive therapists of their own race/ethnicity somewhat more positively than other therapists (Cabral & Smith, 2011). However, while studied more so in cross-racial contexts, ethnically matched dyads may also experience stereotype threat where clients worry about what they report to therapists for fear that it may conform to negative stereotypes about them (Aronson et al., 2013). Tuckwell (2002) mentions in intra-ethnic countertransference that there may be an over-identification, where the therapist fears intrapsychic aspects of the client's problems and/or may affectively distance to prevent this from happening. On the other hand, the closeness of the painful intrapsychic issues may raise anger. Therapists may share the client's ethnic and cultural ambivalence. From the client's perspective, a 'match' may result in idealisation and dependence on the role model or resentment and envy at the therapist's success, equating it with betrayal and 'selling out'. Groups that have experienced racial prejudice and socioeconomic oppression may have internalised racism and not want to work with a therapist from their own group because they experience negative feelings towards themselves and project them onto an ethnically similar therapist.

In the case study, there was no match on ethnicity, gender, age, language, ability but a match in the experience of migration and religion. Where does the reader think this hindered or facilitated the supervisory alliance; how did the intercultural supervision space negotiate differential power? Broaching is mentioned, but gender stays unspoken. The supervisor does her homework on cultural context enough to raise issues in the supervision but in the role of questioner rather than 'expert'. Shadow aspects of client-therapist match need to be explored in supervision. Taking a simple tick box exercise to similarity and difference and assuming that a match circumvents these issues may serve to make these areas invisible.

Broaching conversations about intercultural dynamics in supervision

In the opening vignette from Chapter 2, Bleuer asked several questions that reveal an interest in how we broach conversations about culture, identity, power and privilege in the context of dramatherapy:

> What makes sense to disclose in terms of our culture, or my cultures, in terms of similarities and differences? How do I create a space where clients know that we are going to talk about this and that it is a perfectly normal part of therapy to talk about who I am and who they are – and what it is like to do this work together? What parts of who I am and who they are make this work more challenging or more vulnerable?

Prompts to practice the art of broaching in supervision

In their article entitled "Broaching as a Strategy for Intercultural Understanding in Clinical Supervision", Jones et al. (2019) offer the beginnings of scripts which may be used to generate scenes in intervision to gain practice with broaching conversations about culture and identity or to use in supervision.

Here are two sample prompts they offer to invite reflection on intercultural dimensions at the *beginning* of the supervisory relationship. This first prompt can, in their words, "be used by a supervisor of any marginalised identity to set the stage for continuous and ongoing broaching within the supervisory relationship. It shows that the supervisor is aware of the importance of cultural identities and invites dialogue about them within supervision" (p. 9).

> I am so excited to be working with you in supervision. As a supervisor of colour, I want us to both feel that this is a safe space to discuss our cultural differences and similarities. Doing so allows us to learn more about each other and to have a positive supervisory relationship. In our time together, feel free to share any concerns you may have about the supervision experience, and let's celebrate your successes together.
>
> (p. 9)

This second prompt offers a more general way to extend an invitation from the supervisor to the supervisee while also acknowledging that the supervisor is not an expert yet capable of extending support and modelling ongoing learning and growth.

> I'm looking forward to working with you in supervision. As we get to know each other, I hope you will feel comfortable sharing cultural considerations and concerns with me. I know I need to earn your trust for that to happen. I also know that this (academic or nonacademic) department has areas for growth. I want to be an ally in any way I can, and I'm always eager to learn about my own areas for growth.
>
> (p. 9)

Here are three prompts that may be used during what they define as broachable moments *during* the supervisory relationship. The first may be used to indicate an awareness of cultural factors at play in therapy and to invite reflection of the same in the supervisory relationship in which there is a difference in racial identity.

> Excellent work with this adolescent. It sounds like she is really trying to figure out what it means to be Black Caribbean in the United States. What is it like for you, as an African-American woman, to explore that with her? [Later] Now step back, if you will: What is it like for you to explore these things with me, a White woman?
>
> (p. 10)

These next two prompts might be used to communicate an awareness on the part of the supervisor about comments that take place during group supervision, as well as their own use of biased language where relevant and to signal openness to a conversation.

I heard your coworkers discussing Christmas plans again and wondered what it must be like for you to be in such a Christocentric region of the United States? I have appreciated what you've shared with me about your own practices, and I have noticed more of my own biased language as a result of your willingness to be open with me.

(p. 11)

In group supervision today, as one of your peers discussed his thoughts concerning individuals from working-class families, I noticed your non-verbal behaviour changed. We have talked a little about your financial stressors in the past, so I want to check in with you. Would you like an open space to talk about how the comments made you feel, or do you have any thoughts you want to share?

(p. 11)

It will be useful to exchange examples of these types of prompts in other contexts outside North America. Conversations about the influence of culture in our personal and professional lives take practice and, while these scripts do not cover the gamut of what may arise in intercultural encounters in supervision and therapy, they offer useful points of reference for further reflection.

Relational Roles Assessment Protocol (R-RAP)

Williams (2016a, 2020) proposed the R-RAP[7] as a means of supporting dramatherapists in exploring the therapist-client relationship and as a means of challenging assumptions, biases and stereotypes. Drawing upon a substantial literature concerning the importance of therapeutic alliance, Landy's role theory (2009) and developments in embodied supervision (Landy & Butler, 2012; McMulliam & Burch, 2017), Williams (2020) proposed a structure to enable supervisors and therapists to examine the archetypal, intrapsychic, social and cultural roles that they bring into a relationship and encounter with each other and with clients.

Conclusion

The case study example in this chapter highlights intersectional and intercultural perspectives in dramatherapy supervision. Issues concerning international students and the fact that dramatherapy training has been exported, including unequal power relations, have been discussed in the training chapter. We hope the case study in this chapter and the dramatherapist perspectives on supervision from the survey highlight issues that are important to consider in the supervisory relationship as an intercultural space. To conclude this chapter, we want to refer you back to the two scenarios at the end of Chapter 3, used at the launch of the BADth intercultural good practice guidelines for further exploration.

Notes

1   Interesting to see this in the context of a white European dramatherapy trainer offering training in Asia. This presents intercultural and intersectional issues in prompting questions about the historical and present-day dynamics that make it possible for practitioners from dominant groups and nations to circulate their perspectives. North American and European dramatherapy trainings train many international students; their migration experience and whether/how the trainings enable them to practice, adapt this practice and the power dynamics inherent in this exchange are also discussed in the previous chapter (Chapter 13) on training.

2   See Lahad, M., Schacham, M. and Ayalon, O. eds. (2012). The BASICPh model of coping and resiliency. Jessica Kingsley Pub.

3   Supervisee background: Dramatherapy is a newly introduced practice in a community that has undergone profound social change pertaining to gender roles in a relatively short time.

4   Supervisor research: Park (2016) describes an emotion focused perspective of dramatherapy in Korea: "Dramatherapy is focussed on emotion as a main tool. It refers to emotion as a physical reaction; we can feel and express emotions instantly through our body when we encounter a stimulus. These feelings and the possibility of expression can also actualise invisible emotions" (Park 2016: 6). There are cultural differences in the expression of mental illness, according to Lee et al. (2016). Many Koreans suffer from somatisation of their emotional problems; physical complaints may be a way of expression where expression through verbal language is problematic. Mental illness is seen to occur as a result of suppressed anger in which restraint, suppression of verbal aggression and avoidance of confrontation contribute (Park, 2016). Emotional expression through non-verbal and symbolic representation is viewed as stimulating the possibility of alternative forms of communication. There is also a recognition of psychosocial problems in self-esteem, which can manifest as socially maladaptive behaviour (Lee et al. 2015), whilst for children with ADHD, a structured environment and framework is recommended to reduce distraction and impulsive tendencies.

5   See Solomin, R. M. (2022). Sephardic, Ashkenazi, Mizrahi and Ethiopian Jews https://myjewishlearning.com/article/sepahrdic-askenazic-mizrahi-jews-ethnic-diversity/. Accessed March 17, 2022.

6   Which invisible aspects of our identity we disclose was also discussed in Chapter 5 on sexual orientations, in Chapter 9 about migrant identity and Chapter 10 about class background.

7   View an example of the R-RAP being facilitated within a supervision team: https://bit.ly/3rNWRHx.

Chapter 15

Supporting intercultural practice

Walter, aged 9, has come to the part in his self devised story where the volcano is fed up with the characters that live inside him, the fire babies, being invaded upon by an opposing army, the water babies. The volcano has threatened to explode over a number of sessions but has been unable to do so.

Walter comes from a family that can be very anxious about the potency of feelings, his mum is a white Welsh woman who suffers from bipolar disorder and Walter feels very responsible for her health. His father defines himself as white English, coming from a rural background and suffers from depression and social anxiety problems. The family lives in a large English city. Walter's parents separated or divorced a year ago when Walter was eight and continue to struggle with limited social, emotional, and financial resources. Walter was referred by his parents who were worried by Walter's description of himself as depressed and easily upset; they felt that he was struggling with anger and low self esteem.

Walter and I consider the volcano and the characters that live inside it and the constant war that goes on there. I wonder what would happen if the volcano exploded. Walter replies that the battling characters inside might all die, and that the volcano does not want to be responsible for their deaths. We reflect that this is indeed a difficult dilemma. I ask if there is anyone in the story who can help, there is a dragon, which through the course of the story has learnt to be helpful instead of destructive, and an alien spaceship who only gets involved when asked because, as Walter tells me, "it's not really their war." Walter thinks about who can help, in a deep and loud voice he says "leave me alone for five minutes." This, he says, is the voice of the volcano. He then asks me if we can have a rehearsal of the explosion without the characters being inside the volcano. We remove all the characters from inside Walter's volcano and we fill it with vinegar and bicarbonate of soda. Walter watches with mounting excitement and adds the volcano's voice to the explosion. "Grumble, grumble, grumble" he says.

After the explosion Walter asks that we "do it properly" and wants his dad to witness the eruption. This time he places the characters inside the volcano, calls his dad in and loads up the volcano again. Both Walter and his dad seem excited and focused on watching this part of the story

DOI: 10.4324/9780429431593-18

dramatised. At the end of the session they are able to reflect together on the impact of the eruption on the characters and structure of the volcano. They can see that there have been some changes but ultimately the explosion is survivable. In subsequent sessions, Walter continues to explore, through story, what happens to the volcano, the characters that stayed inside and the characters who were pushed out during the eruption. He creates a park which has rules about interactions and, for the first time, creates two benign parental figures who take responsibility for the care of the younger characters playing.

Sarah Mann Shaw, Dramatherapist, UK

In this chapter, we discuss practices that have been used to support intercultural communication and understanding in the context of dramatherapy. We address practical considerations raised in previous chapters as they relate to specific knowledge, attitudes and skills that encourage exploring, playing, questioning and enabling voice, as well as practice strategies and examples of structures. We see some of these considerations at play in this opening vignette where the dramatherapist sought to attend to the risks associated with inequality and limited resources by aiming to improve the agency of both the child and father.

The dramatherapist reflected that the choice to use objects, often self-made, was Walter's, and she thought this was a good choice. At this point in the work, he did not feel robust enough for role play. Developmentally, Walter felt younger than his chronological years in his choice of play materials. In engaging with objects, Walter could choose to make them, choose them, engage with them, dismiss them, manipulate them with a degree of relative distance and therefore safety. In exploding the volcano, Walter took all of the play objects out of the body of the volcano the first time it exploded, which allowed him to judge and make a decision about whether the objects could be part of the second explosion. In so doing, he could engage with risk taking from a more informed position; he still had the opportunity for rehearsal but he could also be in the role of witness and director and stage manager.

This was important for him; he played projectively but held many roles (author, set designer, prop maker, etc). It still engaged him in an exploration of self, in roles and responsibilities, whilst also experiencing something in the play which was quite potent.

The object play was created by Walter and was a part of Walter, it enabled him to witness and engage with destruction, change and survival. For Walter, it was important that his dad witnessed the potential for destruction but also the capacity for survival. In the words of the practitioner who offered this vignette, "It was a beautiful thing for me to witness, father and son sitting and talking about how the volcano had survived its own potential for destruction and been changed by it. It seemed to bring them closer; they sat close and grinned a lot at each other at the end. Again there was an air of excitement in the room".

This vignette offers an example of (insecure) attachment as a lens through which to explore intercultural communication and how shame dynamics, what the practitioner referred to as low self-esteem and insecurity, benefitted from *dyadic regulation* (Overall & Simpson, 2015). Dyadic regulation, as discussed in Chapter 11, is an approach to managing interdependence dilemmas whereby one, in this case, a parent, supported the regulation of another's responses towards a greater sense of security and well-being in their relationship despite the many material insecurities they faced as a family. Through their co-creation, father and son were able to transform the erupting volcano, a potent symbol of Walter's internalised conflicts, into a playful source of pride in their bond and possibly pride in themselves. The therapist, in this case, benefitted from a sense of awareness about the importance of this co-creation to processes of dyadic regulation, as well as her capacity to notice the impact of their interactions throughout their work together.

As Adams (2020) observed in Chapter 4 in her analysis of systemic racism through the lens of attachment, denigrating experiences related to race, ethnicity, ability, gender, religion, sexuality, age, socio-economic status (SES), legal status may contribute to a sense of insecure attachment, a sense of exile and alienation which can affect how we move, speak and relate with one another. What is shame in this context? Is it "the reaction to an important other's unexpected refusal to co-create an attachment bond that allows for the dyadic regulation of emotions" (Schore, 1998, p. 65)? Shame acts as a "glue to bind the other to the subject" (Turner, 2021, p. 53), yet struggles to move beyond the co-dependent position of compliance. How do we, as dramatherapists, attend to the range of feelings and impacts of othering and being othered in the context of clinical care and community-based practice? What possibilities exist within the embodied, symbolic, playful, improvisational and performance-oriented work of dramatherapy? The vignettes offered throughout this book offer insight into these questions and we will revisit some of the major themes here with a view to ground them in practical strategies for further exploration.

Cultural inheritance: revisiting one's own cultural influences

A core assumption in this book is that it is valuable to explore one's own cultural influences as a basis from which to deepen our personal and professional capacities for intercultural practice. Examining our cultural inheritance permits a greater awareness about ethno-cultural transference (Tuckwell, 2002). Tuckwell highlights the complexities and the potency of racial and cultural phenomena, which can touch deep unconscious feelings that may be enacted in the transference. For example, transferential processes are often associated with internalised attitudes of White superiority and Black subservience, and these may serve as a catalyst for major therapeutic issues such as trust, anger, acknowledgement of ambivalence and acceptance of disparate parts of the self. Tuckwell names mistrust, suspicion and hostility, often rooted in anxiety about being misunderstood and ambivalence in the transference (e.g. struggling with negative feelings towards the therapist whilst also having an attachment to them).

Several respondents to our survey spoke about the value of examining one's cultural inheritance. One respondent wrote,

> My personal drama therapy work with individuals who are nonbinary, gender nonconforming, transitioning, etc... has developed my own understanding of the power of gender narratives and imagery within my own cis male queer experience. In particular it has helped me confront ways in which my experiences have been codified in my body, language, and stories which has helped me look for ways to soften and shift these deep rigidities when working around other forms of difference.

Another dramatherapist was aware of limitations in their consideration of the impact of gender:

> I have a limited understanding of gender myself, so it sometimes takes me a bit longer to understand when a client expresses associating particular behaviours with their gender, and I have to be more actively aware of the ways in which it can influence.

Another respondent wrote about having to "learn – and continue to do so – that different cultures in South Africa view gender roles differently and these do not align with my beliefs...it takes reflection to meet the person in their belief system".

Engaging in one's own therapy, supervision and intervision or intentional creative process can all yield insight into one's own cultural inheritance and current influences. Particular exercises that we have found useful have been excerpted from a previous workshop that we led in Palermo, Sicily, at the 2015 European Consortium of Arts Therapies Training and Education Conference (Sajnani & Dokter, 2015), as well as other exercises.

Mapping landscapes

As a way of warming up, dramatherapists will often invite participants to explore the space in which the work takes place. The space was a vast hall, with very high ceilings. Our 20 participants who sat in a circle of chairs appeared to be drowned by their environment; most were displaced as conference participants in an international conference. The importance of this very basic familiarisation process, before engaging in more exploratory and potentially exposing work about cultural background, is crucial as the following vignette from a workshop participant shows:

I found exploring the space using my senses helped to make the location more real and ground me in the present. By using touch I was able to have a stronger sense of the room and become more aware of my relationship with the space that was grounding and more concrete. In this respect I was able to develop my relationship with both a familiar and unfamiliar space and become more aware of my direct experience through the senses rather than being stuck in my head. By using movement I was given permission to explore and venture into the parts of the room I was drawn to and the parts of the room I felt less drawn to, helping me to notice more of my experience. Being able to move felt important as it gave permission to explore, rather than being limited to sitting in a chair. The invitation to move from the familiarity of a chair to the wider space and its looming uncertainty was fun, tinged with feeling tentative, unaware of what we were being asked to do. As the familiarity with the guidance for exploring the room became more comforting, so did my courage to explore the vastness of the space.

This exercise led to another in which participants were asked to imagine the space differently and to participate in several acts of remembering. For example, they were asked to imagine the landscape as the neighbourhood in which they spent their childhood years and to imagine and embody moving through this landscape.

Painting 'memoryscapes'

Participants were invited to paint or draw the landscapes they had grown up with and to place them in their geographical position on an imaginary world map. This permitted an exploration and commentary about our attachments to certain places and the memories they hold. We polled the group to discover what regions were represented and which were absent, and asked people to introduce themselves to those around them.

The story of your name

Our names carry cultural significance. We asked participants to find a partner and to share the story of their name (which may include different names used in different cultural contexts) and the image that they drew (memoryscape).

Defining culture

We returned to the circle and asked participants to step into the circle and to introduce themselves by name and with a sound and gesture that symbolised some aspect of their culture. This exercise is a challenge because culture cannot be reduced to one movement, yet it is embodied and expressed in our daily lives. After everyone had shared a movement, we asked if we could deduce a definition of culture from the exercises that we had experienced together. Participants offered their thoughts. We then passed out several definitions of culture that were read aloud in the group.

Multiple, changing and contested identities

Another exercise involved creating paper and embodied sculptures of intersecting identities. Participants are asked to brainstorm a list of identity categories – social groups to which they belong that have their own unique culture. Usually, this list includes age, ability, ethnicity, gender identity/expression, military status, legal status, national origin, religion, sexual orientation and SES, etc. They then write down how they identify with each of these categories on their own large sheet of paper, making choices as to how much space each identity takes at this point in their lives. They are invited to fold the paper into any shape and to make choices about how visible or invisible that identity is. We asked participants to reflect on moments in their lives that contributed to the choices they made concerning where and how they placed each identity. This exercise has also been done with an invitation to create a sculpture pertaining to your experience of your identity as a child and another as an adult and compare the two. This is usually enough to prompt conversation about the dynamic, relational and intersectional construction of identity. It also encourages reflection on the role of power, privilege, shame and oppression in how one experiences aspects of one's identity within particular contexts. We have explored this exercise on its feet within a tableau where members of the group assume, under the direction of one participant, different aspects of a paper sculpture. Another version has involved selecting one identity (e.g. gender identity) and asking group participants to work in small groups to create variations of how this identity is inhabited and expressed in their lives.

Continuum

In this and other workshops, we have used an imaginary continuum to explore the influence of socially constructed binaries like young/old, female/male and gay/straight. For example, we asked participants to place themselves on an imaginary continuum between heterosexual and homosexual and to take their time in exploring what moving along the range of the continuum feels like. This can be done in action as a group or individually on paper. Participants were invited to write/share the stories related to those places in their lives and to place themselves on the continuum at different points in their lives. It can be interesting to explore the impact on the continuum beyond the binary; what shapes can emerge?

Acculturation gradient

The same continuum structure may be used to explore acculturation and assimilation. The worldview congruence model (Dokter & Khasnavis, 2008) and acculturation gradient are two theoretical perspectives which can be used experientially to explore differences and potential conflicts in both therapist and client worldviews. Acculturation was first investigated as part of a major study in 1936 by Redfield et al., who defined acculturation as "those phenomena which result when groups of individuals having different cultures come into continuous contact with subsequent changes in the original culture patterns of either or both groups" (cited in Berry, 2005 p. 7): integration, assimilation, separation and marginalisation.

> The *assimilation* path is adopted when the person does not want to maintain either their own cultural identity or contact with outside groups; the *integration* path when it is of value to both maintain one's culture and maintain contact with others; the *marginalisation* path when there is little interest in maintaining one's own cultural identity or contact with others. If the respondent does not wish to maintain relationships with other groups but wants to hold on to his or her own cultural values, *separation* comes into play.
>
> (Berry as cited in Pantiru & Barley, 2014)

However, it is important to add that people do not always have the freedom to choose their own acculturation path due to the attitude of some countries towards cultural diversity.

The relationship between acculturation and psychological adjustment for immigrant groups is an important area of research (Chun et al., 2003). Researchers have been interested in how acculturation influences individual health and wellness (Pawliuk et al., 1996), and in how the acculturation process influences family relationships in migrant families (Hwang & Wood, 2009; Portes & Hao, 2002). Previous studies have examined the link between the acculturation of different family members and family relationships (Luo & Wiseman, 2000; Portes & Hao, 2002). Family members have been seen to move along a continuum of traditional to assimilated to bi-cultural positions. Different generations may also take on different positions.

As an experiential structure, participants may be asked where along the continuum their family would be situated and where they placed themselves. One participant wrote about her experience:

> One of the most memorable aspects of the workshop that has stayed with me was the continuum exercise. By seeing my relationship with my culture "mapped out" and, most significantly, how it related on the scale to others' experiences, I was surprised at how disconnected I felt towards my cultural background. I realised that I felt somewhat envious of some of the other participants, who seemed to have a much stronger sense of their cultural identity than I did and much surer of their place. I was slightly fearful that others would recognise the internal difficulties I was having in conceptualising my cultural identity and lack of

feeling grounded in this. Over the weeks and months that followed, I have returned to this response and feel that this is something I am still processing. I have thought that this may be something to do with cultural shame, or perhaps even a fear of being seen to embody or represent the more shadowy aspects of my cultural identity. Strangely, however, I do feel much more embedded in my professional culture…although why I see this as distinct itself prompts further questions and reflections. … Anyway, I found that the experiential nature and physical engagement of this exercise brought out responses that I was not previously consciously aware of, which was of great interest to me.

Exploring gender identity and sexuality through mixed media and portraiture

Art therapist Millen (2019) offered several prompts designed to support arts therapists in examining their own associations to gender and sexuality through visual art making which could be applied to explore other facets of identity as well. Some of the questions she uses include: How were you perceived and influenced as a child? What were the behavioural expectations? How did you prefer to express yourself in outward appearance and behaviours? Were these expressions impacted by prescribed gender roles, and how? Who did you seek out for friendship and closeness? At what point did you become aware of yourself as a sexual being or become aware of attraction to others as shown through affection and desired closeness? How has this changed over time?

Performance

The role of autobiographical and other forms of therapeutic theatre in training and post-training (Bird, 2017; Dokter, 2021, 2022; Dokter & Gersie, 2016; Sajnani, 2013, 2017; Seymour, 2016) can encourage therapists in an ongoing relationship with their changing identity over time, whilst providing opportunities to share silenced stories and be witnessed. Navigating self-disclosure is an additional area of growth for dramatherapists as it is an integral component of what Emunah calls self-revelatory performance (Emunah, 2016). Connecting that self-disclosure to needed social and environmental change enables the exploration of cultural inheritance, intercultural themes and as a catalyst for dialogue in our professional community as well as a connection between personal and political and personal and professional. Here are four examples:

Autobiographical performance. The use of autobiographical performance in dramatherapy has been known by many names yet shares a commitment to facilitating insight and integration (see Pendzik et al. 2016). Several dramatherapists have used autobiographical performance to examine relationships between culture and care. For example, Maynard (2018) devised a 30-minute solo performance to explore and express her experience of "navigating societal racism and sexism" and the impact of the same on mental health (p. 1). A Taiwanese dramatherapy trainee who participated in Jacques' (2020) research devised and performed a solo performance around her frustration to make her voice heard as an international student, a link to a clip of the performance is available in the article. Dokter (2021, 2022) also devised and performed autobiographical theatre in relation to the impact of migration experiences over the life cycle.

Ethnodramatherapy. *Ethnodrama* and its corollary *ethnotheatre* (Saldaña, 2011) involves the translation of qualitative interviews with a specific group into a dramatic script and, if desired, into a performance. Snow (2021) articulated the hybrid form *ethnodramatherapy* as a means of uniting theatre, therapy, research and activism with a view towards supporting the voice and agency of people who identify as living with disabilities (Snow et al., 2017), as well as other groups who are vulnerable to various and intersecting forms of social exclusion (Snow & D'Amico, 2015).

Devised and therapeutic theatre/affinity groups. Several programmes in dramatherapy provide opportunities for students and alumni to participate in affinity groups focused on themes of interest, including specific issues related to identity, culture, justice and care. Affinity groups are, in and of themselves, a practical strategy to support students and professionals in the creative arts therapies who are vulnerable to social exclusion (Edwards, 2021; Goel, 2022). Examples include the Black Music Therapy Network[1] and the creative affinity groups such as Theatre for Change (TfC) housed at the California Institute of Integral Studies and the Collideoscope Repertory Theatre Company (CRTC) and Disability Justice group housed at New York University blend the supportive function of affinity groups with the benefits of performance. TfC, for example, engages students in devising performances that "raise awareness about diversity" and "invite dialogue at CIIS about oppression, privilege, equality, and alliance" (California Institute of Integral Studies, 2022) The mission of the CRTC is to "advance racial justice through performance and beloved community" (NYU Steinhardt, 2022). Under the leadership of Artistic Director Adam Stevens, the CTRC selects a play by a playwright who identifies as Black, Indigenous or a Person of Colour and students and alums who identify with the primary concerns of the play are invited to participate in its production thereby creating a two-fold opportunity for affinity and a therapeutic theatre process with actors, company members and audiences.[2]

Playback theatre (PT). PT has been practised and researched by dramatherapists. Rowe (2007) researched PT at the company set up in 1991 by David Powley, then course leader of the dramatherapy training in York.

More recently, it has been used to directly address issues related to identity, culture and co-existence in the context of a US arts therapies programme at an institution of higher education (Sajnani & Wager, 2017). In the constrained, managerial and pressured environment that can, at times, characterise institutions of higher education, participants reported valuing (1) the benefit of not remaining overly theoretical or abstract when discussing what is at stake when examining issues related to diversity, equity and justice in training but connecting ideas to lived experience; (2) the transformative effect of enabling a space where each person's story was treated as valuable; (3) the opportunity to bear witness to the stories of faculty of colour in predominantly white institutions; (4) the opening that PT created to affirm the need for ongoing reflection and action. PT companies composed of practising dramatherapists also enable raising a range of diversity issues for both colleagues and clients, an example is Golden Tread PT company where music and dramatherapy colleagues collaborate as performers (Playback Theatre UK, 2022). Volkas (2009) has long used PT as a means of facilitating empathy and understanding between groups who share a legacy of conflict.

Supervision and intervention

Broaching

Thinking about broaching (Jones et al., 2019) in supervision, we quoted Bleuer, who asked several questions that reveal an interest in how we broach conversations about culture, identity, power and privilege in the context of dramatherapy. This is not only a concern for therapists but is something that clients have noted as well. For example, a respondent who identified as a client of dramatherapy wrote about the benefit of being able to "speak to [their] therapist about her privilege as a white person". Who initiates these conversations? When are they best initiated directly and when through metaphor? In certain power dynamics, it might be difficult for the client to raise them, whilst the therapist might assume the client would if it was important to them. As we explored in our chapter on supervision (Chapter 14), broaching such topics takes practice. There are also other methods in which issues related to power, privilege and oppression have been explored within our profession – namely, Boal's work and Developmental Transformations (DvT).

Boalian techniques

As discussed in Chapter 3, variations of forum theatre were used to develop guidelines concerning intercultural and cultural response/ability guidelines. They were inspired by Boal's work on legislative theatre (1998) in which he further develops forum theatre, aiming to create a truer form of democracy and effect social change. Scenes depicting challenges germane to intercultural encounters within the context of an exploratory workshop within our professional community may offer a generative space from which to explore further. Such scenes could be used in the style of forum theatre whereby audience members are invited to replace members of the scene to engage in a collective, embodied exploration of possible strategies to perceived challenges. Other Boalian techniques and systems, such as Rainbow of Desire, wherein internalised oppressed are placed within a larger context, might be employed to explore contradictory forces within the agencies and institutions in which we work (Sajnani et al., 2021).

DvT

A central assumption in DvT (Johnson & Pitre, 2020) is that being is unstable and that, in an attempt to manage uncertainties, including the instability that arises from encountering difference, human beings engage in repeating patterns of behaviour that inevitably reduce difference and, over time, become congealed and accepted as fact. These internalised patterns are enacted and worked through in the dramatic reality of the *playspace* towards a greater tolerance of uncertainty, enhanced capacity to notice and accommodate differences and an increased sense of intimacy, flexibility, collaboration and playfulness about issues related to power and control. DvT has been used in the context of supervision and practice to explore relational dynamics around race, gender, age, and other social constructions of identity where rigid binaries still prevail (Dintino, 1997; Dintino et al., 2015; Johnson & Sajnani, 2015; Landers, 2002; Mayor, 2010, 2012; Miller et al., 2015; Smith, 2000).

Techniques in practice

Witnessing

Witnessing has been understood to be a core process in dramatherapy (Jones, 2007) and takes place in many ways in both process and performance-oriented dramatherapy. In the context of intercultural practice, acts of witnessing serve to heighten experience and ensure a "good enough storying" of the locked-away stories of unfinished grief across generations. It enables us to own our own histories, as in past stories that are also differentiated. As Nisha described in her own story from Chapter 2, the presence of a witness heightened her own experience at the gates of Buckingham palace. In the context of performance, as described in the previous section, witnessing implicates audiences in the struggles portrayed on stage (Sajnani, 2012b). Witnessing is always already embodied in that we are stirred, moved, affected by what we bear witness to. It can also be active wherein, in Boal's (1979) words, spectators are transformed into *spect-actors*, able to interact and engage with scenes directly. Boal's arsenal of techniques, including image, forum, legislative theatre, as well as Rainbow of Desire (Boal, 1995, also see Sajnani et al., 2021), are particularly useful in examining the systemic and structural issues surrounding intercultural communication and intersectional inequities. For example, dramatherapist Jen (2016) used image theatre to identify and explore acculturation experiences of Taiwanese international students in the performing arts. Dramatherapists Hastings and Bleuer (see Sajnani et al., 2021) have used a variety of Boalian forms to explore gender identity and other forms of oppression, whilst Scott-Danter gave an early example of using image and forum theatre to facilitate community healing post-civil war (Scott-Danter, 1998). In the UK, Boalian practice is applied by dramatherapists such as Carr and Bird in their arts-based research, but its practice is foregrounded more by applied theatre practitioners such as Tony Cealy (Sharma, 2019) on ethnicity and race; Rifkin in ACT ESOL (Serpentine, 2022), a theatre and language education project at the Serpentine Gallery for English second language speakers; and Cardboard Citizens, a theatre of the oppressed company that highlights issues such as the impact of the pandemic on those who are homeless (Centre for Homelessness Impact, 2021).

Good enough storying

Many dramatherapists in this book emphasise the importance of storytelling in their practice. The therapist in the borders chapter (Chapter 11) described the use of a variety of story structures which eventually allowed the client to find a way to tell his own painful story. Sharing fictional and sacred stories, the six-part story-making technique (Lahad, 1992; Schacham et al., 2013), writing exercises and poems led to the long process of writing and rewriting his actual life story from early childhood memories to the traumatic events of his adult life. The dramatisations helped him embody and express the feelings behind the words. Letter writing exercises helped him to reconnect to family and friends he had lost and the letters he imagined he might receive in return with messages of love, support and forgiveness.

Dramatherapist Alida Gersie has reflected on the importance of "good enough storying" in her publications (1992, 1997a; Gersie et al., 2022) as a powerful means to interlace historical and cultural factors with personal narrative. In a reflection about one client, Gersie reflected that "she had treated the story of her unfolding life as a series of recent anecdotes without history or tradition" (Gersie, 1991, p. 119). Scott-Danter's (1998) reflections on collective storytelling are also useful here and highlight the value of the therapist as an outsider to the cultural experience of those in their care. Enabling clients to speak their own language meant "the theme of outsiders was paramount within me, coming from a different culture. ... I always felt at least three steps behind what was being said because of the language barrier" (Scott-Danter, 1998, p. 107). Her work reflects the empowerment of a community by sharing different perspectives amongst them and with the actors/

director. Seeing a powerful other struggling to understand, find words, give meaning, provides greater equality in the relationship and models that struggles can be played with and survived. Cultural considerations pertaining to the use of stories in therapy are explored in a section on materials and metaphors later in this chapter.

Working alongside one another in therapeutic solidarity

A lot of the settings we as dramatherapists work in have embedded assumptions and power positions. The possibilities and limitations of advocacy in embedded structural oppressive settings (i.e. psychiatry, age-segregated, white-dominated, patriarchal settings) need to be considered. Is dramatherapy a 'subversive' practice, aiming for inclusion of excluded and marginalised groups and/or is it a profession negotiating for more professional recognition, status and pay? Are these two mutually exclusive or complementary aims? Whether a voice can be heard can depend on status assigned, whether a student debt can be paid off can depend on income from paid employment. As authors, we believe it is important to build bridges between silos and that it is important to be aware of colonial influences in both empire attitudes and political 'wokism'. How can we as dramatherapists engage in dialogue and move beyond the binary opposition? Some of the roles we as dramatherapists adopt may have helpful and hindering aspects; in the book, the one mentioned especially was the therapist as outsider role, identifying both strengths and difficulties with this role (Scott-Danter, 1998). On the advocacy side, there are occupational hazards of the 'therapist as saviour' role, which is problematic in relation to denial of the power relationship, similar to therapist as culture broker and interpreter.

Working alongside our clients and/or participants has been identified as a meta-process in dramatherapy (Cassidy et al., 2014). An example of practice that demonstrates the being with, being alongside, rather than doing for stems from a vignette from a dramatherapist working in a forensic setting, which could be applied in quite a lot of other potentially oppressive settings.

> In the past I did not take part in group exercises, seeing it as interfering with my capacity to facilitate. Now I adopt a participatory role more, to address that issue of power / us and them, and reduce the fear of being judged. Also when working with a co-facilitator, we will share our work alongside everyone else. I have developed this more in recent years, feeling that it takes the tension away from us being "experts"…more a shared experience. That has made a tremendous difference in how we operate. In that process, we are able to recognise the differences, as well as the commonalities we share. Therapists traditionally have quite a lot of power, we have to be sensitive that we are walking around with the keys. We are free to go, they are not. Traditionally therapists can wield quite a lot of power of somehow being the expert, the analyst, the one

who knows how it should be rather than the person who is curious about the other. The therapist as the holder of power, I would rather have a more benign power in terms of saying "I am sharing this journey with you, we are all discovering together." People can let their defences go more readily that way too. They are also human as we are and all can get it wrong. We can celebrate their expertise about their life.

How do we work alongside someone whose values are very different from our own, whom we may perceive as extremist or any other-ist? As therapists, just as a client, we have the right to refuse to work with someone. We do not have to expose ourselves to people we experience as abusive or oppressive. On the other hand, can we find a way of entering into dialogue, a way of staying with that enables potential change for both therapist and client? If and how/where to draw a line as to what is not acceptable, but also work hard on building trust, on coming alongside.

A dramatherapist discussed her practice about working as a white woman with racism in the military.

Sometimes I work overtly within the groups through Theatre of the Oppressed. Otherwise we may be using people's narratives, quite often through doubling seeing the other's perspective. But again, it is about building trust before that. There can be quite a lot of racism within the armed forces for instance. As a therapist I do not just want to say "no, we do not have that". When you hear about their experiences, they may not know any different and are often angry, so can be influenced by others. However, on the flipside, within the military I might be working with someone from the empire (at the time of serving) and he was treated very badly. We think of our veterans as being treated badly, but colonial subjects enrolled within the military are treated even worse. They want them to fight as one of "us", but when they get injured they would hear "we are not responsible for your treatment." They can be from Nigeria, a Gurkha or Australian – less about the colour of their skin, just not part of the tribe. In dramatherapy it is about listening to their narratives. I worked for example with Far East prisoners of War, they were very anti-Japanese, affected by the war. They would not buy Japanese products, when you heard their stories you realise how deeply affected they had been. Sometimes they came round, sometimes not. As the therapist, I would tell them I thought differently, but it was important to develop a trusting relationship, I did not want them to shut down and think "She does not understand either". I would not use Japanese stories as that would immediately set up a barrier. I would consider that generally, for example for those badly affected by a Northern Irish tale or accent. They can overcome that barrier even if it is a group member, but that barrier is there to begin with. We need to work with the barriers through talking about them and working through them.

On materials, metaphors and language

The therapists who offered vignettes in Chapter 4 mentioned the importance of understanding particular cultural references, terms and language and the way they intersect with the experience of racism. The therapist who identified as Black mentioned that she found it easier to explore issues around racism in an individual rather than a group context, while the white therapist found diverse groups the best context for discussion. A critical reader highlighted that the perspectives offered also indicated a need to examine how our inter-actions and the materials, playscripts and stories we choose, the case examples we reference and the approaches we use, may risk reinforcing notions of colour blindness, Eurocentric norms and/or ask racialised (or otherwise othered students) and clients to replace their experience once more with those of their white counterparts (or other dominant groups).

Symbols and metaphors are used across the arts therapies (de Witte et al. 2021) and, indeed, dramatic metaphors facilitate embodied engagement and processing in dramatherapy (Jones, 2007). Physical and verbal languages are part of our professional identity as dramatherapists, whether we draw on the-atre/drama or psychological therapy elements in our practice. However, it is also important to examine ableist notions of physicality as they may appear in our practice (e.g. everyone get up and move around the space). Dramatherapist Hiltunen's (2014) work involving the use of Noh theatre with adults living with severe and profound developmental and intellectual disabilities offers interesting insights into the balance of physicality and words in practice.

Sometimes there seems to be a valuing of the non-verbal over the verbal and a feeling that language is a barrier. Is this part of our professional value system, and will this impede us in effectively exploring language as an aspect of cultural identity? (How) can we incorporate the range of languages avail-able to therapists and clients, be it through therapists and clients and use of all languages available to them (Carr, 2016) and/or using an interpreter?

Some respondents to our survey wrote about the importance of finding shared symbols and language. As one wrote, "[D]ramatherapy is in part ver-bal so how to bridge the verbal and non verbal needs to be negotiated; be it via an interpreter or by creating a shared 'dictionary' of both symbols and words". In connection with this, Dramatherapist Hodemarska critiques what she perceives to be an over-reliance on language to communicate structure and to assess outcomes in dramatherapy and proposes ways of working that are consistent with another's preferred mode of expression. She writes, "[O]ur problematic (read often ableist) use of terms like embodiment and meta-phor, our reliance on the structure of narratives and storytelling, and so much more, needs to be reconsidered and rethought for this new decade" (personal communication, April 15, 2022).

Power issues between therapist and client were also highlighted when working in a second language, with therapists feeling disempowered if clients spoke the dominant language better than them, corrected their language, feeling deskilled clinically when lacking confidence in the majority language. Could this also be an issue when dramatherapists talk about language as a barrier? Some respondents attributed non-verbal communication in sessions to ethnic and cultural preferences. For example, one respondent wrote, "I have to be aware how my eye contact and listening style would be perceived. ... I have to be careful not to generalise whilst still taking culture into consideration". Another wrote about a similar phenomenon as it relates to touch: "I live in a very mixed race society, there has been a melting pot of settlers for over 300 years. ... I have had to change and be aware of touch in some instances, especially between men and women".

Transference, countertransference and self-disclosure

In the opening vignette for this book, Bleuer asked very pertinent questions about therapist self-disclosure. What makes sense to disclose in terms of our culture, in terms of similarities and differences? How do I create a space where clients know that we are going to talk about this and that it is a perfectly normal part of therapy to talk about who I am and who they are – and what it is like to do this work together? What parts of who I am and who they are make this work more challenging or more vulnerable?

If as dramatherapists we aim to work with the transference in the therapeutic relationship, therapist self-disclosure can be seen as impeding that possibility. On the other hand, internalised oppression can also impede working with the (counter) transference. How do we know if we as therapists do not self-disclose because of internalised oppression? For example, sexism can contribute to psychological distress through internalised self-objectification or passive acceptance of gender and other roles. Sheppard quotes Isay's (1991) discussion around erotic transference. He names that non-disclosure can be damaging if the therapist brings shame, guilt and fear into the therapy space, potentially exacerbating the client's internalised identical feelings. Schaverien's edited volume on gender, countertransference and erotic transference (2006) includes some examples of female psychotherapists writing about the erotic transference between them and their female clients. Kavaler-Adler (2003), gives an example of erotic transference in her practice that looks beyond regression to mother-daughter dynamics and acknowledges adult homoerotic desire. In the sexual orientation chapter, a dramatherapist commented about being out on his website and issues related to that. He wonders about it sometimes coming up with straight clients, but always with queer clients. In supervision he discusses being a niche dramatherapist; he might always draw queer clients but wonders if straight clients feel they can benefit from working with him. Do they place him in a box and decide he is not best, even if he might be? He calls those his 'imagined clients', the clients he imagines reading his bio and deciding not to contact him because he is queer. He is also aware that this may be a function of his own experience of homophobia and marginalisation.

As older or younger therapists, we may encounter reverse transference (Heinze, 1987), as illustrated by the opening vignette in that chapter. Therapist anxieties about their own ageing/internalised ageism can promote a fear of engulfment by the client and lead to withdrawal and rejection of the client. Overidentification with problems can block accurate empathy and realistic exploration of the possibilities of change (Atiq, 2006). Creative ageing challenges the emphasis on age segregation. Can we as dramatherapists exchange examples of multigenerational dramatherapy practice, of working with homogenous or heterogenous groups of elders? When do we feel self-disclosure has been helpful; where do we feel it has impeded the client? There can be a mixture of both within the work with one and the same client. Choosing not to self-disclose directly such as in the opening vignette about religion but showing familiarity with the values and metaphors of that religion, may enable a client to explore within their faith, whilst more direct disclosure about migrant status and the feelings about that status may have enabled an emotional connection about alienation.

Making the invisible visible

In closing, dramatherapists have used embodied, metaphoric, performance-based and direct approaches to work through intercultural concerns, including challenging stereotypes, and internalised oppression. We have offered several practical strategies and considerations to aid us in exploring and working through intercultural and intersectional encounters in dramatherapy training, supervision and practice and are grateful to our colleagues whose writing and interviews we have drawn upon here. A final recommendation in writing about practice is that we strive to make relevant aspects of our identity and those we work with more visible, with due consideration to privacy and confidentiality, alongside efforts to discuss the relevance of these experiences in our discussions of care. As authors, this might take the form of including a position statement at the beginning of an essay or research article. In research articles, this may take the form of including more demographic information when we discuss participants. This may enable us to internalise a greater sense of who we are and who we are not working within this field as well as the implications of our differences in how we teach and practice dramatherapy.

Notes

1 For more information on the Black Music Therapy Network, see https://www.blackmtnetwork.or.g
2 For two examples of performances examining issues related to culture and care and hosted by a programme in dramatherapy, see *Turbulence*: https://bit.ly/3xx3cL6 and *Free Play*: https://bit.ly/3rtjAIz.

Chapter 16

Conclusion

As we mentioned in the introduction, this book arose from a series of conversations about the influence of culture in dramatherapy between the authors, some joint workshop facilitation and five years of writing collaboration. The writing took place during a period of rising global conservatism, increasing concerns about climate change, overlapping refugee crises and the coronavirus pandemic. Alongside these challenges have been resurgent efforts to advance racial justice and advocate for a greater ecological understanding of planetary and human health.

Over that time, we sought out stories of how dramatherapists and participants have encountered moments where intersections of identity, power and difference have influenced their experience of dramatherapy. We cast the space between the dramatherapist and participant(s) as an *intercultural space* in which cultural differences, understood in relation to past and present expressions of power, inform care.

We asked questions such as: What is foregrounded, made visible in dramatherapy theory and practice, and what remains invisible? Some voices may be silent or silenced; how do we become aware of the less audible voices and perspectives in dramatherapy? How do we attend to our own cultural experience and that of those we work with in a way that does not repeat dynamics of silencing and marginalisation? An intercultural lens asks us to examine when, why, where, how and to whom culture, always understood in relation to power and inequity, matters in how we conceive of therapy, the role of the therapist, and the therapeutic process. What is the subjectivity of the therapist, what is the intersubjectivity between client and therapist, teacher and pupil, reader and author? Together we create an intersubjective intercultural space, some of it consciously and some of it unconsciously (Thomas, 2019; Tuckwell, 2002).

We are indebted to our community of colleagues, readers and students who contributed to this book, whether as respondents to the survey, providers of vignettes, interviewees and as critical readers for the various drafts of our chapters. These included 66 respondents who completed the survey, 12 interviewees and 14 vignette providers, as well as a minimum of two critical readers per chapter.

DOI: 10.4324/9780429431593-19

As authors, we base ourselves and our practise in specific countries. We have tried as much as possible to be transparent about our influences and acknowledge that the majority of examples are from the US and the UK. This is also noticeable in the vignette contributors to this book who predominantly stem from the US and the UK, with often more singular representations of other continents and countries. In some cases, dominant experiences within marginalised communities such as those of dramatherapists (rather than participants), cisgendered women, Christians and white, gay men, for example, have been foregrounded largely because these were the stories we were able to locate and gather.

Although other countries and perspectives are represented, we hope the book will be a stimulus for others to share, exchange and publish about their lived experience and insights into intercultural and intersectional practice. We prefer to think of equality as a verb, although linguistically a noun, it is always changing, not a permanent state; it is an ongoing process of engagement. The stories and perspectives shared in this book arise from a particular period of struggle and are a call for which we hope there is a response.

The introductory section aimed to set out our backgrounds, both personally and professionally to locate ourselves as authors in particular practices and bodies of knowledge, as well as our involvement with the development of the guidelines. The second section of the book is the main body of the work where we look at the different intersectional identity aspects of race, gender, sexual orientation, age, language, religion, class, ability and national identity. Within the individual chapters, we started with practice vignettes, provided some literature review to contextualise both the vignette and survey responses about that aspect and tried to highlight some of the strengths and struggles we as dramatherapists have in addressing these areas of power difference, oppression and discrimination. How we value difference, communicate across differences and recognise when we may be replicating colonial attitudes and experiences are ongoing themes in these chapters. In the concluding third section, we look at the implications of for dramatherapy training, supervision and practice. Further work should examine how these themes are reflected in research that we undertake in the field.

Chapter 2 introduced our cultural backgrounds as authors and the frameworks influencing our understandings about culture and difference. Intercultural and intersectional understanding, how a social justice framework upholds equality, whilst our theatre backgrounds reinforce the importance of performance, fictional roles, embodiment, encounter and transformation. Chapter 3 narrated the development of the intercultural good practice guidelines, which aim to support our work in this area. The guidelines are part of a professional code of ethics which constitute normative statements to provide guidance on values, issues and choices that a drama therapist may encounter in their professional work. This guidance concerns issues that people tend to have very strong feelings about and about which we may not always agree. This book aims to highlight some of these areas, but again, we acknowledge that this is limited in scope, as we are only offering a comparison of guidelines from the two dramatherapy associations with which we have been involved: the British Association of Dramatherapists and the North American Drama Therapy Association (BADth and NADTA). We hope that the World Alliance of Dramatherapy (WADth) can be a forum for further thinking and exchange about cultural differences so that normative and colonial do not equate yet again.

At the start of each chapter in Section 1, we tried to present practice vignettes for a discussion in relation to equality. A range of working was presented, and the survey elicited further perspectives of dramatherapists to contextualise the different aspects of identity that make up someone's cultural background. We found examples where therapists shared power, working directly or in metaphor to address stereotyped or oppressive perceptions aiming to facilitate empowerment of both clients and communities. In most intersectional aspects of identity, we looked at the impact of socialisation in both therapists and clients and how the therapeutic relationship could be both disempowering and about sharing power and working in partnership.

Good examples of this can be found in Chapter 4 on race. We concluded that chapter by stating that the racialisation of dramatherapists is not dissimilar from the rest of society. As the perspectives shared suggest, there are many ways in which the subject of race and experiences of racism may be silenced; it remains difficult to speak about racism openly despite its exceptionally significant impact on the experience of dramatherapy. According to several of the dramatherapists interviewed and surveyed, there is a desire to continue to work through this but that doing so requires acknowledging the shame and unconscious bias within. The practice reflections offered some examples of the way dramatherapists work with that bias and more spaces are needed to continue this kind of reflection. As one dramatherapist wrote in reference to white privilege, "[I]t is always there, inescapable and requires attending to…there is so much I cannot know because of it. The effort is one of constant humility". The perspectives offered also indicate a need to examine how our interactions and the materials we use (the stories, case examples and approaches), may risk reinforcing notions of colour blindness, Eurocentric norms and/or ask racialised students and clients to replace their experience once more with those of their white counterparts.

In Chapter 5 on gender, dramatherapist perspectives and practice raise questions about the intersecting influence of gender and other aspects of identity and culture in dramatherapy and how these elements might be usefully considered in practice. We focused on gender identity, expression and analysis in connection with the provision of dramatherapy and the experience of dramatherapists. We realised that the history of the profession of dramatherapy is deeply intertwined with the evolving gender dynamics. One must remain vigilant of the impact of sexism on the profession and how care work has often been equated with 'women's work' and consequently devalued. We can also see how the struggle of moving beyond the male/female binary of gender identification has been reflected in writing and perspectives offered in the field. Further exchange about this, the different cultural views on gender and how dramatherapists work with these, are areas of continuous development.

The next chapter, Chapter 6, on sexual orientation highlights an 'invisible' trait where there are choices to be made about therapist self-disclosure and therapist/client match. Representation is often very important and a specific requirement for someone when looking for a 'good fit'; finding a queer therapist may provide permission to start sessions. Inquiring about sexual orientation in the middle of a treatment may be about the therapist's subjectivity – a curiosity, a transference moment, a developmental milestone. Some dramatherapists' perspectives stress a common humanity, but this attempt at equalising may deny those experiences which significantly affect individuals and communities so that they feel pushed to the edge of belonging (Valadas, 2022). The chapter highlights the impact of criminalisation of queer identity at different times and in different places in connection with other aspects of culture and identity such as race, religion, gender, age, national identity, and ability. Trottier (2019) discusses performativity in self-disclosure and the issue of passing when talking about how he regulates his queer performance through non-verbal physical and verbal exchanges, highlighting how a therapist or client may choose to hide these markers in an effort to be seen differently or unintentionally pass as a member of the majority.

Chapter 7 on age is a more visible difference again, whilst subsequent chapters on religion, language, class and ability share issues around choice of passing and self-disclosure to varying degrees. Ageism highlights internalised oppression as a prejudice against the self. Reverse transference and a reluctance to see ageing as anything other than deterioration and loss are challenged by dramatherapists advocating creative ageing and empowerment of elders. Our critical readers challenged our authorial North American and Western European biases in this chapter in particular. The perspectives offered by dramatherapists illuminate how, in the words of one respondent, "as time goes by, the older one gets, and the more experiences one is exposed to, provides a unique way of becoming". This embrace of becoming over the lifespan is something we, as co-authors, value in our own professional community while acknowledging the ongoing presence of ageism. This 'becoming' is present in the dignity brought to elevating the voices of children, the playful approaches that dramatherapists bring to elder care, in the yearning towards beauty, in the search for beginnings, and in the dignity of endings.

Chapter 8 looks at spirituality and religion in dramatherapy and discusses how clients and therapists may experience conflicts between the religious and the therapeutic worldview and may need time to work out how they experience contradictions between the two. It is important for therapists not to prejudge beliefs harshly and be flexible. This can be specifically difficult in the countertransference if the therapist themselves has struggled in their child- and/or adulthood with a particular religious belief system. Jackson-Cherry and Erford (2008) state that when a therapist does not believe what the client believes it is important to understand why that belief is important to them. This may mean working together with a spiritual 'healer' from within the client's belief system; current practice advocates this increasingly, although published examples of dramatherapy practice where this has taken place are still few and far between. Self-disclosure by the therapist is advised by some (Cashwell & Young, 2011), but the more general therapeutic attitude is towards asking clients to be the expert on their own beliefs and for the therapist not to provide their own interpretation because of the risk of the therapist's values becoming dominant.

Chapter 9 showed the importance of being able to use words and using dramatherapy to help (re)find words. The survey findings related more to the interweaving of verbal and non-verbal communication in dramatherapy. The practice reflections highlighted issues of power in relation to language, the importance of having one's story witnessed and understood, the use of interpreters and being able to play with language. Giving clients the choice to work with interpreters is empowering. The therapist's role as interpreter and cultural broker can empower clients and carers to do the work that needs to be done. The therapist as an outsider can be a profoundly helpful role at times. Enabling clients to speak their own language and see a powerful other struggling to understand, find words, give meaning provides greater equality in the relationship and models that these struggles can be played with and survived. Variations in a shared language, such as accent and dialect can intersect with assumptions about class, just like the issue of touch can intersect with gender. Some of this is further explored in the next chapter relating to class.

In Chapter 10, we examined the impact of social class on the experience and provision of dramatherapy. It is important to recognise the strengths of certain class communities and that privilege in wealth may not equal emotional privilege. Some have observed that interdependence is emphasised in working-class communities and that this can facilitate a greater ability to read others' emotions (Graziano et al., 2007; Kraus et al., 2011), a very useful dramatherapeutic skill. Both authors discuss their own background and the impact of (lacking) resources, the practice examples in this chapter do the same. This chapter raises the issue of shame, which we return to in the practices chapter. Turner (2021) studies the shame related to othering and being othered. For those who do not benefit from the current system as a result of their social class, gender, racialisation, etc., encounters with hatred and shame are common. In the context of social class, shame can be related to unconscious complicity. De la Boetie (2015) suggests that the 'class other' is aware of being complicit. Shame acts as a "glue to bind the other to the subject" (Turner, 2021, p. 53), yet struggles to move beyond the co-dependent position of compliance. Shame can be a powerful weapon because it can lead the 'other' to see its authentic, cultural, spiritual, gendered or other identities as shameful, its name, its sexuality, its behavioural norms, even its language. To fit in, to be accepted, one may feel that they have to lose that which makes one other (Bradshaw, 1988).

Globalisation is a highly unequal process. Chapter 11 on migration and national identity shows how this impacts on migrant therapists and clients. Working with socio-political trauma in the therapy room evokes both clients' and therapists' histories. The importance of therapy as witnessing, therapist as witness and client as witness is crucial to ensure "good enough storying" of the locked away stories of unfinished grief across generations. The practice vignette in this chapter shows the parallel process reflected in a powerful poem by the therapist. Blackwell's reflections on othering recognises the sameness and difference in the stories of clients and therapists, which may help us to own the socio-political splits in our communities rather than projecting them on 'the other'. A discussion between dramatherapists internationally owning the impact of politics on our therapeutic relationship, whether they are explicit or implicit, as well as the impact of the settings in the countries we work in, has been evolving over time within national, cross-country and cross-continental professional networks and associations. To slightly paraphrase Beltsiou (2016) when she discusses seeking home in the foreign, otherness and migration, "An immigrant client reaches out to an immigrant therapist; exploring, mapping, creating a place for us. As we encounter each other we move back and forth between our origin and our chosen home, back and forth between past and present" (p. 89).

Chapter 12, the final chapter of Part II, focuses on dis/ability. Dramatherapy as a profession has a long history in this field; reviewing some of the dramatherapy literature over the last 40 years, changes are noticeable. Recent literature from authors such as Critchley and Hodermarska show how a greater awareness of the social model of dis/ability can improve access for disabled people through meaningful partnership and collaboration. Advocacy is evolving from "acting for or on behalf of" to "nothing about us without us". Our research data showed that notions of impairment and the medical model of disability remain part of dramatherapy. We have yet to truly engage with dual experience, the reality of mental illness and other forms of dis/ability as part of dramatherapists' lives. Critchley's work may be a potential start for further developments in this area; can dramatherapists be experts by experience? How does this relate to training and practice? Cultural competencies for working with disabled people are discussed in the wider psychological therapies (Artman & Daniels, 2010; Cornish et al., 2008; Olkin, 2002, 2008) and may be a useful area for further development in dramatherapy.

As with all themes taken up in this book, there remains much more to explore, much more research remains necessary. Sharing power often means having sufficient humility to be aware of our biases and the need for continuous development in our profession. The many contributions of fellow dramatherapists throughout this book reinforced for us as authors the strengths and creative ways of working people have identified in addressing issues around intercultural practice and intersectionality.

In Chapter 13 on training and supervision in Part III, we aim to question what it means to 'decolonise' dramatherapy whilst trying to acknowledge the pitfalls. Nigerian writer, Chimanada Ngozi Adichie, reminds us of the danger of a single story (2009). This warning is at the heart of the movement towards decolonising pedagogy in its acknowledgement of the power dynamics that shape what we know and how we come to know it as well as in its encouragement of pluralism. In this chapter, we laid out ideas relating to decolonising pedagogy and considered implications for dramatherapy. We also offered a framework for teaching cultural response/ability in the context of training within and across borders. The supervision chapter gives an extended case study of an intercultural supervisory relationship and the impact of intersectional differences. Dramatherapists' perspectives on supervision to think about client-therapist match, therapist self-disclosure and issues around privilege are addressed. The concept of 'broaching' (Jones et al., 2019) in supervision as a very useful concept for practice is introduced.

Recommendations for practice, as discussed in Chapter 15, followed up from Part II and the training and supervision chapters; issues around therapist self-disclosure, broaching, particular dramatherapy structures, good enough storying and implications for the transference in the therapeutic relationship were raised. We will be interested to discover further issues with other dramatherapists and participants of dramatherapy. As mentioned, we aim to treat equality as a verb, always changing and developing; our particular perspectives need further development through exchange and sharing. The way in which identity aspects intersect is one area for further development, working beyond the binary another, inclusive embodiment in the context of ability and ageing another. How do we give voice to invisible stories, especially those that are placed outside our borders?

To enable a client to become aware of the othering which they carry with them, Totton summarises the importance of acknowledging such areas by identifying three frameworks:

> Firstly that therapy…(is)…tied firmly to the social and political context in which the therapy takes place; secondly that therapists and counsellors exercise political agency in their work, whether or not they are aware of it; and thirdly that, conscious or unconscious support from the therapist for mainstream cultural positions – at the expense of the positions of the client – can be both damaging and wounding.
>
> (2008, p. 145)

Haugh and Paul described the changing attitude within counselling training and practice:

> Traditionally issues of diversity, power and anti-oppressive practice were not considered central to practice. At the very best, they were thought of as something that needed to be considered in addition to theory and practice training rather than being seen as pivotal to the counselling relationship. In the last five to ten years we are happy to note that this

omission is being addressed. At least to some extent. Ironically, in our experience this has led some to assert, for example, that they do not physically see a person's colour/sex/physical abilities/age. In this example we have used physically obvious aspects of a person. This dynamic can also happen for those aspects of a person's lived experience that may not be so immediately obvious, such as ethnicity, sexuality or class. We believe that approaches to practice which ignore such dimensions are limited and counterproductive, adding to a person's (the client's) distress'.

(2008, p. 5)

They highlight the difficulties around invisibility. In this book, we have tried to provide a shift in perspective in relation to dramatherapy theory and practice, including supervision and training.

An area that we have not explicitly looked at is that of research. The intercultural research guidelines outlined in Chapter 3 are very similar between the NADTA and BADth. They elaborate on cultural issues around consent and the need to include excluded voices in research, as well as the need to be familiar with relevant research pertaining to the impact of discrimination on health and culturally relevant practices. We tried to take these guidelines into account for our methodology. We chose the survey for its accessibility, open phenomenological interviewing (based on questions from the survey) and vignette research where dramatherapists provided practice vignettes with their reflections about that practice.[1] We included voices who did not have English as a first language, but the majority of voices were in English. We included dramatherapists of colour, of a range of ages and sexual orientations, dramatherapists who are migrants, dramatherapists from different religious orientations, different genders, abilities, classes and from different continents. There remain many, many unheard perspectives, especially from those who have experienced dramatherapy.

As two authors whose intersectional identities sometimes overlapped, but very often did not, who came from different perspectives, we needed to engage in continuous dialogue, share new writings and viewpoints, check with others who as critical readers pointed out missing issues and often suggested important references, vignette contributors who may or may not have agreed with the way we represented their work. This book aims to be an ongoing dialogue, we as authors certainly feel we have gained and learned a significant amount in the writing and consulting. We hope that the book provides enough stimulation for others to feel they can take up the baton, either go on where we left off, or express disagreement, different voices and opinions.

Note

1 To view the survey and interview questions, see link: https://bit.ly/3lfr7HA.

References

Abrams, D., Lamont, R. A., & Swift, H. J. (2015). A review and meta-analysis of age-based stereotype threat: Negative stereotypes, not facts, do the damage. *Psychology and Aging, 30*(1), 180–193. https://doi.org/10.1037/a0038586

Abrams, Z. (2018). When therapists face discrimination. *Monitor on Psychology, 49*(4). http://www.apa.org/monitor/2018/04/therapists-discrimination

Adams, S. E. (2020). Being with black: Windrush suitcase performance and drama-therapy to meet with trauma, and dialogues about racism and the transatlantic slave trade. *Dramatherapy, 41*(1), 5–24. https://doi.org/10.1177/0263067220964432

Adichie, C. (2009, July). *The danger of a single story* [Video]. TED Conferences. https://www.ted.com/talks/chimamanda_ngozi_adichie_the_danger_of_a_single_story?language=en

Ahmed, S. (2013). Making feminist points. *Feministkilljoys.* http://feministkilljoys.com/2013/09/11/making-feminist-points/

Alegría, M., NeMoyer, A., Falgàs Bagué, I., Wang, Y., & Alvarez, K. (2018). Social determinants of mental health: Where we are and where we need to go. *Current Psychiatry Reports, 20*(11), 95. https://doi.org/10.1007/s11920-018-0969-9

Allegranti, B. (2013). The politics of becoming bodies: Sex, gender and intersubjectivity in motion. *The Arts in Psychotherapy, 40*(4), 394–403. https://doi.org/10.1016/j.aip.2013.05.017

Allen, C. T., Swan, S. C., & Raghavan, C. (2009). Gender symmetry, sexism, and intimate partner violence. *Journal of Interpersonal Violence, 24*(11), 1816–1834. https://doi.org/10.1177/0886260508325496

American Art Therapy Association. (2011). *Art therapy multicultural/diversity competencies.* https://arttherapy.org/wp-content/uploads/2017/06/Multicultural-Competencies.pdf

American Music Therapy Association. (2013). *American music therapy association professional competencies.* https://www.musictherapy.org/about/competencies/.

American Psychological Association. (1998). Resolution on appropriate therapeutic responses to sexual orientation. *American Psychologist, 43*, 934–935.

American Psychological Association. (2003). Guidelines on multicultural education, training, research, practice, and organizational change for psychologists. *American Psychologist, 58*(5), 377–402. https://doi.org/10.1037/0003-066X.58.5.377

American Psychological Association. (2009). *Report of the American Psychological Association task force on appropriate therapeutic responses to sexual orientation.* http://www.apa.org/pi/lgbt/resources/therapeutic-response.pdf

American Psychological Association. (2012). Guidelines for psychological practice with lesbian, gay, and bisexual clients. *American Psychologist*, *67*(1), 10–42. https://doi.org/10.1037/a0024659

American Psychological Association. (2015). Professional practice guidelines: Guidance for developers and users. *American Psychologist*, *70*(9), 823–831, https://doi.org/10.1037/a0039644.

American Psychological Association (APA). (2017). *Work, stress, and mealth & socioeconomic status*. https://www.apa.org/pi/ses/resources/publications/work-stress-health

American Psychological Association. (2020). *Publication manual of the American Psychological Association* (7th ed.). https://doi.org/10.1037/0000165-000

American Psychological Association. (2021). *APA resolution on gender identity change efforts*. https://www.apa.org/about/policy/resolution-gender-identity-change-efforts.pdf

Americans with Disabilities Act. (2017). *Guidelines for writing about people with disabilities*. National Network Information, Guidance and Training on the Americans with Disabilities Act. https://adata.org/factsheet/ADANN-writing

Anderson, C. (2020, August 26). A review of Trump immigration policy. *Forbes*. https://www.forbes.com/sites/stuartanderson/2020/08/26/fact-check-and-review-of-trump-immigration-policy/?sh=2e87538a56c0

Andersen-Warren, M., & Grainger, R. (2008). *Practical approaches to dramatherapy: The shield of Perseus* (1st ed.). Jessica Kingsley Publishers.

Applewhite, A. (2017, August 23). *Let's end ageism* [Video]. *YouTube*. https://www.youtube.com/watch?v=WfjzkO6_DEI; http://feministkilljoys.com/2013/09/11/making-feminist-points/

Arber, S., Davidson, K., & Ginn, J., Eds. (2005). *Gender and ageing. Changing roles and relationships*. Open University Press.

Ariarajah, S. W. (2005). Intercultural hermeneutics – a promise for the future? *Exchange*, *34*(2), 89–101. https://doi.org/10.1163/1572543054068523

Aronson, J., Burgess, D., Phelan, S. M., & Juarez, L. (2013). Unhealthy interactions: The role of stereotype threat in health disparities. *American Journal of Public Health*, *103*(1), 50–56. https://doi.org/10.2105/AJPH.2012.300828.

Arredondo, P., Toporek, M. S., Brown, S., Jones, J., Locke, D. C., Sanchez, J. and Stadler, H. (1996). *Operationalization of the multicultural counseling competencies*. Association for Multicultural Counseling & Development.

Artman, L., & Daniels, J. (2010). Disability and psychotherapy practice: Cultural competence and practical tips. *Professional Psychology: Research And Practice*, *41*(5), 442–448. https://doi.org/10.1037/a0020864

Association for Dance Movement Psychotherapy. (2013). *Code of professional practice*. https://admp.org.uk/dance-movement-psychotherapy/code-of-professional-practice/

Association for Multicultural Counseling & Development. (1996). *AMCD multicultural counselling competencies*. https://www.counseling.org/resources/competencies/multcultural_competencies.pdf

Atiq, R. (2006). Common themes and issues in geriatric psychotherapy. *Psychiatry (Edgmont, Pa.: Township)*, *3*(6), 53–56.

Aujla, A. (2000). Others in their own land: Second generation South Asian Canadian women, racism, and the persistence of colonial discourse. *Canadian Woman Studies*, *20*(2). https://cws.journals.yorku.ca/index.php/cws/article/view/7608

Awais, J. Y., & Blausey, D. (2021). *Foundations of art therapy supervision: Creating common ground for supervisees and supervisors* (1st ed.). Routledge.

Ayalon, L., Chasteen, A., Diehl, M., Levy, B. R., Neupert, S. D., Rothermund, K., Tesch-Römer, C., & Wahl, H. W. (2021). Aging in times of the COVID-19 pandemic: Avoiding ageism and fostering intergenerational solidarity. *The Journals of Gerontology. Series B, Psychological Sciences and Social Sciences, 76*(2), e49–e52. https://doi.org/10.1093/geronb/gbaa051

Ayalon, L., & Tesch-Römer, C. (Eds.). (2018). *Contemporary perspectives on ageism. International perspectives on aging* (Vol. 19). Springer Open.

Bachmann, C., & Gooch, B. (2018). *LGBT in Britain: Health report.* Stonewall and YouGov. https://www.stonewall.org.uk/system/files/lgbt_in_britain_health.pdf

Bailey, S. (2009). Performance in drama therapy. In D. R. Johnson & R. Emunah (Eds.), *Current approaches in drama therapy* (pp. 374–389). Charles C. Thomas Publishers.

Bailey, S. (2010). *Barrier-free theatre: Including everyone in theatre arts-in schools, recreation, and arts programs-regardless of (dis)ability.* Idyll Arbor.

Bailey, S., Burr, B., Dickinson, P., Marie, T., Woolsey, P., & Yadon, M. (2018, October 25–28). *Making an inclusive community through inclusive, Barrier-Free Theatre* [Paper presentation]. North American Drama Therapy Association Conference, Kansas City, MO, United States.

Baldor, C. (2021, March 31). Reversing Trump, Pentagon releases new transgender policies. *The Associated Press.* https://www.militarytimes.com/news/pentagon-congress/2021/03/31/reversing-trump-pentagon-to-release-new-policy-for-transgender-people-to-serve-in-the-military/

Balboni, T. A., VanderWeele, T. J., Doan-Soares, S. D., Long, K.N.G., Ferrell, B. R., Fitchett, G., Koenig, H. G., Bain, P. A., Puchalski, C., Steinhauser, K. E., Sulmasy, D. P., & Koh, H. K. (2022). Spirituality in serious illness and health. *JAMA, 328*(2), 184–197. https://doi.org/10.1001/jama.2022.11086

Bambling, M., King, R., Raue, P., Schweitzer, R., & Lambert, W. (2006). Clinical supervision: Its influence on client-rated working alliance and client symptom reduction in the brief treatment of major depression. *Psychotherapy Research, 16*(3), 317–331. https://doi.org/10.1080/10503300500268524

Bannister, A. (1997). *The healing drama: Psychodrama and dramatherapy with abused children.* Free Association Books.

Barber, J. P., & Muenz, L. R. (1996). The role of avoidance and obsessiveness in matching patients to cognitive and interpersonal psychotherapy: Empirical findings from the treatment for depression collaborative research program. *Journal of Consulting and Clinical Psychology, 64*(5), 951–958. https://doi.org/10.1037/0022-006X.64.5.951

Barnett, J., & Johnson, B. (2011). Integrating spirituality and religion into psychotherapy: Persistent dilemmas, ethical issues and a proposed decision-making process. *Ethics & Behavior, 21*(2), 147–164. https://doi.org/10.1080/10508422.2011.551471

Bartoli, E., Michael, A., Bentley-Edwards, K., Stevenson, H. C., Shor, R. E., & McClain, S. E. (2016). Training for colour-blindness: White racial socialisation. *Whiteness and Education, 1*(2), 125–136. https://doi.org/10.1080/23793406.2016.1260634

Barucha, R. (1993). *Theatre and the world: Performance and the politics of culture* (1st ed.). Routledge. https://doi.org/10.4324/9780203168172

Basting, A. (2009). *Forget memory: Creating better lives for people with dementia.* JHU Press.

Bauermeister, J. A., Connochie, D., Jadwin-Cakmak, L., & Meanley, S. (2017). Gender policing during childhood and the psychological well-being of young adult sexual minority men in the United States. *American Journal of Men's Health, 11*(3), 693–701. https://doi.org/10.1177/1557988316680938

Baum, C. (2018, September 14). The ugly truth about ageism: It's a prejudice targeting our future selves. *The Guardian*. https://www.theguardian.com/lifeandstyle/2018/sep/14/the-ugly-truth-about-ageism-its-a-prej

Bayley, B. (1999). Feeling queer in dramatherapy: Transformation, Alice & the caterpillar. *Dramatherapy, 21*(1), 3–9. https://doi.org/10.1080/02630672.1999.9689502

Bayley, B. (2000). *The queer carnival gender transgressive images in contemporary queer performance and their relationship to carnival and the grotesque* [Doctoral dissertation, University of Exeter]. Bruce Howard Bayley website. https://www.brucebayley.co.uk/The_Queer_Carnival_-_Bruce_Bayley_2000.pdf

Bayley, B. (2003). Splitting and mirroring: Working with gender transgressive issues in dramatherapy. [Presentation]. Anthroposophical Society of Great Britain, Park Road, London, UK. http://www.brucebayley.co.uk/Splitting_and_Mirroring.pdf

Bayley, B. (2022.). *Tirubhavan three-fold drama therapy: Freedom-individuality-love.* http://www.brucebayley.co.uk/trib-bhb.htm

Beauregard, M., & Long, K. (2019). Attuning to the needs of LGBTQ youth: Trauma, attachment, and healing relationships. In B. MacWilliam, B. T. Harris, D. G. Trottier, & K. Long (Eds.), *Creative arts therapies and the LGBTQ community: Theory and practice* (pp. 119–138). Jessica Kingsley Publishers.

Beauregard, M., & Moore, D. (2011). Creative approaches to working with gender variant and sexual minority boys. In C. Haen (Ed.), *Engaging boys in treatment: Creative approaches to the therapy process* (pp. 293–316). Routledge.

Beauregard, M., Stone, R., Trytan, N., & Sajnani, N. (2016). Drama therapists' attitudes and actions regarding LGBTQI and gender nonconforming communities. *Drama Therapy Review, 2*(1), 41–63. https://doi.org/10.1386/dtr.2.1.41_1

Beauregard, M., Stone, R., Trytan, N., & Sajnani, N. (2017). Systemic barriers in mental health care for LGBTQI and gender nonconforming drama therapists and clients. *Drama Therapy Review, 3*(2), 285–312. https://doi.org/10.1386/dtr.3.2.285_

Beck, D. F. (1988). Counselor characteristics: How they affect outcomes. *Family Service of America*.

Beinart, H. (2014). Building and sustaining the supervisory relationship. In C. E. Watkins Jr. & D. L. Milne (Eds.), *The Wiley international handbook of clinical supervision* (pp. 257–281). Wiley. https://doi.org/10.1002/9781118846360.ch11

Beltsiou, J. (Ed.). (2016). *Immigration in psychoanalysis: Locating ourselves*. Routledge.

Benjamin, J. (2018). *Beyond doer and done to: Recognition theory, intersubjectivity and the third*. Routledge.

Benjamin, J. N. (2020, February 17). Review: Death of England at national theatre. *Exeunt Magazine*. http://exeuntmagazine.com/reviews/review-death-england-national-theatre/

Ben-Moshe, L., & Magaña, S. (2014). An introduction to race, gender, and disability: Intersectionality, disability studies, and families of color. *Women, Gender, and Families of Color, 2*(2), 105–114. https://doi.org/10.5406/womgenfamcol.2.2.0105

Bergman, J. (2001). Using dramatherapy to uncover genuineness and deception in civilly committedsexual offenders. In A. Schlank (Ed.), *The sexual predator: Legal issues, clinical issues, special populations* (1st ed., Vol. 2, pp. 8-1–8-15). The Civic Research Institute.

Bernard, J. M., & Goodyear, R. K. (2014). *Fundamentals of clinical supervision* (5th ed.). Pearson Education.

Bernard, J. M., & Luke, M. (2015). A content analysis of 10 years of clinical supervision articles in counseling. *Counselor Education and Supervision, 54*(4), 242–257. https://doi.org/10.1002/ceas.12024

Bernard, M., & Rickett, M. (2017). The cultural value of older people's experiences of theater-making: A review. *The Gerontologist*, *57*(2), e1–e26.

Bernstein, R. J. (1991). Incommensurability and otherness revisited. In E. Deutsch (Ed.), *Culture and modernity: East-west philosophic perspectives* (pp. 85–103). University of Hawaii Press.

Berriz, B. R., Wager, A. C., & Poey, V. M. (2019). *Art as a way of talking for emergent bilingual youth: A foundation for literacy in preK–12 schools* (1st ed.). Routledge.

Berry, J. W. (2005). Acculturation: Living successfully in two cultures. *International Journal of Intercultural Relations*, *29*(6), 697–712. https://doi.org/10.1016/j.ijintrel.2005.07.013

Bhabha, H. K. (1994). *The location of culture*. Routledge.

Bhopal, K (2018). *White privilege: The myth of a post-racial society*. Policy Press.

Bilodeau, S., Carr, M., Bleuer, J., Dokter, D., Sajnani, N., & Tomczyk, P. (2016). Guidelines on cultural response/ability in training, research, practice, supervision, advocacy and organizational change. *Drama Therapy Review*, *2*(1), 139–146.

Bilodeau, S., Carr, M., Dokter, D., Sajnani, N., & Bleuer, J. (2017). *Intercultural good practice guidelines in dramatherapy*. British Association of Dramatherapists. http://www.badth.org.uk.

Bird, D. (2017). Playback theatre, autoethnography and generosity. *Dramatherapy*, *38*(1), 32–42. https://doi.org/10.1080/02630672.2017.1291845

Bissoondath, N. (1994). *Selling illusions: The cult of multiculturalism in Canada*. Penguin.

Bitar, G. W., Kimball, T., Bermúdez, J. M., & Drew, C. (2014). Therapist self-disclosure and culturally competent care with Mexican–American court mandated clients: A phenomenological study. *Contemporary Family Therapy: An International Journal*, *36*(3), 417–425. https://doi.org/10.1007/s10591-014-9308-4

Blackman, N. (2008). Making space for thought: Supervision in a learning disability context. In P. Jones & D. Dokter (Eds.), *Supervision of dramatherapy* (pp. 185–198). Routledge.

Blackwell, D. (2005). *Counselling and psychotherapy with refugees*. Jessica Kingsley Publishers.

Blau, Francine D., & Kahn, L. M. (2017). The gender wage gap: Extent, trends, and explanations. *Journal of Economic Literature*, *55*(3): 789–865. https://doi.org/10.1257/jel.20160995

Bleiweis, R. (2020, March 24). *Quick facts about the gender wage gap*. The Center for American Progress. https://www.americanprogress.org/article/quick-facts-gender-wage-gap/

Bloom, M. (2014). Creativity in older adults. In T. P. Gullotta & M. Bloom (Eds.), *Encyclopedia of primary prevention and health promotion* (2nd ed., pp. 1933–1941). Springer.

Blundell, R., Joyce, R., Costa Dias, M., & Xu, X. (2020). *Covid 19: The impacts of the pandemic on inequality*. Institute for Fiscal Studies https://ifs.org.uk/publications/14879

Boal, A. (1979). *Theatre of the oppressed*. Pluto Press. (Original work published in 1974).

Boal. A. (1992). *Games for actors and non-actors*. Routledge.

Boal, A. (1995). *Rainbow of desire. The Boal method of theatre and therapy*. Routledge.

Boal, A. (1998). *Legislative theatre: Using performance to make politics* (A. Jackson, Trans). Routledge.

Boal, A. (2002). *Games for actors and non-actors*. Psychology Press.

Bodner, E., Palgi, Y., & Wyman, M. F. (2018). Ageism in mental health assessment and treatment of older adults. In L. Ayalon & C. Tesch-Römer (Eds.), *Contemporary perspectives on ageism: International perspectives on aging* (Vol. 19, pp. 241–263). Springer. https://doi.org/10.1007/978-3-319-73820-8_15

Boduroglu, A., Yoon, C., Luo, T., & Park, D. C. (2006). Age-related stereotypes: A comparison of American and Chinese cultures. *Gerontology, 52*(5), 324–333.

Boffey, D. (2018, February 18). Orbán claims Hungary is last bastion against 'Islamisation' of Europe. *The Guardian.* https://www.theguardian.com/world/2018/feb/18/orban-claims-hungary-is-last-bastion-against-islamisation-of-europe

Bohart, A. C., & Wade, A. G. (2013). The client in psychotherapy. In M. J. Lambert (Ed.), *Bergin and Garfield's handbook of psychotherapy and behavior change* (6th ed., pp. 219–257). John Wiley & Sons, Inc.

Booker, M. (2011). *Developmental drama: Dramatherapy approaches for people with profound or severe multiple disabilities, including sensory impairment.* Jessica Kingsley Publishers.

Bosworth, M. L., Ayoubkhani, D., Nafilyan, V., Foubert, J., Glickman, M., Davey, C., & Kuper, H. (2021). Deaths involving COVID-19 by self-reported disability status during the first two waves of the COVID-19 pandemic in England: A retrospective, population-based cohort study. *The Lancet Public Health, 6*(11), e817–e825. https://doi.org/10.1016/S2468-2667(21)00206-1

Bottomley, G. (1997). Identification: Ethnicity, gender and culture. *Journal of Intercultural Studies, 18*(1), 41–50. https://doi.org/10.1080/07256868.1997.9963440

Bowling, A., & Dieppe, P. (2005). What is successful ageing and who should define it? *British Medical Journal, 331*(7531), 1548–1551. https://doi.org/10.1136/bmj.331.7531.1548

Bradshaw, J. (1988). *Healing the shame that binds you.* Health Communications Inc.

Braithwaite, T. (1997). The Trinidad carnival. A cross-cultural drama of seduction and communal therapy. In S. Jennings (Ed.), *Dramatherapy theory and practice 3* (p. 330). Routledge.

Brecht, B. (1936). Alienation effects in Chinese acting. [Reprinted from *Brecht on theatre: The development of an aesthetic,* 91–99 by J. Willet, Ed., 1964/1978, Methuen].

Brennan, R., Bush, M., Trickey, D., Levene, C., & Watson, J. (2019). *Adversity and trauma-informed practice.* YoungMinds. https://youngminds.org.uk/media/3091/adversity-and-trauma-informed-practice-guide-for-professionals.pdf.

Brians, P. (2008, September 17). *The irrelevance of "postcolonialism" to South Asian literature.* Washington State University. https://brians.wsu.edu/2016/10/19/paul-brians-the-irrelevance-of-postcolonialism-to-south-asian-literature

British Association for Counselling and Psychotherapy. (2013). *Ethical framework for good practice in counselling and psychotherapy (ethics & guidance).* https://www.bacp.co.uk/events-and-resources/ethics-and-standards/ethical-framework-for-the-counselling-professions/

British Association of Art Therapists. (2014). *Code of ethics and principles of professional practice for art therapists.* https://www.baat.org/Assets/Docs/General/BAAT%20CODE%20OF%20ETHICS%202014.pdf

British Association of Dramatherapists. (2016). *Intercultural good practice guidelines.* http://badth.org.uk/sites/default/files/content/pdf/badth_intercultural_good_practice_for_conference_

Brook, O., O'Brien, D., & Taylor, M. (2018). *Panic! Social class, taste and inequalities in the creative industries*. Create London. https://createlondon.org/wp-content/uploads/2018/04/Panic-Social-Class-Taste-and-Inequalities-in-the-Creative-Industries1.pdf

Brouillent, R. (2016). Why therapists should talk politics. *New York Times*. http://opinionator.blogs.nytimes.com/2016/03/15/why-therapists-should-talk-politics/?_r

Brown, L. (2011, August 4). *The significance of semantics: Person-first language: Why it matters*. Autistic Hoya. https://www.autistichoya.com/2011/08/significance-of-semantics-person-first.html

Brown, N., & Leigh, J. (2018). Ableism in academia: Where are the disabled and ill academics?. *Disability & Society*, *33*(6), 985–989. https://doi.org/10.1080/09687599.2018.1455627

Brownell, P. (2014). Neglect, abuse and violence against older women: Definitions and research frameworks. *South Eastern European Journal of Public Health*, *1*. https://doi.org/10.4119/UNIBI/SEEJPH-2014-28

Burns, E. (1972). *Theatricality: A study of convention in the theatre and in social life*. Longman.

Burns, J. K. (2015). Poverty, inequality and a political economy of mental health. *Epidemiology and Psychiatric Sciences*, *24*(2), 107–113. https://doi.org/10.1017/S2045796015000086

Busfield, J., & Campling, J. (1996). *Men, women, and madness: Understanding gender and mental disorder*. Palgrave.

Butler, R. (1975). The elderly: An overview. *American Journal of Psychiatry*, *132*(9), 893–900. https://doi.org/10.1176/ajp.132.9.893

Butler, J. (1990). *Gender trouble: Feminism and the subversion of identity*. Routledge.

Butler-Sloss, E. (2015). *Report of the commission on religion and belief in British public life: Living with difference, community, diversity and the common good*. Cambridge, the Woolf Institute. https://www.woolf.cam.ac.uk/research/publications/reports/report-of-the-commission-on-religion-and-belief-in-british-public-life

Bytheway, B. (1995). *Ageism*. Open University Press.

Cabral, R. R., & Smith, T. B. (2011). Racial/ethnic matching of clients and therapists in mental health services: A meta-analytic review of preferences, perceptions, and outcomes. *Journal of Counseling Psychology*, *58*(4), 537–554. https://doi.org/10.1037/a0025266

Cajete, G. (2000). *Native science: Natural laws of interdependence*. Clear Light Publishers.

California Institute of Integral Studies. (2022). *Theatre for change*. https://www.ciis.edu/academics/graduate-programs/drama-therapy/theatre-for-change

Calisch, A. C. (1996). Multiculturalism and art therapy: Looking back and seeing beyond *Canadian Art Therapy Journal*, *10*(2), 63–68.

Cameron, D., & Johnson, R. (2015). How gay rights have spread around the world over the last 224 years. *Washington Post*. https://www.washingtonpost.com/graphics/world/gay-rights-history/.

Campbell, J., Liebmann, M., Brooks, F., Jones, J., & Ward, C. (Eds.). (1999). *Art therapy, race and culture*. Jessica Kingsley Publishers.

Canadian Association for Music Therapy. (1999). *Code of ethics*.

Cant, B., & Hemmings, S. (1988). *Radical records: Thirty years of lesbian and gay history, 1957–1987*. Routledge.

Carr, M. (2012). Romeo and Juliet and dramatic distancing: Chaos and anger contained for innercity adolescents in multicultural schools. In L. Leigh, I. Gersch, A. Dix, & D. Haythorne (Eds.), *Dramatherapy with children, young people and schools* (pp. 91–97). Routledge.

Carr, M. (2016). Dramatherapy across languages. In M. Dokter & M. Hills de Zarate (Eds.), *Intercultural art therapies research* (1st ed., pp. 15–33). Routledge.

Carr, M., & Andersen-Warren, M. (2012). Clinical comment – a research interview: Dramatherapy and cross-cultural awareness. *Journal of the British Association of Dramatherapists*, *34*(2), 92–100.

Carr, M., Dokter, D., Ioannou, A., Southern, H., & Valladas, R. C. (2015). *Diversity survey British Association of Dramatherapists*. British Association of Drama Therapy. https://www.badth.org.uk

Cashwell, C., & Young, J. (2011). *Integrating spirituality and religion into counseling: A guide to competent practice* (2nd ed., pp. 1–18). American Counseling Association. https://www.counseling.org/Publications/FrontMatter/72906-FM.PDF.

Cassidy, S., Turnbull, S., & Gumley, A. (2014). Exploring core processes facilitating therapeutic change in dramatherapy: A grounded theory analysis of published case studies. *The Arts in Psychotherapy*, *41*(4), 353–365. https://doi.org/10.1016/j.aip.2014.07.003

Casson, J. (2004). *Drama, psychotherapy and psychosis: Dramatherapy and psychodrama with people who hear voices* (1st ed.). Routledge.

Casson, J. (2005). The ageing fool: The importance of humour and stimulus for older people, *Dramatherapy*, *27*(4), 14–17.

Casson, J. (2018). On being a gay therapist: A reflective memoir. *Dramatherapy*, *39*(3), 181–182. https://doi.org/10.1080/02630672.2018.1508604

Castora-Binkley, M., Noelker, L., Prohaska, T., & Satariano, W. (2010). Impact of arts participation on health outcomes for older adults. *Journal of Aging, Humanities, and the Arts*, *4*(4), 352–367.

Centre for Better Ageing. (2020, September 29). *Double jeopardy? The cumulative inequalities of age and ethnicity*. https://ageing-better.org.uk/events/double-jeopardy

Centre for Disease and Control and Prevention. (2020, September 16). *Disability and health overview*. https://www.cdc.gov/ncbddd/disabilityandhealth/disability.html

Centre for Homelessness Impact. (2021). *2021 impact forum*. https://impactfestival.homelessnessimpact.org/

Center for Substance Abuse Treatment. (2009). *What are peer recovery support services?* (HHS Publication No. SMA 09-4454). Substance Abuse and Mental Health Services Administration, U.S. Department of Health and Human Services. https://store.samhsa.gov/sites/default/files/d7/priv/sma09-4454.pdf

Centre for Transpersonal Psychology. (2014). *Welcome to the centre for transpersonal psychology*. http://www.transpersonalcentre.co.uk/

Ceobanu, A. M., & Escandell, X. (2010). Comparative analyses of public attitudes toward immigrants and immigration using multinational survey data: A review of theories and research. *Annual Review of Sociology*, *36*, 309–328. https://doi.org/10.1146/annurev.soc.012809.102651

Césaire, A. (2000). *Discourse sur le colonialism* (J. Pinkham Trans.). Monthly Review Press.

Chan, C. D., & Erby, A. N. (2018). A critical analysis and applied intersectionality framework with intercultural queer couples. *Journal of Homosexuality*, *65*(9), 1249–1274. https://doi.org/10.1080/00918369.2017.1411691

Chan, K. J., Young, M. Y., & Sharif, N. (2016). Well-being after trauma: A review of posttraumatic growth among refugees. *Canadian Psychology/Psychologie canadienne, 57*(4), 291–299. https://doi.org/10.1037/cap0000065

Chandrasegaram, V. (2009). Cultural diversity in dramatherapy in the Malaysian context. *Dramatherapy, 31*(2), 9–13. https://doi.org/10.1080/02630672.2009.9689771

Chang, M. (2009). Cultural consciousness and the global context of dance/movement therapy. In S. Chaiklin & H. Wengrower (Eds.), *The art and science of dance/movement therapy: Life is dance* (pp. 299–316). Routledge.

Chasen, L. R. (2011). *Social skills, emotional growth and dramatherapy: Inspiring connection on the autism spectrum.* Jessica Kingsley Publishers.

Chaudhuri, P. (1991). Nonparametric estimates of regression quantiles and their local bahadur representation. *The Annals of Statistics, 19*(2), 760–777. https://doi.org/10.1214/aos/1176348119

Chesner, A. (1995). *Dramatherapy for people with learning disabilities; A world of difference.* Jessica Kingsley Publishers.

Chesner, A., & Zografou, L. (Eds.). (2014). *Creative supervision across modalities: Theory and applications for therapists, counsellors and other helping professionals.* Jessica Kingsley Publishers.

Chin, D. (1991). From popular to pop. The arts in/of commerce: Mass media and the new imagery. *Performing Arts Journal, 13*(1), 5–20. https://doi.org/10.2307/3245500

Choi, S. K., & Meyer, I. H. (2016). *LGBT aging: A review of research findings, needs, and policy implications.* The Williams Institute.

Chun, K. M. E., Organista, P. B. E., & Marin, G. E. (2003). *Acculturation: Advances in theory, measurement, and applied research.* American Psychological Association.

Clair, M., & Denis, J. S. (2015). Sociology of racism. *The International Encyclopedia of the Social and Behavioral Sciences, 19*, 857–863. http://www.sciencedirect.com/science/article/pii/B9780080970868321225

Clark, S. (1989). *Moo.* Playwrights Canada Press.

Clarke, I. (Ed.). (2010). *Psychosis and spirituality: Consolidating the new paradigm* (2nd ed.). Wiley Blackwell. https://doi.org/10.1002/9780470970300

Clausen, J. A. (1968). *Socialization and society.* Little, Brown and Company.

Coates, T. (2015). *Between the world and me.* Spiegel & Grau.

Cohen, A. B., & Varnum, M. E. W. (2016). Beyond east vs. west: Social class, region, and religion as forms of culture. *Current Opinion in Psychology, 8*, 5–9. https://doi.org/10.1016/j.copsyc.2015.09.006

Cohn, K. (1997). Movement therapy as a bridge to biculturalization of Ethiopian immigrants in Israel. *The Arts In Psychotherapy, 24*(3), 281–289. https://doi.org/10.1016/S0197-4556(97)00036-1

Colkett, D. (2007). Child survivors of a tsunami in Sri Lanka. In P. Jones (Ed.), *Drama as therapy. Theory, practice and research* (p. 4). Routledge.

Collins, P. H. (1990). *Black feminist thought: Knowledge, consciousness, and the politics of empowerment.* Routledge.

Conger, J. J. (1975). Proceedings of the american psychological association, incorporated, for the year 1974: Minutes of the annual meeting of the council of representatives. *American Psychologist, 30*(6), 620–651. https://doi.org/10.1037/h0078455

Constantine, M. G., & Kwan, K. L. (2003). Cross-cultural considerations of therapist self-disclosure. *Journal of Clinical Psychology, 59*(5), 581–588. https://doi.org/10.1002/jclp.10160

Cook, R. M., & Welfare, L. E. (2018). Examining predictors of counselor-in-training intentional nondisclosure. *Counselor Education and Supervision, 57*(3), 211–226. https://doi.org/10.1002/ceas.12111

Cornell, S., & Hartmann, D. (2006). *Ethnicity and race: Making identities in a changing world* (2nd ed.). Pine Forge Press.

Cornish, J., Gorgens, K., Monson, S., Olkin, R., Palombi, B., & Abels, A. (2008). Perspectives on ethical practice with people who have disabilities. *Professional Psychology: Research and Practice, 39*(5), 488–497. https://doi.org/10.1037/a0013092

Council of Europe. (2016). *Intercultural cities: Governance and policies for diverse communities.* https://edoc.coe.int/en/living-together-diversity-and-freedom-in-europe/6909-intercultural-cities-governance-and-policies-for-diverse-communities.html.

Counselors for Social Justice. (2011). The counselors for social justice code of ethics. *Journal for Social Action in Counseling & Psychology, 3*(2), 1–21. https://doi.org/10.33043/JSACP.3.2.1-21

Couroucli-Robertson, K. (1992). Cultural differences and similarities in drama therapy. *The Arts in Psychotherapy, 19*(2), 117–121.

Cowan, L. (2021). *Border nation: A story of migration.* Pluto Press.

Cox, M., & Theilgaard, A. (1987). *Mutative metaphors in psychotherapy: The Aeolian Mode.* Routledge.

Crenshaw, K. W. (1988). Race, reform, and retrenchment: Transformation and legitimation in antidiscrimination law. *Harvard Law Review, 101*(7), 1331–1387. https://doi.org/10.2307/1341398

Crenshaw, K. W. (2004). *Intersectionality: The double bind of race and gender interview with Kimberlé Crenshaw.* American Bar Association, Spring.

Crimmens, P. (1998). *Storymaking and creative groupwork with older people.* Jessica Kingsley Publishers.

Crisis. (2021). *Chapter 12 ending migrant homelessness.* https://www.crisis.org.uk/ending-homelessness/the-plan-to-end-homelessness-full-version/solutions/chapter-12-ending-migrant-homelessness/

Critchley, A., Dokter, D., Odel-Miller, H., Power, N., & Sandford, S. (2019). Starting from scratch: Co-production with dramatherapy in a recovery college. *Dramatherapy, 40*(2), 63–80. https://doi.org/10.1177/0263067219843442

Cunningham-Younger, E. (2016). Muslim students talk stereotypes, Islamic faith. *The Collegian.* https://www.kstatecollegian.com/2016/01/26/muslim-students-talk-stereotypes-islamic-faith/

Curtis, S. (2013). On gender and the creative arts therapies. *The Arts in Psychotherapy, 40*(3), 371–372. https://doi.org/10.1016/j.aip.2013.05.014

Daccache, Z. (2016). The unheard stories of those forgotten behind bars in Lebanon. In S. Pendzik, R. Emunah, & D. R. Johnson (Eds.), *The self in performance* (pp. 227–239). Palgrave.

Dalal, F. (2002). *Race, colour and the process of racialization: New perspectives from group analysis, psychoanalysis, and sociology.* Brunner-Routledge.

D'Ardenne, P., & Mahtani, A. (1999). *Transcultural counselling in action.* SAGE Publications.

David, E. J. R., Schroeder, T. M., & Fernandez, J. (2019). Internalized racism: A systematic review of the psychological literature on racism's most insidious consequence. *Journal of Social Issues, 75*(4), 1057–1086. https://doi.org/10.1111/josi.12350

Davidson, S. (2016). Gender inequality: Nonbinary transgender people in the workplace. *Cogent Social Sciences*, *2*(1). https://doi.org/10.1080/23311886.2016.1236511

Davies, D. (1996). Towards a model of gay affirmative therapy. In D. Davies & C. Neal (Eds.), *Pink therapy: A guide for counsellors and therapists working with lesbian, gay and bisexual clients* (pp. 24–40). Open University Press.

Davies, D., & Neal, C. (Eds.). (1996). *Pink Therapy: A guide for counsellors and therapists working with lesbian, gay and bisexual clients*. Open University Press.

de Haas, H., Castles, S., & Miller, M. J. (2020). *The age of migration: International population movements in the modern world* (6th ed.). MacMillan.

De la Boetie, E. (2015). *The politics of obedience: The discourse of voluntary servitude*. Ludwig von Mises Institute.

de Witte, M., Orkibi, H., Zarate, R., Karkou, V., Sajnani, N., Malhotra, B., Ho, R., Kaimal, G., Baker, F. A., & Koch, S. C. (2021). From therapeutic factors to mechanisms of change in the creative arts therapies: A scoping review. *Frontiers in Psychology*, *12*, 678397. https://doi.org/10.3389/fpsyg.2021.678397

Dechavez, Y. (2018, October 8). It's time to decolonize that syllabus. *Los Angeles Times*. https://www.latimes.com/books/la-et-jc-decolonize-syllabus-20181008-story.html.

DeGruy, J. (2017). *Post traumatic slave syndrome: America's legacy of enduring injury and healing* (rev. ed.). Joy DeGruy Publications.

Dembo, R., Iklé, D. N., & Ciarlo, J. A. (1983). The influence of client–clinician demographic match on client treatment outcomes. *Journal of Psychiatric Treatment & Evaluation*, *5*(1), 45–53.

Denzin, N. K., Lincoln, Y. S., & Smith, L. T. (Eds.). (2008). *Handbook of critical and Indigenous methodologies*. SAGE publications.

Department of Health (DOH). (2009). *Policies on ageing*. Centre for Policy on Ageing. http://www.cpa.org.uk/cpa/policies_on_ageing.html

Dhingra, S., Killaspy, H., & Dowling, S. (2021). Gender equality in academic psychiatry in the UK in 2019. *BJPsych Bulletin*, *45*(3), 153–158. https://doi.org/10.1192/bjb.2020.116

DiAngelo, R. J. (2018). *White fragility: Why it's so hard for white people to talk about racism*. Penguin Books.

Dintino, C. (1997). Playing with the perpetrator: Gender dynamics in developmental drama therapy. In S. Jennings (Ed.), *Dramatherapy: Theory and practice* (Vol. 3, pp. 205–221). Routledge.

Dintino, C. (2021). Drama therapy in midlife and beyond: A reformative proposal. *Drama Therapy Review*, *7*(1), 115–132, https://doi.org/10.1386/dtr_00064_1

Dinitino, C., & Johnson, D. (1997). Playing with the perpetrator: Gender dynamics in developmental drama therapy. In S. Jennings (Ed.), *Drama therapy: Theory and practice* (Vol. 3, pp. 191–220). Routledge.

Dintino, C., Steiner, N., Smith, A., & Carlucci Galway, K. (2015). Developmental transformations and playing with the unplayable. *A Chest of Broken Toys: A Journal of Developmental Transformations*, *1*, 12–31.

Disabled Peoples' International. (2022). *About us*. https://disabledpeoplesinterna tional.org/about-us/

Dix, A. (2015). Telling stories: Dramatherapy and theatre in education with boys who have experienced parental domestic violence. *Dramatherapy*, *37*(1), 15–27. https://doi.org/10.1080/02630672.2015.1055778

Dixon, C. (2018). Family Dramatherapy (FDT) and LGBTQ+. *Dramatherapy*, *39*(3), 186–191. https://doi.org/10.1080/02630672.2018.1514062

Dokter, D. (1993). Dramatherapy across Europe, cultural contradictions: An inquiry into the parameters of British training and practice. In H. Payne & J. Rowan (Eds.), *Handbook of inquiry in the arts therapies: One river, many currents* (pp. 79–90). Jessica Kingsley Publishers.

Dokter, D. (Ed.). (1994). *Arts therapies and clients with eating disorders*. Jessica Kingsley Publishers.

Dokter, D. (1998a). *Arts therapists, refugees, and migrants: Reaching across borders*. Jessica Kingsley Publishers.

Dokter, D. (1998b). Being a migrant, working with migrants. In D. Dokter (Ed.), *Reaching across borders: Arts therapists, refugees and migrants* (pp. 145–154). Jessica Kingsley Publishers.

Dokter, D. (2000a). *Exile: Refugees and the arts therapies*. University of Hertfordshire Press.

Dokter, D. (2000b). Intercultural dramatherapy practice: A research history. *Dramatherapy*, *22*(3), 3–8. https://doi.org/10.1080/02630672.2000.9689554

Dokter, D. (2004). Exile, arts therapies and refugees. In S. Scoble (Ed.), *Arts therapies communication* (pp. 14–20). Munster Verlag.

Dokter, D. (2005/6). The fool and 'stranger anxiety': Creative and destructive possibilities. *Dramatherapy*, *27*(4), 9–13. https://doi.org/10.1080/02630672.2005.9689673

Dokter, D. (2008). Immigrant mental health: Acculturation stress and the response of the UK 'host'. In M. Finkelstein & K. Dent-Brown (Eds.), *Psychosocial stress in immigrants and in members of minority groups as a factor of terrorist behaviour* (pp. 168–179). IOS Press.

Dokter, D. (Ed.). (2009). Editorial. *Dramatherapy*, *31*(2). https://doi.org/10.1080/026 30672.2009.9689768

Dokter, D. (2010). Embodying difference: To join or not to join the dance. In P. Jones (Ed.), *Drama as therapy: Clinical work and research into practice* (Vol. 2, pp. 208–233). Routledge.

Dokter, D. (2011). Outcomes in dramatherapy: Standardised or individualised? In D. Read Johnstone and S. Pendzik (Eds.), *Assessment in dramatherapy* (pp. 333–361). Charles C. Thomas Publishers.

Dokter, D. (2016). Developing intercultural good practice guidelines in dramatherapy. In D. Dokter, & M. Hills De Zárate (Eds.), *Intercultural arts therapies research: Issues and methodologies* (pp. 79–97). Routledge.

Dokter, D. (2021). The transformative body. In S. Reeve (Ed.), *Body and awareness* (pp. 221–234). Triarchy Press.

Dokter, D. (2022). Arts based research and self reflexive autobiographical performance. In C. Frizell & M. Rova (Eds.), *Research and practice that brings us home. The creative body as catalyst*. Routledge. In press.

Dokter, D., & Gersie, A. (2016). Dramatherapists remember: A retrospective study of autobiographical performance during dramatherapy training. In S. Pendzik, R. Emunah, & D. R. Johnson (Eds.), *The self in performance: Autobiographical, self-revelatory, and autoethnographic forms of therapeutic theatre* (pp. 181–197). Palgrave Macmillan.

Dokter, D., & Hills de Zárate, M. (2016). *Intercultural arts therapies research: Issues and methodologies* (1st ed.). Routledge.

Dokter, D., & Hughes, P. (2007a). *Analysis of dramatherapy equal opportunities survey.* http://www.badth.org.uk

Dokter, D., & Hughes, P. (2007b). *Equal opportunities survey.* British Association of Drama Therapy. www.badth.org.uk

Dokter, D., & Khasnavis, R. (2008). Intercultural supervision: The issue of choice. In P. Jones & D. Dokter (Eds.), *Supervision of dramatherapy* (pp. 111–129). Routledge/Taylor & Francis Group.

Dokter, D., Lea-Weston, L., & Thornewood, T. (2020). Secondary traumatisation and therapist illness. In A. Chesner & S. Lykou (Eds.), *Trauma in the creative and embodies therapies: When words are not enough* (pp. 143–154). Routledge.

Donald, D., Glanfield, F., & Sterenberg, G. (2011). Culturally relational education in and with an Indigenous community. *In Education, 17*(3), pp. 72–83. https://doi.org/10.37119/ojs2011.v17i3.73

Dooman, R. (2007). Research vignette: Abui. In P. Jones (Ed.), *Drama as therapy. Theory, practice and research* (pp. 127–133). Routledge.

Drescher, J. (2015). Queer diagnoses revisited: The past and future of homosexuality and gender diagnoses in DSM and ICD. *International Review of Psychiatry, 27*(5), 386–395. https://doi.org/10.3109/09540261.2015.1053847

Du Bois, W. E. B., & Edwards, B. H. (2008). *The souls of black folk.* Oxford University Press.

Duncan, P. (2017, July 27). Gay relationships are still criminalised in 72 countries, report finds. *The Guardian.* https://www.theguardian.com/world/2017/jul/27/gay-relationships-still-criminalised-countries-report

Dunn, D. S., & Andrews, E. E. (2015). Person-first and identity-first language: Developing psychologists' cultural competence using disability language. *The American Psychologist, 70*(3), 255–264. https://doi.org/10.1037/a0038636

Dunphy, K., Baker, F., Dumaresq, E., Carroll-Haskins, K., Eikholt, J., Ercole, M., Kaimal, G., Meyer, K., Sajnani, N., Shamir, O., Wosch, T., & (2019). Creative arts interventions to address depression in older adults: A systematic review of outcomes, processes and mechanisms. *Frontiers in Psychology, 9*, 2655. https://doi.org/10.3389/fpsyg.2018.02655

Dyer, R. (1997). *White: Essays on race and culture.* Routledge.

Eddo-Lodge, R. (2017). *Why I'm no longer talking to white people about race.* Bloomsbury Publishing.

Edward, J. (2021). Living in "turbulence": Reflections on a therapeutic theatre performance. *Voices, 21*(1). https://doi.org/10.15845/voices.v21i1.3165

Elliott, I. (2016). *Poverty and mental health: A review to inform the Joseph Rowntree foundation's anti poverty strategy.* Mental Health Foundation.

Emmons, R. A. (2003). Personal goals, life meaning and virtue: Wellsprings of a positive life. In C. M. L. Keynes (Ed.), *The positive person and the good life* (pp. 105–128). American Psychological Association.

Emunah, R. (1989). The use of dramatic enactment in the training of drama therapists, *The Arts in Psychotherapy, 16*(1), 29–36.

Emunah, R. (2016). Self-revelatory performance: A form of drama therapy and theatre. *Drama Therapy Review, 1*(1), 71–85.

Emunah, R., & Johnson, D. R. (1983). The impact of theatrical performance on the self-images of psychiatric patients. *The Arts in Psychotherapy, 10*, 233–239.

Epstein, M. (2009). Transculture: A broad way between globalism and multiculturalism. *The American Journal of Economics and Sociology, 68*(1), 327–352. http://www.jstor.org/stable/27739771

Fagan, A. (2021). *The class-blindness of human rights*. Universal Rights Group Geneva. https://www.universal-rights.org/blog/the-class-blindness-of-human-rights

Fanon, F. (1961). *The wretched of the earth*. Penguin Classics.

Fellows, M. L., & Razack, S. (1998). The race to innocence: Confronting hierarchical relations among women. *Journal of Gender, Race & Justice, 1*, 335–352. https://scholarship.law.umn.edu/faculty_articles/274

Ferrant, G., Pesando, L. M., & Nowacka, K. (2014). *Unpaid care work: The missing link in the analysis of gender gaps in labour outcomes*. OECD Development Centre. https://www.oecd.org/dev/development-gender/Unpaid:care_work.pdf

Fiji Islands Bureau of Statistics. (2008, April 14). Survey statistics. https://www.stats fiji.gov.fj/

Finklestein, M. and Dent-Brown, K. (Eds.). (2008). *Psychosocial stress in immigrants and in members of minority groups as a factor of terrorist behavior*. IOS Press.

Fiske, A., Kitayama, S., Markus, H. R., & Nisbett, R. E. (1998). The cultural matrix of social psychology. In D. Gilbert, S. Fiske, & G. Lindzey (Eds.), *The handbook of social psychology* (4th ed., Vol. 2, pp. 915–981). McGraw-Hill.

Flanders, C. E., Robinson, M., Legge, M. M., & Tarasoff, L. A. (2016). Negative identity experiences of bisexual and other non-monosexual people: A qualitative report. *Journal of Gay & Lesbian Mental Health, 20*(2), 152–172. https://doi.org/10.1080/19359705.2015.1108257

Ford, T. (2020, September 13). Why do women appear to bear the brunt of ageism at work? *BBC.Com*. https://www.bbc.com/news/business-54080397.

Frankish, P. (2015). *Disability psychotherapy: An innovative approach to trauma-informed care*. Routledge.

Fraser, K. D., O'Rourke, H. M., Wiens, H., Lai, J., Howell, C., & Brett-MacLean, P. (2015). A scoping review of research on the arts, aging, and quality of life. *The Gerontologist, 55*(4), 719–729. https://doi.org/10.1093/geront/gnv027

Frederick, A., & Shifrer, D. (2019). Race and disability: From analogy to intersectionality. *Sociology of Race and Ethnicity, 5*(2), 200–214. https://doi.org/10.1177/2332649218783480

Freire, P. (1971). *Pedagogy of the oppressed*. Continuum.

French, S. (1994). *On equal terms: Working with disabled people*. Butterworth Heinemann.

Freud, S. (1905). *On psychotherapy. Standard edition of the complete psychological works of Sigmund Freud* (Vol. 7.). Hogarth.

Friel, B. (1981). *Translations*. Faber and Faber.

Frost, D. M., Lehavot, K., & Meyer, I. (2013). Minority stress and physical health among sexual minority individuals. *Journal of Behavioral Medicine, 38*(1), 1–8.

Frydman, J., & Segall, J. (2016). Investigating the glass escalator effect among registered drama therapists: A gender-based examination of professional trajectory. *Drama Therapy Review, 2*(1), 25–39. https://doi.org/10.1386/dtr.2.1.25_1

Fryer, P. (1984). *Staying power: The history of black people in Britain*. Pluto Press.

Fukuyama, F. (2018). *Identity: The demand for dignity and the politics of resentment*. Farrar, Strauss and Giroux.

Fuller, C., Chang, D., & Rubin, L. (2009). Sliding under the radar: Passing and power among sexual minorities. *Journal of LGBT Issues in Counseling, 3*, 128–151. https://doi.org/10.1080/15538600903005334

Gaines, A. M. (2021). Therapeutic teaching artistry: Towards a wellness model for enhancing vitality in older adults, *Drama Therapy Review, 7*(1), 95–113. https://doi.org/10.1386/dtr_00063_1

Gaines, A. M., & Butler, J. D. (2016). The history, trends and future of North American drama therapy. In S. Jennings & C. Holmwood (Eds.), *Routledge international handbook of dramatherapy* (pp. 52–64). Routledge. https://doi.org/10.4324/9781315728537

Gallardo, M. E. (2014). *Developing cultural humility: Embracing race, privilege and power*. SAGE Publications.

Gates, G. (2011, April). *How many people are lesbian, gay, bisexual and transgender?* Williams Institute. https://williamsinstitute.law.ucla.edu/publications/how-many-people-lgbt/

Geertz, C. (1993). *The interpretation of cultures: Selected essays*. Fontana Press.

Genevay, B., & Katz, R. S. (1990). *Countertransference and older clients*. SAGE publications.

Gersie, A. (1987). Dramatherapy and play. In S. Jennings (Ed.), *Dramatherapy: Theory and practice for teachers and clinicians* (pp. 46–72). Croom Helm.

Gersie, A. (1991). *Storymaking in bereavement: Dragons fight in the meadow*. Jessica Kingsley Publishers.

Gersie, A. (1992). *Earthtales: Storytelling in times of change*. Merlin Press.

Gersie, A. (1997a). *Reflections on therapeutic storymaking: The use of stories in groups*. Jessica Kingsley Publishers.

Gersie, A. (1997b). 'To feel absent from one's voice': Trial therapy with a young immigrant woman. In S. Jennings (Ed.), *Dramatherapy: Theory and practice* (Vol 3, pp. 113–128). Routledge.

Gersie, A., & King, N. (1989). *Storymaking in education and therapy* (1st ed.). Jessica Kingsley Publishers.

Gersie, A., Nanson, A., Schieffelin, E. L. (2022). *Storytelling for nature connection*. Hawthorn Press.

Giebel, C., Corcoran, R., Kullu, C., Campbell, N., Gabbay, M., Daras, K., Barr, B., Wilson, T., & Goodall, M. (2020). Do people living in disadvantaged circumstances receive different mental health treatments than those from less disadvantaged backgrounds? *BMC Public Health, 20*(651). https://doi.org/10.1186/s12889-020-08820-4

Gieseking, J. J. (2008). Queer theory. In V. N. Parrillo, M. Andersen, J. Best, W. Kornblum, C. M. Renzetti, & M. Romero (Eds.), *Encyclopedia of social problems* (1st ed., pp. 737–738). SAGE Publications.

Goel, S. (2022). *Beyond silence: Affinity spaces for the marginalized creative arts therapist* [Unpublished Master's Thesis]. New York University.

Goffman, E. (1963). *Stigma: Notes on the management of spoiled identity*. Prentice-Hall.

Goldstein, E. G. (1994). Self-disclosure in treatment: What therapists do and don't talk about. *Clinical Social Work Journal, 22*(4), 417–433. https://doi.org/10.1007/BF02190331

Goldstein, A. (Ed.). (2015). *The complete works of Primo Levi*. Penguin Classics.

Gonçalves, D. C. (2009). From loving grandma to working with older adults: Promoting positive attitudes towards aging. *Educational Gerontology, 35*(3), 202–225. https://doi.org/10.1080/03601270802466884

Gough, K. (1968). *Anthropology and imperialism*. New England Free Press.

Graham, A. (2016). Womanist preservation: An analysis of black women's spiritual coping. *International Journal of Transpersonal Studies, 35*(1), 106–117. http://dx.doi.org/10.24972/ijts.2016.35.1.106

Grainger, R. (1990). *Drama and healing: The roots of drama therapy*. Jessica Kingsley Publishers.

Grainger, R. (1995). *The glass of heaven: The faith of the dramatherapist*. Jessica Kingsley Publishers.

Grainger, R. (1996). The therapeusis of the audience. *Dramatherapy, 18*(1), 27–30.

Grande, S. (2011). Confessions of a full-time Indian. *Journal of Curriculum and Pedagogy, 8*(1), 40–43. https://doi.org/10.1080/15505170.2011.572523

Graziano, W., Habashi, M., Sheese, B., & Tobin, R. (2007). Agreeableness, empathy, and helping: A person × situation perspective. *Journal of Personality and Social Psychology, 93*(4). 583–599. https://doi.org/10.1037/0022-3514.93.4.583

Green, M. S., & Dekkers, T. D. (2010). Attending to power and diversity in supervision: An exploration of supervisee learning outcomes and satisfaction with supervision. *Journal of Feminist Family Therapy, 22*(4), 293–312.

Greenaway, R. (2016). *Active reviewing guide experiential learning articles + critiques of David Kolb's theory*. Reviewing.co. https://reviewing.co.uk/research/experiential.learning.htm#ixzz5ws8QAc1s

Gutierrez, G. (1988). *A theology of liberation: History, politics, and salvation*. Orbis Books.

Gutin, J. A. C. (1994, November 1). The end of the rainbow. *Discover Magazine*. https://www.discovermagazine.com/health/end-of-the-rainbow

Gutman, L., Joshi, H., Parsonage, M., & Schoon, I. (2015). *Children of the new century: Mental health findings from the millennium cohort study*. Centre for Mental Health. https://www.centreformentalhealth.org.uk/sites/default/files/2018-09/new century.pdf

Gutman, S. A., Raphael-Greenfield, E. I., & Rao, A. K. (2012). Effect of motor-based roleplay intervention on the social behaviours of adolescents with high functioning autism: Multiple base single subject design. *American Journal of Occupational Therapy, 66*, 529–537.

Hadley, S. (2013a). Dominant narratives: Complexity and the need for vigilance in the creative arts therapies. *The Arts in Psychotherapy, 40*(4), 373–381.

Hadley, S. (2013b). *Experiencing race as a music therapist: Personal narratives*. Barcelona Publishers.

Haen, C. (2002). The dramatherapeutic use of the superhero role with male clients. *Dramatherapy, 24*(1), 16–22. https://doi.org/10.1080/02630672.2002.9689602

Hahna, N. (2013). Towards an emancipatory practice. Incorporating feminist pedagogy in the creative arts therapies. *The Arts in Psychotherapy, 40*(4), 436–440.

Hakim, C. (2007). Women, careers and work-life preferences. *British Journal of Guidance and Counselling 34*(3), 279–294. https://doi.org/10.1080/03069880600769118

Hall, S. (1986). Gramsci's relevance for the study of race and ethnicity. *Journal of Communication Inquiry, 10*(2), 5–27. https://doi.org/10.1177/019685998601000202

Hall, W. J., Chapman, M. V., Lee, K. M., Merino, Y. M., Thomas, T. W., Payne, B. K., Eng, E., Day, S. H., & Coyne-Beasley, T. (2015). Implicit racial/ethnic bias among health care professionals and its influence on health care outcomes: A systematic review. *American Journal of Public Health, 105*(12), e60–e76. https://doi.org/10.2105/AJPH.2015.302903

Hamilton, N. (2014). *Awakening through dreams: The journey through the inner landscape* (1st ed.). Routledge.

Handa, A. (2003). *Of silk saris and mini-skirts: South asian girls walk the tightrope of culture*. Women's Press.

Hanna, G. P., Noelker, L. S., & Bienvenu, B. (2015). The arts, health, and aging in America: 2005–2015. *The Gerontologist, 55*(2), 271–277. https://doi.org/10.1093/geront/gnu183

Hawkins, P., & Shohet, R. (1989). *Supervision in the helping professions.* Open University Press.

Hawkins, P., & Shohet, R. (2012). *Supervision in the helping professions* (4th ed.). Open University Press.

Hays, P. A. (1996). Addressing the complexities of culture and gender in counseling. *Journal of Counseling and Development, 74*(4), 332–338. https://doi.org/10.1002/j.1556-6676.1996.tb01876.x

Hays, D. G., & Chang, C. Y. (2003). White privilege, oppression, and racial identity development: implications for supervision. *Counselor Education and Supervision, 43*(2), 134–145. https://doi.org/10.1002/j.1556-6978.2003.tb01837.x

Haythorne, D., & Seymour, A. (Eds.). (2016). *Dramatherapy and autism.* Routledge.

Health & Care Professions Council. (2013). *The standards of proficiency for arts therapists. Arts Therapists.* https://www.hcpc-uk.org/standards/standards-of-proficiency/arts-therapists/

Heinze, E. (1987). Transference and countertransference in the psychoanalytic treatment of older patients. *International Review of Psycho-Analysis, 14*, 465–473.

Helbling, M., Hoeglinger, D., & Wuest, B. (2010). How political parties frame European integration. *European Journal of Political Research, 49*(4), 495–521. https://ejpr.onlinelibrary.wiley.com

Henretty, J. R., & Levitt, H. M. (2010). The role of therapist self-disclosure in psychotherapy: A qualitative review. *Clinical Psychology Review, 30*(1), 63–77. https://doi.org/10.1016/j.cpr.2009.09.004

Hermann, U. (2016). Touching insights: Visual and tactile cultures in research art psychotherapy with congenitally blind children. In D. Dokter & M. Hills de Zarate (Eds.), *Intercultural arts and therapies research* (pp. 30–52). Routledge.

Hill-Collins, P. (2000). *Black feminist thought: Knowledge, consciousness, and the politics of empowerment* (2nd ed.). Routledge.

Hills, J. (2010). *An anatomy of economic inequality in the UK: Report of the national equality panel.* Centre for Analysis of Social Exclusion, LSE. https://ssrn.com/abstract=1546894

Hiltunen, S. M. K. (2014). *Therapeutic Noh theater: SohKiDo pathway VII of the seven pathways of transpersonal creativity.* Two Harbors Press.

Hiscox, A. R., & Calisch, A. C. (1998). *Tapestry of cultural issues in art therapy.* Jessica Kingsley Publishers.

Hodermarska, M. (2013). Autism as performance. *Dramatherapy, 35*(1), 64–76. https://doi.org/10.1080/02630672.2013.773129

Hodermarska, M. (2015, July 16). *An unexpected alliance [Audio podcast episode].* The Moth. https://themoth.org/stories/an-unexpected-alliance

Hodermarska, M., & Filson, V. (2018). *Excavating ableism in the academy.* Critical Pedagogy in the Art Therapies. https://www.criticalpedagogyartstherapies.com/single-post/2018/07/01/Excavating-Ableism-in-the-Academy

Hodermarska, M., Stevens, A., Johnson, J., Jones, E., Manzi, M., & McGowan, S. (2021). Disability justice: Drama therapy as collective liberation. In R. Parasuram & S. Parasuram (Eds.), *Artability: Creative arts and disabilities* (pp. 184–205). Notion Press.

Hoffman, K. M., Trawalter, S., Axt, J. R., & Oliver, M. N. (2016). Racial bias in pain assessment and treatment recommendations, and false beliefs about biological differences between blacks and whites. *Proceedings of the National Academy of Sciences of the United States of America, 113*(16), 4296–4301. https://doi.org/10.1073/pnas.1516047113

Hogan, S. (Ed.). (2020). *Arts therapies and gender issues: International perspectives on research*. Routledge.

Hoggart, K. (1997). The middle classes in rural England 1971–1991. *Journal of Rural Studies, 13*(3), 253–273.

Holledge, J., & Tompkins, J. (2000). *Women's intercultural performance*. Routledge.

Hollingshead, A. B., & Redlich, F. C. (2007). Social class and mental illness: A community study. *American Journal of Public Health, 97*(10), 1756–1757. https://doi.org/10.2105/ajph.97.10.1756

Holloway, P., & Seebohm, H. (2011). When worlds elide: Culture, dialogue and identity in multi-professional settings. *Dramatherapy, 33*(1), 4–15. https://doi.org/10.1080/02630672.2010.549634

Holmwood, C. (2016). Dramatherapy and theatre: Current interdisciplinary discourses. In S. Jennings & C. Holmwood (Eds.), *The international handbook of dramatherapy* (pp. 160–169). Routledge.

Holt, L., Bowlby, S., & Lea, J. (2018). Disability, special educational needs, class, capitals, and segregation in schools: A population geography perspective. *Popul Space Place, 25*(4), e2229. https://doi.org/10.1002/psp.2229

Home Office. (2016). *Asylum policy instruction, sexual orientation in asylum claims*. https://assets.publishing.service.gov.uk/government/uploads/system/uploads/attachment_data/file/543882/Sexual-orientation-in-asylum-claims-v6.pdf

Hoogvelt, A. M. M. (1997). *Globalization and the postcolonial world: The new political economy of development*. Johns Hopkins University Press.

Hooks, B. (1989). Choosing the margin as a space of radical openness. *Framework: Journal of Cinema and Media, 36*, 15–23. https://www.ias.edu/sites/default/files/sss/pdfs/Crisis-and-Critique-2018-19/hooks_choosing_the_margins.pdf

Hooks, B. (1990) *Yearning- rce, gender and cultural politics*. Southend Press.

Hook, J. N., Davis, D. E., Owen, J., Worthington Jr, E. L., & Utsey, S. O. (2013). Cultural humility: Measuring openness to culturally diverse clients, *Journal of Counseling Psychology, 60*(3), 353–366.

Hughes, D., Rodriguez, J., Smith, E. P., Johnson, D. J., Stevenson, H. C., & Spicer, P. (2006). Parents' ethnic-racial socialization practices: A review of research and directions for future study. *Developmental Psychology, 42*(5), 747–770. https://doi.org/10.1037/0012-1649.42.5.747

Hwang, W. C., & Wood, J. J. (2009). Acculturative family distancing: Links with self-reported symptomatology among Asian Americans and Latinos. *Child psychiatry and human development, 40*(1), 123–138. https://doi.org/10.1007/s10578-008-0115-8

Innes, C. D. (1993). *Avant garde theatre, 1892–1992*. Routledge.

Institute of Medicine. (2011). *The health of lesbian, gay, bisexual and transgender people: Building a foundation for better understanding*. The National Academies Press. https://www.ncbi.nlm.nih.gov/books/NBK64806/

Isay, R. A. (1991). The homosexual analyst. Clinical considerations. *The Psychoanalytic study of the child, 46*, 199–216. https://doi.org/10.1080/00797308.1991.118223

Jaaniste, J. (2011). Dramatherapy and spirituality in dementia care. *Dramatherapy, 33*, 16–27. https://doi.org/10.1080/02630672.2011.558355

Jaaniste, J. (2022). *Dramatherapy with elders and people with dementia: Enabling developmental wellbeing*. Routledge.

Jackson-Cherry, L. R., & Erford, B. T. (2008). *Crisis assessment, intervention, and prevention* (1st ed.). Pearson.

Jacobi, J. (Ed.). (2014). *C.G.Jung: Psychological reflections: A new anthology of his writings 1905–1961*. Routledge.

Jacobs, L. (2000). For whites only. *British Gestalt Journal, 9*(1), 3–14.

Jacobs, M. (2003). *Sigmund Freud – key figures in counselling and psychotherapy* (2nd ed.). SAGE Publications.

Jacques, J. F. (2020). Investigation into the production of meaning in autobiographical performance in dramatherapy. *The Arts in Psychotherapy, 69*, 101659. http://doi.org/10.1016/j.aip.2020.101659

James, J. (1996). Dramatherapy and clients with learning disabilities. In S. Mitchell (Ed.), *Dramatherapy clinical studies* (Chapter 2). Jessica Kingsley Publishers.

Jay, S. and Muldoon, O. T. (2018). Social class and models of agency: Independent and interdependent agency as educational (dis) advantage. *Journal of Community and Applied Psychology, 28*(5), 318–331. https://doi.org/10/1002/casp.2370

Jen, W. (2016). The use of image theatre to examine the acculturation process of Taiwanese international performing arts students in New York City. *Drama Therapy Review, 2*(1), 79–97, https://doi.org/10.1386/dtr.2.1.79_1

Jenkyns, M. (1997). Gender issues in supervision. In S. Jennings (Ed.), *Drama therapy: Theory and practice 3* (1st ed., pp. 189–197). Routledge.

Jennings, S. (1974). *Remedial drama: A handbook for teachers and therapists*. Pitman Publishing.

Jennings, S. (1981). Dramatherapy origins and the physically disabled. In G. Schatner & S. Courtney (Eds.), *Drama in therapy* (Vol. 1). Drama Book Specialists.

Jennings, S. (Ed.). (1987). *Drama therapy: Theory and practice 1* (1st ed.). Croom Helm.

Jennings, S. (1992). *Shakespeare comes to Broadmoor*. Jessica Kingsley Publishers.

Jennings, S. (1994). An incomplete rite of passage. In D. Dokter (Ed.), *Arts therapies and clients with eating disorders* (pp. 124–143). Jessica Kingsley Publishers.

Jennings, S. (1995). *Theatre, ritual and transformation: The Senoi Temiars* (1st ed.). Routledge.

Jennings, S. (1999). Theatre-based dramatherapy supervision: A supervisory model for multidisciplinary supervisees. In E. Tselikas-Portman (Ed.), *Supervision and dramatherapy* (pp. 62–79). Jessica Kingsley.

Jennings, S. (2005). The ageing fool: The importance of humour and stimulus for older people. *Dramatherapy, 27*(4), 14–16. https://doi.org/10.1080/02630672.2005.968967

Jennings, S. (Ed.). (2009). *Dramatherapy and social theatre: Necessary dialogues*. Routledge.

Jennings, S. (2020). The gendered body in arts therapies research and practice. In S. Hogan (Ed.), *Arts therapies and gender issues: International perspectives on research* (pp. 138–146). Routledge.

Jennings, S., Cattanach, A., Mitchell, S., Chesner, A., Meldrum, B., & Nfa, S. M. (1993). *The handbook of dramatherapy* (1st ed.). Routledge.

Jennings, S., & Holmwood, C. (Eds.). (2016). *The international handbook of dramatherapy*. Routledge.

Joffe-Walt, C. (2013). *Unfit for work: The startling rise of disability in America*. NPR. https://apps.npr.org/unfit-for-work/

Johnson, D. R. (1986). The developmental method in drama therapy: Group treatment with the elderly. *The Arts in Psychotherapy, 13*, 17–33.

Johnson, D. R. (1994). Shame dynamics among creative arts therapists. *Arts in Psychotherapy, 21*(3), 173–178.

Johnson, D. R. (2009). Developmental transformations: Towards the body as presence. In D. Johnson & R. Emunah (Eds.), *Current approaches in drama therapy* (2nd ed., pp. 89–116). Charles C. Thomas Publishers.

Johnson, D. R. (2014). Trauma centered developmental transformations. In D. R. Johnson & N. Sajnani (Eds.), *Trauma informed dramatherapy: Transforming clinics, classrooms and communities* (pp. 68–92). Charles C. Thomas Publishers.

Johnson, D. R., & Pitre, R. (2020). Developmental transformations. In D. R. Johnson & R. Emunah (Eds.), *Current approaches in drama therapy* (pp. 123–158). Charles C. Thomas Publishers.

Johnson, D. R., & Sajnani, N. (2014). The role of drama therapy in trauma treatment. In N. Sajnani & D. R. Johnson (Eds.), *Trauma informed drama therapy: Transforming clinics, classrooms, and communities* (pp. 5–23). Charles C Thomas Publishers.

Johnson, D. R., & Sajnani, N. (2015). Conversare: Developmental transformations and social justice. *A Chest of Broken Toys: A Journal of Developmental Transformations* (pp. 57–77). Institute of Developmental Transformations.

Jones, C. T., Welfare, L. E., Melchior, S., & Cash, R. (2019). Broaching as a strategy for intercultural understanding in clinical supervision. *The Clinical Supervisor*, 38(1), 1–16. https://doi.org/10.1080/07325223.2018.1560384

Jones, E. E., & Zoppel, C. L. (1982). Impact of client and therapist gender on psychotherapy process and outcome. *Journal of Consulting and Clinical Psychology*, 50(2), 259–272. https://doi.org/10.1037/0022-006X.50.2.259

Jones, P. (1996). *Drama as therapy: Theory, practice and research* (Vol. 1). Routledge.

Jones, P. (2005). *The arts therapies: A revolution in healthcare*. Routledge. https://doi.org/10.4324/9781315788098

Jones, P. (2007). *Drama as therapy: Theory, practice, and research* (2nd ed.). Routledge.

Jones, P. (2009a). Research into therapists' perceptions of therapeutic change using vignettes and aMSN messenger. *European Journal of Psychotherapy, Counseling and Health*, 11(3), 251–266. https://doi.org/10.1080/13642530903230376

Jones, P. (2009b). *Rethinking childhood: Attitudes in contemporary society*. Continuum.

Jones, P. (Ed.). (2010). *Drama as therapy: Clinical work and research into practice (Vol. 2.)*. Routledge.

Jones, P. (2021). *The arts therapies: A revolution in healthcare* (2nd ed.). Routledge.

Jones, P., Cedar, L., Coleman, A., Haythorne, D., Merceica, D., & Ramsden, E. (2020). *Child agency and voice in therapy*. Routledge.

Jones, P., & Dokter, D. (Eds.). (2008). *Supervision of dramatherapy*. Routledge.

Jones, R. (2016). *Violent borders: Refugees and the right to move*. Verso Pub.

Joppke, C. (2018). War of words: Interculturalism v. multiculturalism. *Comparative Migration Studies*, 6(1), 11. https://doi.org/10.1186/s40878-018-0079-1

Jung, C. G. (1968). *The collected works of C. G. Jung (I): The archetypes and the collective unconscious* (Vol. 9, 2nd ed.). Princeton University Press.

Kafer, R. A., Rakowski, W., Lachman, M., & Hickey, T. (1980). Ageing opinion survey: A report on instrument development. *The International Journal of Aging & Human Development*, 11(4), 319–333. https://doi.org/10.2190/JQF5-XDCV-H1AH-3E1Y

Kahn, M. (2001). *Between therapist and client. The new relationship*. Holt Paperbacks.

Kalmanovitz, D., & Lloyd, B. (2005). *Art therapy and political violence: With art, without illusion* (1st ed.). Routledge.

Kapilashrami, A., & Hankivsky, O. (2018). Intersectionality and why it matters to global health. *The Lancet*, 391, 2589–2591. https://doi.org/10.1016/S0140-6736(18)31431-4

Kapp, S. K., Steward, R., Crane, L., Elliott, D., Elphick, C., Pellicano, E., & Russell, G. (2019). 'People should be allowed to do what they like': Autistic adults' views and experiences of stimming. *Autism: The International Journal of Research and Practice, 23*(7), 1782–1792. https://doi.org/10.1177/13623613198296

Karasu, T. B., Stein, S. P., & Charles, E. S. (1979). Age factors in patient-therapist relationship. *The Journal of nervous and mental disease, 167*(2), 100–104. https://doi.org/10.1097/00005053-197902000-00005

Kareem, J., & Littlewood, R. (Eds.). (1992). *Intercultural therapy: Themes, interpretation and practice.* Blackwell Scientific Publications.

Karkou, V., & Sanderson, P. (2006). *The arts therapies: A research based map of the field.* Elsevier Press.

Kaufman, J. S., Carlozzi, A. F., Boswell, D. L., Barnes, L. L. B., Wheeler-Scruggs, K., & Levy, P. A. (1997). Factors influencing therapist selection among gays, lesbians and bisexuals. *Counselling Psychology Quarterly, 10*(3), 287–297. https://doi.org/10.1080/09515079708254180

Kaur, E. (2021, March 1). *Such a Gorgeous Paradox: I am a Sikh Dramatherapist* [Audio podcast]. https://anchor.fm/gorgeous-paradox/episodes/Im-a-Sikh-Dramatherapist--Eshmit-Kaur-eq5v9v

Kavaler-Adler, S. (2003). Lesbian homoerotic transference in dialective with developmental mourning: On the way from symbolism from the protosymbolic. *Psychoanalytic Psychology, 20*(1), 131–152. Routledge

Kawano, T., Cruz, R. F., & Tan, X. (2018). Dance/movement therapists' attitudes and actions regarding LGBTQI and gender nonconforming communities. *American Journal of Dance Therapy, 40*(2), 202–223. https://doi.org/10.1007/s10465-018-9283-7

Keisari, S., Gesser-Edelsburg, A., Yaniv, D., & Palgi, Y. (2020b). Playback theatre in adult day centers: A creative group intervention for community-dwelling older adults. *PLoS One, 15*(10), e0239812.

Keisari, S., Palgi, Y., Yaniv, D., & Gesser-Edelsburg, A. (2020a). Participation in life-review playback theater enhances mental health of community-dwelling older adults: A randomized controlled trial. *Psychology of Aesthetics, Creativity, and the Arts.* https://doi.org/10.1037/aca0000354

Keisari, S., Yaniv, D., Palgi, Y., & Gesser-Edelsburg, A. (2018). Conducting playback theatre with older adults—A therapist's perspective. *The Arts in Psychotherapy, 60,* 72–81.

Kelinspen-Ammerlahn, A., Kotter-Gruhn, D., & Smith, J. (2008). Self perceptions of ageing: Do subjective age and satisfaction with age change during old age? *Journal of Gerontology, 63*(3), 377–385.

Kende, A., & Kreko, P. (2020). Xenophobia, prejudice and right wing populism in east-central Europe. *Current Opinion in Behavioral Sciences, 34,* 29–33. https://doi.org/10.1016/j.cobeha.2019.11.011

Kendig, H., Hussain, R., O'Loughlin, K., & Cannon, L. (2019). Australian attitudes to intergenerational equity: Impacts of social and policy change. *Ageing and Society. 39.* 1–28. https://doi.org/10.1017/S0144686X18000703.

Kennedy, S., Gheera, M., Keen, R., Mackley, A., & Bellis, A. (2018). *Claimant experience of the personal independence payment process.* House of Commons Library. https://www.parliament.uk/globalassets/documents/commons-library/Claimant-experience-of-the-Personal-Independence-Payment-process-CDP-2018-0020.pdf

Kim, O. M., & Ginther, A. M. (2019). I am who I am: Archetypal dramatherapy workshops for Asian American adoptees. *Drama Therapy Review, 5*(2), 251–266.

Kim, S.-A., & Whitehead-Pleaux, A. (2015). Music therapy and cultural diversity. In B. L. Wheeler (Ed.), *Music therapy handbook* (pp. 51–63). Guilford Publications.

Kim, Y. M., & Cho, S. I. (2020). Socioeconomic status, work-life conflict, and mental health. *American Journal of Industrial Medicine, 63*(8), 703–712. https://doi.org/10.1002/ajim.23118

King, D. E. (2005). *Encyclopedia of anthropology*. SAGE Publications.

King, R. (2010). Religion as a concept in Christianity. In D. Patte (Ed.), *The Cambridge dictionary of Christianity*. Cambridge University Press.

Kinsey, A., Pomeroy, W., & Martin, C. (1948). Sexual behavior in the human male. *Social Forces, 26*(3), 348–350. https://doi.org/10.2307/2572063

Kinsey, A., Wardell, P., Martin, C., & Gebhard, P. (1954). Sexual behavior in the human female. *The Annals of the American Academy of Political and Social Science, 292*(1), 178. https://doi.org/10.1177/000271625429200147

Kirshner, L., Hauser, S., & Genack, A. (1978). Effects of gender on short-term therapy. *Psychotherapy: Theory, Research, and Practice, 15.* 158–167.

Klimczuk, A. (2016). Creative aging: Drawing on the arts to enhance healthy aging. In N. Pachana (Ed.), *Encyclopedia of geropsychology* (pp. 608–612) Springer. https://doi.org/10.1007/978-981-287-080-3_363-1

Knight, B. G. (2004). Transference and countertransference with older clients. In *Psychotherapy with older adults* (pp. 67–95). SAGE publications. https://dx.doi.org/10.4135/9781452204574.n4

Knowles, C. (2010). 'Mobile sociology'. *The British Journal of Sociology, 61*(1), 373–379. https://doi.org/10.1111/j.1468-4446.2009.01295.x

Koenig, H. G. (2009). Research on religion, spirituality and mental health: A review. *Canadian Journal of Psychiatry, 54*(5), 283–291. 10.1177/070674370905400502.

Koh, J. (2012). The history of the concept of gender identity disorder. *Seishin Shinkeigaku Zasshi = Psychiatria Et Neurologia Japonica, 114*(6), 673–680.

Kolb, D. A. (1984). *Experiential learning: Experience as the source of learning and development*. Pearson Education.

Kontos, P. and Martin, W. (2013). Embodiment and dementia: Exploring critical narratives of selfhood, surveillance, and dementia care. *Dementia, 12*(3), 288–302.

Kooden, H. (1991). Self-disclosure: The gay male therapist as agent of social change. In C. Silverstein (Ed.), *Gays, lesbians, and their therapists: Studies in psychotherapy* (pp. 143–154). W.W. Norton & Company.

Kramer, C. H. (2013). Revealing our selves. In M. Baldwin (Ed.), *The use of self in therapy* (3rd ed., pp. 36–63). Taylor & Francis.

Kraus, M. W., Piff, P. K., & Keltner, D. (2011). Social class as culture: The convergence of resources and rank in the social realm. *Current Directions in Psychological Science, 20*(4), 246–250. https://doi.org/10.1177/0963721411414654

Krause, I. (1998). *Therapy across culture*. SAGE Publications.

Kroll-Zeldin, O. (2016). *Colonialism*. Oxford Bibliographies.

Kronner, H. W., & Northcut, T. (2015). Listening to both sides of the therapeutic dyad: Self-disclosure of gay male therapists and reflections from their gay male clients. *Psychoanalytical Social Work, 22*(2), 162–181. https://doi.org/10.1080/15228878.2015.1050746

Kuftinec, S. (2009). *Theatre, facilitation, and nation formation in the Balkans and Middle East*. Basingstoke: Palgrave Macmillan.

Kurt, D. (2021). *The cost of studying at New York University (NYU)*. Investopedia. https://www.investopedia.com/articles/personal-finance/010915/cost-studying-new-york-university-nyu.asp

Labov, W. (1966). *The social stratification of English in New York City*. Center for Applied Linguistics.

Ladany, N., Ellis, M. V., & Friedlander, M. L. (1999). The supervisory working alliance: Trainee self-efficacy, and satisfaction. *Journal of Counseling & Development, 77*(4), 447–455. https://doi.org/10.1002/j.1556-6676.1999.tb02472.x

Ladany, N., Mori, Y., & Mehr, K. E. (2013). Effective and ineffective supervision. *The Counseling Psychologist, 41*(1), 28–47. https://doi.org/10.1177/0011000012442648

Lago, C. (2006). *Race, culture, and counselling: The ongoing challenge*. Open University Press.

Lahad, M. (1992). Story-making in assessment method for coping with stress: Six-piece story-making and BASIC Ph. In S. Jennings (Ed.), *Dramatherapy theory and practice 2* (pp. 150–163). Routledge.

Lahad, M. (2000). *Creative supervision: The use of expressive arts methods in supervision and self-supervision*. Jessica Kingsley Publishers.

Lambert, M. J. (2016). Does client-therapist gender matching influence therapy course or outcome in psychotherapy? *Evidence Based Medical Practice 2* (108). https://doi.org/10.4172/2471-9919.1000108

Landers, F. (2002). Dismantling violent forms of masculinity through developmental transformations. *The Arts In Psychotherapy, 29*(1), 19–29. https://doi.org/10.1016/s0197-4556(01)00132-0

Landis, H. (2014). Drama therapy with newly arrived refugee women. In N. Sajnani & D. R. Johnson (Eds.), *Trauma-informed drama therapy: Transforming clinics, classrooms, and communities* (pp. 287–305). Charles C. Thomas.

Landy, R. (1982). Training the drama therapist—A four-part model. *The Arts in Psychotherapy, 9* (2), 91–99.

Landy, R. (1986). *Drama therapy: Concepts and practices*. Charles C. Thomas Publishers.

Landy, R. (2009). Role theory and the role method of drama therapy. In D. R. Johnson & R. Emunah (Eds.), *Current approaches in drama therapy* (pp. 65–88). Charles C. Thomas Publishers.

Landy, R., & Butler, J. D. (2012). Assessment through role theory. In D. R. Johnson, S. Pendzik, & S. Snow (Eds.), *Assessment in drama therapy* (pp. 148–176). Charles C. Thomas.

Landy, R., McLellan, L., & McMullian, S. (2005). The education of the drama therapist: In search of a guide. *The Arts in Psychotherapy, 32*(4), 275–292.

Lareau, A. (2011). *Unequal childhoods: Class, race, and family life* (2nd ed.). University of California Press.

Layton, L. (2017). Racialised enactments and normative unconscious processes: Where haunted identities meet. In S. Grand & J. Salberg (Eds.), *Transgenerational trauma and the other: Dialogues across history and difference* (pp. 144–164). Routledge.

Lazarus, R. J. (2000). Environmental racism! That's what it is. *University of Illinois Law Review, 2000*, 255–274. https://scholarship.law.georgetown.edu/facpub/160

Leamy, M., Bird, V., Boutillier, C., Williams, J., & Slade, M. (2011). Conceptual framework for personal recovery in mental health: Systematic review and narrative synthesis. *British Journal Of Psychiatry, 199*(6), 445–452. https://doi.org/10.1192/bjp.bp.110.083733

Lee, K., Volans, P. J., & Gregory, N. (2003). Trainee clinical psychologists' view on recruitment to work with older people. *Ageing & Society*, *23*(1), 83–97.

Lee, S. Y., Kim, S. H., & Kerr, C. (2015). Art therapy with Korean families. In C. Kerr (Ed.), *Multicultural family art therapy* (pp. 178–189). Routledge.

Lee Soon, R. (2016). Nohona i Waena i na Mo'olelo/living between the stories: Contextualizing drama therapy within an indigenous hawaiian epistemology. *Drama Therapy Review*, *2*(2), 257–271.

Leffler, E. (2022). *Applied theatre and intercultural dialogue: Playfully approaching difference*. Springer.

Legari, S., & Steiner, N. (2019). The direct transmission of DvT. http://www.develop mentaltransformations.com/images/Journal_Current.pdf

Lev-Aladgem, S. (1999). Dramatic play amongst the aged. *Dramatherapy*, *21*(3), 3–10. https://doi.org/10.1080/02630672.1999-2000.9689522

Levinas, E. (2006). *Humanism of the other*. University of Illinois Press.

Liddle, B. J. (1996). Therapist sexual orientation, gender, and counseling practices as they relate to ratings on helpfulness by gay and lesbian clients. *Journal of Counseling Psychology*, *43*(4), 394–401. https://doi.org/10.1037/0022-0167.43.4.394

Linden, S. (Ed.). (2013). *The heart and soul of psychotherapy. A transpersonal approach through theatre arts*. Trafford Publishing.

Lindkvist, B. (1981). Movement and drama with autistic children. In G. Schatner & S. Courtney (Eds.), *Drama in therapy* (Vol. 1). Drama Book Specialists.

Litman, L., Robinson, J., Rosen, Z., Rosenzweig, C., Waxman, J., & Bates, L. M. (2020). The persistence of pay inequality: The gender pay gap in an anonymous online labor market. *PLoS One*, *15*(2), e0229383. https://doi.org/10.1371/journal.pone.0229383

Littlewood, R., & Lipsedge, M. (1982). *Aliens and alienists: Ethnic minorities and psychiatry*. Penguin Books.

Liu, W. M. (2010). *Social class and classism in the helping professions: Research, theory and practice* (1st ed.). SAGE publications.

Long, K. (2020). Fractured stories: Self-experiences of third culture kids. *Journal of Infant, Child, and Adolescent Psychotherapy*, *19*(2), 134–147. https://doi.org/10.108 0/15289168.2020.1756030

Luo, S-H. & Wiseman, R. (2000) Ethnic language maintenance among Chinese immigrant children in the United States. *International Journal of Intercultural Relations*, *24*(3.1), 307–324. https://doi.org/10.106/SQ147-1767(00)00003-1

Mackelprang, R. W., & Salsgiver, R. O. (2016). *Disability: A diversity model approach in human service practice* (3rd ed.). Oxford University Press.

Mackey, K., Ayers, C. K., Kondo, K. K., Saha, S., Advani, S. M., Young, S., Spencer, H., Rusek, M., Anderson, J., Veazie, S., Smith, M., & Kansagara, D. (2020). Racial and ethnic disparities in COVID-19–related infections, hospitalizations, and deaths: A systematic review. *Annals of Internal Medicine*, *174*(3), 362–386. https://doi.org/10.7326/M20-6306

MacWilliam, B., Harris, B., Trottier, D., Long, K., & Williams, B. (Eds.). (2019). *Creative arts therapies and the LGBTQ community*. Jessica Kingsley Publishers.

Makanya, S. (2014). The missing links: A South African perspective on the theories of health in drama therapy. *The Arts in Psychotherapy*, *41*(3), 302–306. https://doi.org/10.1016/j.aip.2014.04.007

Mall, R. A. (1998). Philosophy and philosophies – cross-culturally considered. *Topoi: An International Review of Philosophy*, *17*(1), 15–27. https://doi.org/10.1023/A:1005924122195

Mall, R. A. (2000). The concept of an intercultural philosophy. *Polylog: Forum for Intercultural Philosophy, 1*. https://them.polylog.org/1/fmr-en.htm

Manstead, A. (2018). The psychology of social class: How socioeconomic status impacts thought, feelings, and behaviour. *The British Journal of Social Psychology, 57*(2), 267–291. https://doi.org/10.1111/bjso.12251

Marmot, M., Goldblatt, A. J., Boyce, P., McNeish, T, Grady, D., & Geddes, I. (2010) *Fair society, healthy lives.* (Strategica Review of Health Inequities in England post-2010). Institute of Health Equity. https://www.instituteofhealthequity.org/resources-reports/fair-society-healthy-lives-the-marmot-review

Marotta, V. (2009). Intercultural hermeneutics and the cross-cultural subject. *Journal of Intercultural Studies, 30*(3), 267–284. https://doi.org/10.1080/07256860903003575

Marotta, V. (2014). The multicultural, intercultural and the transcultural subject. In F. Mansouri & B. E. de B'beri (Eds.), *Global perspectives on the politics of multiculturalism in the 21st century* (pp. 90–102). Routledge.

Martin, R. (2020). Look at me! Representing self, representing ageing: Older women represent their own narratives of ageing, using re-enactment phototherapeutic techniques. In S. Hogan (Ed.), *Arts therapies and gender issues: International perspectives on research* (pp. 188–209). Routledge.

Marx, K. (1977). *Capital* (Vol. 1). Vintage Books.

Matsick, J., Wardecker, B., & Oswald, F. (2020). Treat sexual stigma to heal health disparities: Improving sexual minorities' health outcomes. *Policy Insights from the Behavioral and Brain Sciences, 7*(2), 205–213. https://doi.org/10.1177/2372732220942250

Maynard, K. (2018). To be black. To be a woman. Can dramatherapy help black women to discover their true self despite racial and gender oppression? *Dramatherapy, 39*(1), 31–48. https://doi.org/10.1080/02630672.2018.1432668

Mayor, C. (2010). Contact zones: The ethics of playing with "the Other". *Poiesis: A Journal of the Arts and Communication, 12*, 82–90.

Mayor, C. (2012). Playing with race: A theoretical framework and approach for creative arts therapists. *The Arts in Psychotherapy, 39*(3), 214–219. https://doi.org/10.1016/j.aip.2011.12.008

Mayor, C., & Dotto, S. (2014). De-railing history: Trauma stories off the track. In N. Sajnani & D. R. Johnson (Eds.), *Trauma-informed drama therapy: Transforming clinics, classrooms, and communities.* Charles C. Thomas.

Mbeki, L., & van Rossum, M. (2017). Private slave trade in the Dutch Indian ocean world: A study into the networks and backgrounds of the slavers and the enslaved in South Asia and South Africa. *Slavery and Abolition, 38*(1), 95–116. https://doi.org/10.1080/0144039X.2016.1159004

McAllister, M. (2011). From transitional object to symbol: Spiderman in a dramatherapy group for mentally disordered offenders. In D. Dokter & H. Seebohm (Eds.), *Dramatherapy and destructiveness.* Routledge.

McCall, L. (2005). The complexity of intersectionality. *Signs: Journal of Women in Culture and Society, 30*(3), 1771–1800. https://doi.org/10.1086/426800

McElroy, S. (2005). A soldier's story: An art therapy intervention in Sri Lanka. In D. Kalmanovitz & B. Lloyd (Eds.), *Art therapy and political violence: With art, without illusion* (pp. 183–196). Routledge.

McGoldrick, M., Giordano, J., & Pearce, J (Eds.). (1996). *Ethnicity and family therapy* (2nd ed.). Guilford Press.

McGoldrick, M., Giordano, J., & Preto, N. G. (2005). *Ethnicity and family therapy* (3rd ed.). Guilford Press.

McKenzie Mavinga, I. (2019). The challenge of racism in clinical supervision. In B. Ababio & R. Littlewood (Eds.), *Intercultural therapy: Challenges, insights and developments* (1st ed., pp. 167–177). Routledge.

McMulliam, S., & Burch, D. (2017). 'I am more than my disease': An embodied approach to understanding clinical populations using Landy's Taxonomy of Roles in concert with the DSM-5. *Drama Therapy Review, 3*(1). 29–43. https://doi.org/10.1386/dtr.3.1.29_1

Meerloo, J. A. M. (1955). Transference and resistance in geriatric psychotherapy. *Psychoanalytical Review, 42*, 72–82.

Mehra, B., Lemieux, P., & Stophel, K. (2019). An exploratory journey of cultural visual literacy of "non-conforming" gender representations from pre-colonial sub-saharan africa. *Open Information Science, 3*, 1–21. https://doi.org/10.1515/opis-2019-0001

Mental Health Foundation. (2016). *Fundamental facts about mental health.* https://www.mentalhealth.org.uk/sites/default/files/fundamental-facts-about-mental-health-2016.pdf

Meyer, I. H. (2015). Resilience in the study of minority stress and health of sexual and gender minorities. *Psychology of Sexual Orientation and Gender Diversity, 2*(3), 209–213. https://doi.org/10.1037/sgd0000132

Michaels, C. (1981). Geriadrama. In R. Courtney & G. Patte (Eds.), *Drama in therapy* (Vol. 2, pp. 175–186). Drama Book Specialist.

Milioni, D. (2001). Social constructionism and dramatherapy: Creating alternative discourses. *Dramatherapy, 23*(2), 10–17. https://doi.org/10.1080/02630672.2001.9689579

Millar, S., Chambers, M., & Giles, M. (2015). Service user involvement in mental health care: An evolutionary concept analysis. *Health Expectations, 19*(2), 209–221. https://doi.org/10.1111/hex.12353

Millen, M. (2019). Exploring gender identity and sexuality through portraiture. In B. MacWilliam, B. T. Harris, D. G. Trottier, & K. Long. (Eds.), *Creative arts therapies and the LGBTQ community: Theory and practice* (pp. 201–216). Jessica Kingsley Publishers.

Miller, C. (2009). Colonialism and dramatheraoy in Fiji. *Dramatherapy, 31*(2), 3–8.

Miller, C. (2000). Therapy at the end of one's life – What's the point?, *Dramatherapy, 22*(1), 25–27. https://doi.org/10.1080/02630672.2000.9689535

Miller, R., Vgenopoulou, S., & Johnson, D. R. (2015). Tending to the supervisory relationship through developmental transformations. *A Chest of Broken Toys: A Journal of Developmental Transformations, 1*, 35–51.

Mitchell, S. (2012). The theatre of self-expression: A brief introduction to the theory and practice of this ritual theatre form in clinical dramatherapy. In C. Schrader (Ed.), *Ritual theatre: The power of dramatic ritual in personal development groups and clinical practice* (pp. 240–254). Jessica Kingsley Publishers.

Mitchell, S. (2016). Ritual theatre in short-term group dramatherapy. In S. Jennings & C. Holmwood (Eds.), *Routledge international handbook of dramatherapy* (pp. 325–334). Routledge.

Modood, T. (2016). What is multiculturalism and what can it learn from interculturalism? *Ethnicities, 16*(3), 480–489. http://dx.doi.org/10.1186/s40878-018-0079-1

Moleiro, C., & Pinto, N. (2015). Sexual orientation and gender identity: Review of concepts, controversies and their relation to psychopathology classification systems. *Frontiers in Psychology, 6*, 1511. http://dx.doi.org/10.3389/fpsyg.2015.01511

Morgensen, S. L. (2011). *Spaces between us: Queer settler colonialism and indigenous decolonization.* University of Minnesota Press.

Morreira, S., Luckett, K., Kumalo, S. H., & Ramgotra, M. (2020). Confronting the complexities of decolonising curricula and pedagogy in higher education. *Third World Thematics: A TWQ Journal*, 5(1–2), 1–18. https://doi.org/10.1080/2380201 4.2020.1798278

Morris, N. (2011). Unspoken depths: Dramatherapy and dementia. *Dramatherapy*, 33(3), 144–157. https://doi.org/10.1080/02630672.2011.621262

Morrison, T. (2017). *The origin of others*. Harvard University Press.

Mullen-Williams, J. (2016). Translating the cultural subtext: An auto-ethnographical narrative of creating a reflexive space for newly qualified teachers. In D. Dokter & M. Hills de Zárate (Eds.), *Intercultural arts therapies research*. Routledge.

Mushfiqur, R., Mordi, C., Oruh, E. S., Nwagbara, U., Mordi, Tonbara, & Turner, I. M. (2018). The impacts of work-life-balance (WLB) challenges on social sustainability: The experience of Nigerian female medical doctors. *Employee Relations*, 40(5), 868–888. https://doi.org/10.1108/ER-06-2017-0131/full/html

Myers, L (1992). *Understanding an Afrocentric world view: Introduction to optimal psychology* (1st ed.). Kendall Hunt Publishing.

Nanda, S. (1996). Hijras: An alternative sex and gender role in India. In G. Herdt (Ed.), *Third sex, third gender: Beyond sexual dimorphism in culture and history* (pp. 373–418). Zone Books.

Narayan, U. (1997). Cross-cultural connections, border-crossings, and "death by culture": Thinking about dowry-murders in India and domestic-violence murders in the United States. In U. Narayan (Ed.), *Dislocating cultures* (1st ed., pp. 79–116). Routledge.

National Health Service England (NHS). (2017). *Prevent training and competencies framework*. https://www.somersetccg.nhs.uk/wp-content/uploads/2021/10/Prevent-Training-and-Competencies-Framework-2017.pdf

Nawaz, H., & Brett, A. S. (2009). Mentioning race at the beginning of clinical case presentations: A survey of US medical schools. *Medical Education*, 43(2), 146–154.

Nealy, E. (2017). *Transgender children and youth: Cultivating pride and joy with families in transition*. W. W. Norton & Company.

Neeganagwedgin, E. (2013). A critical review of Aboriginal education in Canada: Eurocentric dominance impact and everyday denial. *International Journal of Inclusive Education*, 17(1), 15–31. https://doi.org/10.1080/13603116.2011.580461

New York University Steinhardt. (2022). *Therapeutic theatre series*. https://steinhardt.nyu.edu/programs/drama-therapy/student-experience

Ng-A-Fook, N. (2013). Fishing for knowledge beyond colonial disciplines: Curriculum, social action projects, and indigenous communities. In A. Kulnieks, D. Roronhiakewen Longboat, & K. A. Young (Eds.), *Contemporary studies in environmental and indigenous pedagogies: A curricula of stories and place* (pp. 285–305). Sense Publishers. https://doi.org/10.1007/978-94-6209-293-8_16

Nimako, K., & Willemsen, G. (2011). *The dutch atlantic: Slavery, abolition and emancipation*. Pluto Press. https://doi.org/10.2307/j.ctt183p3kr

Nkrumah, K. (1970). *Consciencism: Philosophy and ideology for de-colonization*. Monthly Review Press.

Noice, H., & Noice, T. (2006). Theatrical intervention to improve cognition in intact residents of long term care facilities. *Clinical Gerontologist*, 3, 59–76.

Noice, H., & Noice, T. (2009). An arts intervention for older adults living in subsidized retirement homes. *Aging, Neuropsychology & Cognition*, 16(1), 56–79.

Noice, H. & Noice, T. (2013) Extending the reach of an evidence based theatrical intervention. *Experimental Ageing Research*, 39(4), 398–418. https://www.ncbi.nlm.nih.gov/pmc/articles PMCID: PMC3769171

Noice, H. & Noice, T. (2021) A theatrical evidence-based cognitive intervention for older adults. *Drama Therapy Review, 7*(1), 9–22.

Noice, H., Noice, T., Perrig-Chiello, P., & Perrig, W. (1999). Improving memory in older adults by instructing them in professional actors' learning strategies. *Applied Cognitive Psychology, 13*(4), 315–328.

Noice, H., Noice, T., & Staines, G. (2004). Short-term intervention to enhance cognitive and affective functioning in older adults. *Journal of Aging and Health, 16*(4), 562–585.

Noice, T., Noice, H., & Kramer, A. F. (2014). Participatory arts for older adults: A review of benefits and challenges. *The Gerontologist, 54* (5). 741–774.

Noice, T., Noice, H., & Kramer, A. F. (2015). Theatre arts for improving cognitive and affective health. *Activities, Adaptation & Aging, 39*, 19–31. https://doi.org/10.1080/01924788.2015.994440

North American Drama Therapy Association. (2013). *NADTA code, ethical principles*. https://www.nadta.org/assets/documents/updated-nadta-code-of-ethics-2019.pdf

North American Drama Therapy Association. (2016). *Guidelines on cultural response/ability in training, research, practice, supervision, advocacy & organizational change*. https://www.nadta.org/about-nadta/diversity/Cultural_Responsibility_Guidelines.html

North American Drama Therapy Association. (2019). *Timeline*. https://www.nadta.org/about-nadta/diversity/timeline.html

Novy, C. (2019). From reality disjunctions to dramatic reality: Bridging realities through the performance of life stories in dementia care. *Dramatherapy, 40*(3), 122–133. https://doi.org/10.1177/0263067220915419

Nyerere, J. K. (1968). *Freedom and socialism. Uhuru na ujamaa; a selection from writing and speeches 1965–1967*. Oxford University Press.

Office for National Statistics. (2021). *Ethnic group, national identity and religion*. https://www.ons.gov.uk/methodology/classificationsandstandards/measuringequality/ethnicgroupnationalidentityandreligion#religion

Office for National Statistics. (2022). *Coronavirus and the social impacts on disabled people in Great Britain*. https://www.ons.gov.uk/peoplepopulationandcommunity/healthandsocialcare/disability/datasets/coronavirusandthesocialimpactsondisabledpeopleingreatbritainmay2020

Olkin, R. (1999). *What psychotherapists should know about disability*. Guilford Press.

Olkin, R. (2002). Could you hold the door for me? Including disability in diversity. *Cultural Diversity And Ethnic Minority Psychology, 8*(2), 130–137. https://doi.org/10.1037/1099-9809.8.2.130

Olkin, R. (2007). Disability-affirmative therapy and case formulation: A template for understanding disability in a clinical context. *Counseling and human development, 39*(8), 1–20.

Olkin, R. (2017). *Disability-affirmative therapy. A case formulation template for clients with disabilities*. Oxford University Press.

Olkin, R., & Pledger, C. (2003). Can disability studies and psychology join hands? *American Psychologist, 58*(4), 296–304. https://doi.org/10.1037/0003-066X.58.4.296

Olkin, R., & Taliaferro, G. (2006). Evidence based practices have ignored people with disabilities. In J. Norcross, L. Beutler, & R. Levant (Eds.), *Evidence based practices in mental health: Debate and dialogue on the fundamental questions* (pp. 353–359). American Psychological Association.

Olumide, Y. M. (2016). *The vanishing black African woman. A Compendium of global skin lightening practice*. Langaa Research and Publishing CIG.

Olusoga, D. (2016). *Black and British: A forgotten history*. Macmillan Education.

Orth, J., & Verburght, J. (1998). One step beyond: Music therapy with traumatised refugees in a psychiatric clinic. In D. Dokter (Ed.), *Arts therapists, refugees and migrants: Reaching across borders* (1st ed., pp 80–94). Jessica Kinglsey Publishers.

Ortiz, F. (1947). *Cuban counterpoint: Tobacco and sugar*. Duke University Press.

Overall, N. C., & Simpson, J. A. (2015). Attachment and dyadic regulation processes. *Current Opinion in Psychology, 1*, 61–666. https://doi.org/10.1016/j.copsyc.2014.11.008

Palmore, E. (2015). Ageism comes of age. *Journals of Gerontology: Series B*, 70 (6), 873–875. https://doi.org/10.1093/geronb/gbv079

Panhofer, H., Zelaskowski, P., & Bräuninger, I. (2016). Dance movement therapy training: The challenges of interculturality and cross-cultural communication within a diverse student group-analytic large group. In D. Dokter & M. Hills de Zárate (Eds.), *Intercultural arts therapies research: Issues and methodologies* (pp. 56–74). Routledge. https://doi.org/10.4324/9781315726441-4

Pantiru, S. A., & Barley, R. (2014). The acculturation process of Romanian immigrants in the UK. *Reinvention: An International Journal of Undergraduate Research, 7*(1). https://warwick.ac.uk/fac/cross_fac/iatl/reinvention/archive/volume7issue1/pantiru/

Park, M. (2016). The development of a Korean drama therapy: From a late comer to the leading special practical human science in art therapy. In S. Jennings & C. Holmwood (Eds.), *The international handbook of dramatherapy* (pp. 3–7). Routledge.

Pattison, S. (2007). *The challenge of practical theology*. Jessica Kingsley Publishers.

Pawliuk, N., Grizenko, N., Chan-Yip, A., Gantous, P., Mathew, J., & Nguyen, D. (1996). Acculturation style and psychological functioning in children of immigrants. *The American Journal of Orthopsychiatry, 66*(1), 111–121. https://doi.org/10.1037/h0080161

Payne, H. (Ed.). (2008). *Supervision of dance movement psychotherapy: A practitioner's handbook*. Routledge.

Pendzik, S. (2006). On dramatic reality and its therapeutic function in drama therapy. *The Arts in Psychotherapy, 33*(4), 271–280. https://doi.org/10.1016/j.aip.2006.03.001

Pendzik, S. (2016). The feminist tradition in dramatherapy. In S. Jennings & C. Holmwood (Eds.), *International handbook of dramatherapy* (pp. 306–316). Routledge.

Pendzik, S., Emunah, R., & Johnson, D. R. (Eds.). (2016). *The self in performance: Autobiographical, self revelatory and autoethnographic forms of therapeutic theatre*. Palgrave Macmillan.

Peréz-Torres, R. (1993). Nomads and migrants: Negotiating a multicultural postmodernism. *Cultural Critique*, (26), 161–189. https://doi.org/10.2307/1354459

Pew Research Center. (2013). *A survey of LGBT Americans: Attitudes, experiences and values in changing times*. https://www.pewresearch.org/social-trends/2013/06/13/a-survey-of-lgbt-americans/

Plamondon, B. (2013). *The truth about Trudeau* (1st ed.). Great River Media Inc.

Playback Theatre UK. (2022). *The golden thread playback company*. https://playbacktheatreuk.wordpress.com/wales/

Porter, L. (2000). The bifurcated gift: Love and intimacy in drama psychotherapy. *Arts in Psychotherapy, 27*, 309–320.

Porter, J., Hulbert-Williams, L., & Chadwick, D. (2015). Sexuality in the therapeutic relationship: An interpretive phenomenological analysis of the experiences of gay therapists. *Journal of Gay and Lesbian Mental Health, 19*, 165–183.

Portes, A., & Hao, L. (2002). The price of uniformity: Language, family and personality adjustment in the immigrant second generation. *Ethnic & Racial Studies*, *25*(6), 889–912.

Potash, J. S., Bardot, H., Moon, C. H., Napoli, M., Lyonsmith, A., & Hamilton, M. (2017). Ethical implications of cross-cultural international art therapy. *The Arts in Psychotherapy*, *56*, 74–82. https://doi.org/10.1016/j.aip.2017.08.005

Powell, A. (2016). Embodied multicultural assessment: An interdisciplinary training model. *Drama Therapy Review*. 2 (1), 111–121.

Prentki, T. & Abraham, N. (2020). *The applied theatre reader*. Routledge.

Pruchno, R. A., Wilson-Genderson, M. R., & Rose, M. (2010). Successful ageing: Early influences and contemporary characteristics. *The Gerontologist*, *50*(6), 821–833. https://doi.org/10.1093/genront/gnq041

Pyke, K. D. (2010). What is internalized racial oppression and why don't we study it? Acknowledging racism's hidden injuries. *Sociological Perspectives*, *53*(4), 551–572. https://doi.org/10.1525/sop.2010.53.4.551

Quinn, J. F., & Burkhauser, R. V. (1994). Public policy and the plans and preferences of older Americans. *Journal of Aging & Social Policy*, *6*(3), 5–20. https://doi.org/10.1300/j031v06n03_03

Quinodoz, D. (2009). *Growing old: A journey of self discovery* (1st ed.). Routledge.

Ramsden, E., & Guarnieri, M. (2010). Dramatherapy and victim empathy: A workshop approach in a forensic setting. In P. Jones (Ed.), *Drama as therapy: Clinical work and research into practice* (Vol. 2, pp. 152–171). Routledge.

Ratts, M., Singh, A. A., Nassar-McMillan, S., Butler, S. K., & McCullough, J. R. (2015). *Multicultural and social justice counseling competencies*. AMCD.

Raucher, G. (2011). Towards a meta psychology of ritual in dramatherapy. In C. Schrader (Ed.), *Ritual theatre: The power of dramatic ritual in personal development groups and clinical practice* (pp. 60–78). Jessica Kingsley Publishers.

Razaq, A., Harrison, D., Karunanithi, S., Barr, B., Asaria, M., Routen, A., & Khunti, K. (2020). *BAME COVID-19 DEATHS – What do we know? Rapid data & evidence review*. Centre for Evidence-Based Medicine (CEBM). https://www.cebm.net/covid-19/bame-covid-19-deaths-what-do-we-know-rapid-data-evidence-review/

Redfield, R., Linton, R., & Herskovits, M. (1936). Memorandum on the study of acculturation. *American Anthropologist*, *38*, 149–152.

Redhouse, R. (2014). Life story: Meaning making through dramatherapy in a palliative care context. *Dramatherapy*, *36*(2–3), 66–80. https://doi.org/10.1080/02630672.2014.996239

Reidi, T. (2018, August 31). Is studying the arts the preserve of the middle classes? *The Guardian*. https://www.theguardian.com/education/2018/aug/31/how-working-class-arts-students-get-locked-out

Reinstein, M. (2002). When I am an old woman… Using dramatherapy as a treatment for depression with functional elderly people. *Dramatherapy*, *24*(2), 10–15. https://doi.org/10.1080/02630672.2002.9689611

Reiss, F., Meyrose, A. K., Otto, C., Lampert, T., Klasen, F., & Ravens-Sieberer, U. (2019). Socioeconomic status, stressful life situations and mental health problems in children and adolescents: Results of the German BELLA cohort-study. *PLoS One*, *14*(3), e0213700. https://doi.org/10.1371/journal.pone.0213700

Remigi, E. (2017). *In limbo: Brexit testimonies from EU citizens in the UK*. CreateSpace Independent Publishing Platform.

Richards, P. S., & Bergin, A. (2014). *Handbook of psychotherapy and religious diversity* (2nd ed.). American Psychological Association.

Richards, P. S., & Bergin, A. E. (Eds.). (2000). *Handbook of psychotherapy and religious diversity*. American Psychological Association. https://doi.org/10.1037/10347-000

Richardson, H. (2020, July 30). Black pupils face trebled exclusion rate in some areas of England. *BBC News*. https://www.bbc.com/news/education-53516009

Riddle, T., & Sinclair, S. (2019). Racial disparities in school-based disciplinary actions are associated with county-level rates of racial bias. *PNAS Proceedings of the National Academy of Sciences of the United States of America, 116*(17), 8255–8260. https://doi.org/10.1073/pnas.1808307116

Rigaud, K. K.., de Sherbinin, A., Jones, B., Bergmann, J., Clement, V., Ober, K., Schewe, J., Adamo, S., McCusker, B., Heuser, S., & Midgley, A. (2018). *Groundswell: Preparing for internal climate migration*. World Bank. https://doi.org/10.1596/29461

Rollins, J. (2009, July 29). *Connecting with clients of faith*. Counseling Today Online. http://ct.counseling.org/2009/08/connecting-with-clients-of-faith/

Rosen, D. C., Miller, A. B., Nakash, O., Halperin, L., & Alegría, M. (2012). Interpersonal complementarity in the mental health intake: A mixed-methods study. *Journal of Counseling Psychology, 59*(2), 185–196. https://doi.org/10.1037/a0027045

Rousseau, C., Benoit, M., Gauthier, M, & Lacroix, L. (2007). Classroom dramatherapy program for immigrant and refugee adolescents: A pilot study. *Clinical Child Psychology and Psychiatry, 12*(3), 451–465.

Rowe, N. (2007). *Playing the other*. Jessica Kingsley Publisher.

Rowley, J., Richards, N., Carduff, E., & Gott, M. (2021). The impact of poverty and deprivation at the end of life: A critical review. *Palliative Care and Social Practice, 15*, 1–19. https://doi.org/10.1177/26323524211033873

Royal College of Psychiatrists. (2016). *Spirituality and mental health*. www.rcpsych.ac.uk/mentalhealthinfo/treatments/spirituality.aspx

Ryan, C., Russell, S., Huebner, D., Diaz, R., & Sanchez, J. (2010). Family acceptance in adolescence and the health of LGBT young adults. *Journal Of Child And Adolescent Psychiatric Nursing, 23*(4), 205–213. https://doi.org/10.1111/j.1744-6171.2010.00246.x3

Ryde, J. (2000). Supervising across difference. *International Journal of Psychotherapy, 5*(1), 37–48.

Ryde, J. (2009). *Being white in the helping professions: Developing effective intercultural awareness*. Jessica Kingsley Publishers.

Said, E. W. (1994). *Orientalism*. Vintage Books.

Sajnani, N. (2003). The body politic: Four conversations on gender and the nation. *Graduate Researcher: Interdisciplinary Journal, 1*(1), 9–18. https://doi.org/10.1016/j.aip.2013.05.001

Sajnani, N. (2004). Strategic narratives: The embodiment of minority discourse in biographical performance. *Canadian Theatre Review, 117*, 33–37.

Sajnani, N. (2009). Theatre of the oppressed: Drama therapy as cultural dialogue. In D. R. Johnson & R. Emunah (Eds.), *Current approaches in drama therapy* (pp. 461–482). Charles C. Thomas Publishers.

Sajnani, N. (2012a). Response/ability: Imagining a critical race feminist paradigm for the creative arts therapies. *The Arts in Psychotherapy, 39*(3), 186–191. https://doi.org/10.1016/j.aip.2011.12.009

Sajnani, N. (2012b). The implicated witness: Towards a relational aesthetic in dramatherapy. *Dramatherapy, 34*(1), 6–21.

Sajnani, N. (2013). The body politic: The relevance of an intersectional framework for therapeutic performance research in drama therapy. *The Arts in Psychotherapy, 40*(4), 382–385. https://doi.org/10.1016/j.aip.2013.05.001

Sajnani, N. (2016a). On being home. In M. Agosin (Ed.), *Home: An imagined land-scape* (pp. 113–120). Solis Press.

Sajnani, N. (2016b). Toward a critical aesthetic paradigm in drama therapy. In C. Holmwood & S. Jennings (Eds.), *International handbook of dramatherapy* (pp. 161–163). Routledge.

Sajnani, N. (2017). Advancing theory and technique in drama therapy. *Drama Therapy Review, 3*(2), 161–163. https://doi.org/10.1386/dtr.3.2.161_2

Sajnani, N. (2018). The trouble with the word 'client'. https://tinyurl.com/troubling-language

Sajnani, N., & Dokter, D. (2015, September 16–19). *Teaching intercultural good practice guidelines through experiential learning in dramatherapy* [Workshop]. *ECArTE: 13th European Arts Therapies Conference*, Palermo, Sicily, Italy.

Sajnani, N., & Dokter, D. (2017). An experiential framework and approach to teaching cultural response/ability. In R. Houghham, S. Pitruzella, & S. Scoble (Eds.), *Cultural landscapes in the arts therapies* (pp. 253–274). University of Plymouth Press.

Sajnani, N., & Johnson, D. R. (2014). *Trauma informed drama therapy: Transforming clinics, classrooms, and communities*. Charles C. Thomas Publishers.

Sajnani, N., Mayor, C., & Boal, J. (2021). Theatre of the oppressed. In D. R. Johnson & R. Emunah (Eds.), *Current approaches in drama therapy* (pp. 561–581). Charles C. Thomas Publishers.

Sajnani, N., & Nadeau, D. (2006). Creating safer spaces with immigrant women of colour: Performing the politics of possibility. *Canadian Woman Studies, 25*(1–2), 45–53.

Sajnani, N., Tomczyk, P., Bleuer, J., Dokter, D., Carr, M., & Bilodeau, S. (2016). Guidelines on cultural response/ability in training, research, practice, supervision, advocacy and organizational change. *Drama Therapy Review, 2*, 141–148. https://doi.org/10.1386/dtr.2.1.141_7

Sajnani, N., & Wager, A. (2017, June 19). *Gaps, complicities, and connections: Stories from a movement towards racial justice in higher education by Nisha Sajnani and Amanda Wager*. Playback Theatre Reflects. https://playbacktheatrereflects.net/2017/06/19/gaps-complicities-and-connections-stories-from-a-movement-towards-racial-justice-in-higher-education-by-nisha-sajnani-and-amanda-wager/

Sakellariou, D., & Rotarou, E. (2017). Access to healthcare for men and women with disabilities in the UK: Secondary analysis of cross-sectional data. *BMJ Open, 7*(8), e016614. https://doi.org/10.1136/bmjopen-2017-016614

Salamon, G. (2010). *Assuming a body: Transgender and rhetorics of materiality*. Columbia University Press.

Saldaña, J. (2011). *Ethnotheatre: Research from page to stage* (1st ed.). Routledge.

Saldaña, J. (2016). *The coding manual for qualitative researchers*. SAGE Publications.

Samuels, A. (1989). *The plural psyche*. Routledge.

Samuels, A. (2001). *Politics on the couch: Citizenship and the internal life*. Karnac Books.

Samuels, E. J. (2003). My body, my closet: Invisible disability and the limits of coming-out discourse. *GLQ: A Journal of Lesbian and Gay Studies 9*(1), 233–255. https://www.muse.jhu.edu/article/40803

Sartre, J.-P. (1945). *Existentialism is a humanism* (C. Macomber, Trans.). Yale University Press.

Satterly, B. (2006). Therapist self-disclosure from a gaymale perspective. *Families in Society: The Journal of Contemporary Social Services, 87*, 240–247. https://doi.org/10.1606/1044-3894.3517

Savage, M., Devine, F., Cunningham, N., Taylor, M., Jaojun, L., Johns, H., Le Rous, B., Friedman, S., & Miles, A. (2013). A new model of social class: Findings from the BBC's great British class survey experiment. *Sociology, 47*(2), 219–250.

Savarese, N., & Fowler, R. (2001). 1931 Antonin Artaud sees Balinese theatre at the Paris colonial exposition. *TDR: The Drama Review, 45*(3), 51–77. https://doi.org/10.1162/10542040152587114

Scannell, M. (2016). *The big book of conflict resolution games.* McGraw-Hill.

Schacham, M. Ayalon, O., & Lahad, M. (2013). *The BASIC Ph Model of coping and resiliency: Theory, research and cross cultural application.* Jessica Kingsley Publishers.

Schattner, G., & Courtney, R. (Eds.). (1981). *Drama in therapy: Adults.* Drama Book Specialists.

Schaverien, J. (2004). Boarding school: The trauma of the 'privileged' child. *The Journal of Analytical Psychology, 49*(5), 683–705. https://doi.org/10.1111/j.0021-8774.2004.00495.x

Schaverien, J. (Ed.). (2006). *Gender, countertransference and the erotic transference: Perspectives from analytical psychology and psychoanalysis.* Routledge/Taylor & Francis Group.

Schaverien, J. (2011). Boarding school syndrome: Broken attachments a hidden trauma. *British Journal of Psychotherapy, 27*(2), 138–155. https://doi.org/10.1111/j.1752-0118.2011.01229.x

Schechner, R. (1988). *Performance theory.* Routledge.

Schechner, R. (2002). *Performance studies: An introduction.* Routledge.

Schilt, K., & Westbrook, L. (2009). Doing gender, doing heteronormativity: "Gender normals," transgender people, and the social maintenance of heterosexuality. *Gender & Society, 23*(4), 440–464. https://doi.org/10.1177/0891243209340034

Schleutker, E. (2016). Women's work-life preferences: Reconceptualization and cross country description over time. *European societies, 19*(3), 292–312. https://doi.org/10.1080/14616696.2017.1290266

Schore, A. N. (1998). Early shame experiences and infant brain development. In P. Gilbert & B. Andrews (Eds.), *Shame: Interpersonal behavior, psychopathology, and culture* (pp. 57–77). Oxford University Press.

Schrader, C. (2012). *Ritual theatre: The power of dramatic ritual in personal development groups and clinical practice.* Jessica Kingsley Publishers.

Schreurs, A. (2002). *Psychotherapy and spirituality: Integrating the spiritual dimension into therapeutic practice.* (1st ed.). Jessica Kingsley Publishers.

Scope. (2020). *The disability report: Disabled people and the coronavirus crisis.* https://www.scope.org.uk/campaigns/disabled-people-and-coronavirus/the-disability-report/

Scott, B. (2019). Dramatherapy in a nursing home: Exploring resonances between sensory experience and embodied interaction in people with dementia through fairy tales. *Dramatherapy, 40*(2), 81–95.

Scott-Danter, H. (1998). Between theatre and therapy: Experiences of a dramatherapist in Mozambique. In D. Dokter (Ed.), *Arts therapists, refugees and migrants: Reaching across borders* (pp. 94–110). Jessica Kingsley Publishers.

Serpentine.(2022). *ACTESOL: Language, resistance, theatre.* Retrieved April 30, 2022, from https://www.serpentinegalleries.org/whats-on/act-esol-language-resistance-theatre/

Seymour, A. (2016). Personal theatre and pedagogy: A dialectical process. In S. Pendzik, R. Emunah, & D. R. Johnson (Eds.), *The self in performance* (pp. 199–212). Palgrave Macmillan.

Seymour, A., & Holloway, P. (2019, January 7). *Marx and dramatherapy pedagogy*. Critical Pedagogies in the Art Therapies. http://www.criticalpedagogyartstherapies. com/single_post/2019/01/07/Marx_and_Dramatherapy_Pedagogy/index.html

Shakespeare, T., & Watson, N. (2001). The social model of disability: An outdated ideology? In S. Barnartt & B. Altman (Eds.), *Exploring theories and expanding methodologies: Where we are and where we need to go* (Vol 2, pp. 9–28). Emerald Publishing.

Shapiro, J. (2020, June 9). *COVID-19 infections and deaths are higher among those with intellectual disabilities*, NPR. https://www.npr.org/2020/06/09/872401607/covid-19-infections-and-deaths-are-higher-among-those-with-intellectual-disabili

Sharma, A. (2019). *In conversation with Tony Cealy: Theatre practitioner, cultural producer, activist*. Ideas Alliance. https://www.ideas-alliance.org.uk/hub/2019/10

Sheppard, B. (2018). Should a dramatherapist disclose their sexual orientation to their clients? Perhaps they should be prepared to. *Dramatherapy*, *39*(3), 127–140. https://doi.org/10.1080/02630672.2018.1510019

Shorter, E. (2005). *Written in the flesh: A history of desire*. University of Toronto Press.

Showalter, E. (1987). *The female malady: Women, madness and English culture, 1830–1980*. Virago.

Silvers, L. (2021). *About drag therapy*. Drag Therapy. http://www.drag-therapy.com/dragtherapy.html

Simonds, L. M., & Spokes, N. (2017). Therapist self-disclosure and the therapeutic alliance in the treatment of eating problems. *Eating Disorders: The Journal of Treatment & Prevention*, *25*(2), 151–164.

Simplican, S. C., Leader, G., Kosciulek, J., & Leahy, M. (2015). Defining social inclusion of people with intellectual and developmental disabilities: An ecological model of social networks and community participation. *Research in Developmental Disabilities*, *38*, 18–29. https://doi.org/10.1016/j.ridd.2014.10.008

Sinason, V. (1992). *Mental handicap and the human condition: New approaches from the Tavistock*. Free Association Books.

Sinason, V. (2010). *Mental handicap and the human condition: An analytic approach to intellectual disability: Second updated edition*. Free Association Books.

Singer, A., Skorc, B., & Ognenovic, V. (2016). Voices within intercultural arts psychotherapy research and practice: An ethnographic approach. In D. Dokter & M. Hills de Zárate (Eds.), *Intercultural arts therapies research: Issues and methodologies*. (pp 133–151). Routledge.

Sins Invalid. (2019). *Skin, tooth, and bone: The basis of movement is our people, A disability justice primer* (2nd ed.). Sins Invalid.

Skaife, S. (2000). Keeping the balance: Further thoughts on the dialectics of art therapy. In A. Gilroy & G. McNeilly (Eds.), *The changing shape of art therapy: New developments in theory and practice* (pp. 115–142). Jessica Kingsley Publishers.

Skutbnabb-Kangas, T. (1981). *Bilingualism or not: The education of minorities*. Multilingual Matters.

Slife, B. D., Stevenson, T. D., & Wendt, D. C. (2010). Including God in psychotherapy: Strong vs weak theism. *Journal of psychology and theology*, *38*(3). 163–174. https://doi.org/10.1177/009164711003800301

Smail, M. (2016). Open sesame and the soul cave. In S. Jennings & C. Holmwood (Eds.), *International handbook of drama therapy* (1st. ed., pp. 180–188). Routledge.

Smith, A. (2000). Exploring death anxiety with older adults through developmental transformations. *The Arts in Psychotherapy*, *22*(5), 321–334.

Smith, S. D., Ng, K.-M., Brinson, J., & Mityagin, E. (2008). Multiculturalism, diversity, and social advocacy: A 17-year content analysis of counselor education and supervision. *Counselor Education and Supervision*, *47*(4), 249–263. https://doi.org/10.1002/j.1556-6978.2008.tb00055.x

Snell, J. (2014). Social class and language. In J. Östman & J. Verschueren (Eds.), *Handbook of pragmatics: 2014 installment*. John Benjamins.

Snow, S. (2022). *Ethnodramatherapy: Integrating research, therapy, theatre and social activism into one method* (1st ed.). Routledge.

Snow, S., D'Amico, M., Mongerson, E., Anthony, E., Rozenberg, M., Opolko, C., & Anandampillai, S. (2017). Ethnodramatherapy applied in a project focusing on relationships in the lives of adults with developmental disabilities, especially romance, intimacy and sexuality. *Drama Therapy Review*, *3*(2), 241–260. https://doi.org/10.1386/dtr.3.2.241_1

Snow, S., D'Amico, M., & Tanguay, D. (2003). Therapeutic theatre and well-being. *The Arts in Psychotherapy*, *30*(2), 73–82.

Snow, S., & D'Amico, M. (2015). The application of ethnodrama with female adolescents under youth protection within a creative arts therapies context. *Drama Therapy Review*, *1*(2), 201–218. https://doi.org/10.1386/dtr.1.2.201_1

Soheilian, S. S., Inman, A. G., Klinger, R. S., Isenberg, D. S., & Kulp, L. E. (2014). Multicultural supervision: Supervisees' reflections on culturally competent supervision. *Counseling Psychology Quarterly*, *27*(4), 379–392.

Solomon, P., O'Brien, K., Wilkins, S., & Gervais, N. (2014). Aging with HIV: A model of disability. *Journal of the International Association of Providers of AIDS Care (JIAPAC)*, 519–525. https://doi.org/10.1177/2325957414547431

Sommers-Flanagan, R., & Sommers-Flanagan, J. (2015). *Becoming an ethical helping professional: Cultural and philosophical foundations, with video resource center* (1st ed.). Wiley.

Song, J. E., Lee, Y. H., & Jung, H. E. (2009). *Family and life culture*. Yang Seo Won

Sorrells, K. (2015). *Intercultural communication: Globalization and social justice*. SAGE Publications.

Southern, H. (2018). I am such a woman: The complexities of being a bisexual dramatherapist. *Dramatherapy*, *39*(3), 183–185. https://doi.org/10.1080/02630672.2018.1508603

Sparrow, S., Cicchetti, D. V., & Balia, D. A. (2006). *Vineland adaptive behavior scales—Second edition* (2nd ed.). Pearson.

Spiderwoman Theatre. (n.d.). *Projects*. Retrieved May 4, 2022, from https://www.spiderwomantheater.org/current

Stamp, S. (2000). A fast-moving floorshow – The space between acting and thinking in dramatherapy with offenders. *Dramatherapy*, *22*(1), 10–15. https://doi.org/10.1080/02630672.2000.9689532

Stanfeld, S., Clark, C., Bebbington, P., King, M., Jenkin, R., & Hinchliffe, S. (2016). *Mental health and wellbeing in England: Adult psychiatric morbidity survey 2014*. NHS Digital.

Steele, L., Dewa, C., & Lee, K. (2007). Socio economic status and self reported barriers to mental health service use. *Canadian Journal of Psychiatry*, *52*(3), 201–207. https://doi.org/10.1177/070674370705200312

Steinbugler, A. C., Press, J. E., & Dias, J. J. (2006). Gender, race, and affirmative action: Operationalizing intersectionality in survey research. *Gender & Society*, *20*(6), 805–825. https://doi.org/10.1177/0891243206293299

Stevens, A. (2021, January 6). *Being black and strong* [Video]. *NYU Theatre & Health Lab YouTube*. https://www.youtube.com/watch?v=cV8BJ0P_C7E&t=4923s

Stevens, M. (2020, November 8). Kamala Harris's vice president-elect acceptance speech. *The New York Times*. https://www.nytimes.com/article/watch-kamala-harris-speech-video-transcript.html

Sturm, D. C., & Gibson, D. M. (Eds.). (2012). *Social class and the helping professions: A clinician's guide to navigating the landscape of class in America*. Taylor & Francis Group.

Sue, D. W., Arredondo, P., & McDavis, R. J. (1992). Multicultural competencies/standards: A pressing need. *Journal of Counseling & Development*, 70, 477–486.

Sue, S. (1998). In search of cultural competence in psychotherapy and counseling. *American Psychologist*, *53*(4), 440–448. https://doi.org/10.1037/0003-066X.53.4.440

Sykes, S. (2020, December 29). Black physician's Covid-19 death demonstrates bias of U.S. health care system, peers say. *NBC News*. https://www.nbcnews.com/news/us-news/black-physician-s-covid-19-death-demonstrates-bias-u-s-n1252290

Tajfel, H. (1981). Social stereotypes and social groups. In J. C. Turner & H. Giles (Eds.), *Intergroup behaviour* (pp. 144–167). Blackwell.

Talwar, S. (2016). Is there a need to redefine art therapy? *Art Therapy*, *33*(3), 116–118. https://doi.org/10.1080/07421656.2016.1202001

Taylor, M. (2020). *How the British establishment resisted the abolition of slavery*. The Bodley Head.

Teesri Duniya Theatre. (n.d.). *About*. Retrieved May 4, 2022, from https://teesridun iyatheatre.com/

Tennant, R., Hiller, L., Fishwick, R. et al. (2007). The Warwick-Edinburgh Mental Well-being Scale (WEMWBS): Development and UK validation. *Health Qual Life Outcomes* 5, 63 https://doi.org/10.1186/1477-7525-5-63

Tervalon, M., & Murray-García, J. (1998). Cultural humility versus cultural competence: A critical distinction in defining physician training outcomes in multicultural education. *Journal of Health Care for the Poor and Underserved*, *9*(2), 117–125. https://doi.org/10.1353/hpu.2010.0233

The Equality Trust. (2016, November 10). *The mindless gap: Why gender pay inequality harms us all*. https://equalitytrust.org.uk/blog/mindless-gap-why-gender-pay-inequality-harms-us-all

The Fawcett Society. (2021). *Coronavirus: Making women visible*. Fawcett. https://www.fawcettsociety.org.uk/coronavirus-making-women-visible

TED. (2018, May 4). Fatmah AlQuadfan: Finding drama therapy and bringing it home. YouTube. https://www.youtube.com/watch?v=l44lSx5yPsA

Thomas, J. E., & Lyles, K. (Eds.). (2007). *Creativity and aging: Best practices*. National Endowment for the Arts.

Thomas, L. (2018, November 24). *What's normal*. [Webinar]. *The Black and Asian Therapy Network website*. https://www.confer.uk.com/biogs/biog_thomas.html

Thomas, L. (2019). Intercultural psychoanalytic psychotherapy and generationally transmitted trauma. In J. Kareem & R. Littlewood (Eds.), *Intercultural therapy* (1st ed.). Blackwell Science.

Thompson, J., Balfour, M., & Hughes, J. (2009). *Performance in place of war*. Seagull Books.

Thorn, R. (2011). Sugar and spice and all things nice. A black woman's anger in a forensic setting. In D. Dokter, P. Holloway, & H. Seebohm (Eds.), *Dramatherapy and destructiveness* (pp. 133–144). Routledge.

Thornton-Dill, B., & Zambrana, R. (2009). *Emerging intersections: Race, class, and gender in theory, policy, and practice*. Rutgers University Press.

Thorpe, V. (2020, August 15). 'We must give black talent the stage' says Young Vic's Kwame Kwei-Armah. *The Guardian*. https://www.theguardian.com/stage/2020/aug/15/we-must-give-black-talent-the-stage-says-young-vics-kwame-kwei-armah

Thorsteinsson, E. B., James, J. E., & Gregg, M. E. (1998). Effects of video-related social support on hemodynamic reactivity and salivary cortisol during laboratory-based behavioral challenge. *Health Psychology*, *17*(5), 436–444. https://doi.org/10.1037//0278-6133.17.5.436

Todd, M. (2016). *Straight jacket: How to be gay and happy*. Penguin Random House.

Todman, V. (2020, February 5). *Access to university for working class students: The rural/urban divide*. What Works Dept: Kings College London. https://blogs.kcl.ac.uk/behaviouralinsights/2020/02/05/access-to-university-for-working-class-students-the-rural-urban-divide/

Tomczyk, P. (2015, March 26). Is there a queer drama therapy? *The Dramascope*. https://thedramascope.wordpress.com/2015/03/26/is-there-a-queer-drama-therapy/

Tomczyk, P, (2019). Queer bodies and queer practices: The implications of queer theory for dramatherapy. In S. Hogan (Eds.), *Arts therapies and gender issues: International perspectives on research* (pp. 110–119). Routledge. https://doi.org/10.4324/9781351121958

Tomczyk, P. (2020). Queer bodies and queer practice: The implications of queer theory for dramatherapy. In S. Hogan (Ed.), *Arts therapies and gender issues: International perspectives on research* (pp. 116–126). Routledge.

Tonghou-Ngong, D. (Ed.). (2017). *A new history of African Christian thought. From Cape to Cairo*. Routledge.

Totton, N. (2008). In and out of the mainstream: Therapy in its social and political context. In S. Haugh & S. Paul (Eds.), *The therapeutic relationship: Perspectives and themes*. PCCS Books.

Tovah, L. (2016). *Crip lit: Toward an intersectional crip syllabus*. Autostraddle. https://www.autostraddle.com/crip-lit-an-intersectional-queer-crip-syllabus-333400/

Tran, D. (2019, September 24). *How 'slave play' got 800 black people to the theatre*. American Theatre. https://www.americantheatre.org/2019/09/23/how-slave-play-got-800-black-people-to-the-theatre/.

Trilling, D. (2018). *Light in the distance: Exile and refuge on the borders of Europe*. Picador.

Trottier, D. G. (2019). Therapist as guide. In B. MacWilliam, B. Harris, D. Trottier, K. Long, & B. Williams (Eds.), *Creative arts therapies and the LGBTQ community* (pp. 75–100). Jessica Kingsley Publishers.

Tselikas-Portmann, E. (Ed.). (1999). *Supervision and drama therapy*. Jessica Kingsley Publishers

Tuck, E., Wayne, Y. K., & Gaztambide-Fernández, R. (2015, April). Citation practices. *Critical Ethnic Studies*. http://www.criticalethnicstudiesjournal.org/citation-practices.

Tuckwell, G. (2002). *Racial identity, white counsellors and therapists*. Open University Press.

Turner, D. (2021). *Intersections of privilege and otherness in counselling and psychotherapy* (1st ed.). Routledge. https://doi.org/10.4324/9780367854423

Tyagi, A. (2008). Individuation: The jungian process of spiritual growth. In A. Hussain (Ed.), *Explorations of human spirituality* (pp. 128–153). Global Vision.

U.K. Council for Psychotherapy. (2009). *Ethical principles and code of professional conduct*. http://gpti.org.uk/wp-content/uploads/2013/09/UKCP-Ethical-Principles-and-Code-of-Professional-Conduct.pdf.

U.K. Parliament (1957). *Wolfenden report*. https://www.parliament.uk/about/living-heritage/transformingsociety/private-lives/relationships/collections1/sexual-offences-act-1967/wolfenden-report-/

United Nations. (1948). *Universal declaration of human rights*. https://www.un.org/en/about-us/universal-declaration-of-human-rights

United Nations. (2013). *World population ageing 2013*. Department of Economic and Social Affairs Population Division. http://www.un.org/en/development/desa/population/publications/pdf/ageing/WorldPopulationAgeing2013.pdf

Vaïs, M. (2019). Lepage and mnouchkine collide with cultural appropriation. *PAJ: A Journal of Performance and Art, 41*(3), 71–74. https://doi.org/10.1162/pajj_a_00488

Valadas, R.C. (2018). From isolation towards intimacy: Healing emotional wounds in HIV+ Gay men. *Dramatherapy.* 39 (3), 163–178. https://doi.org/10.1080/02630672.2018.152630

Valadas, R. C. (2022). *Current reflexion*. https://ryancvaladas.com/current-reflexion

Valadas, R. C., & Carr, M. (2018). Editorial. *Dramatherapy Special Issue: LGBTQ+ Perspectives, 39*(3), 123–126. https://doi.org/10.1080/02630672.2018.152631

Valikhani, A. (2000). Male adolescents and adults in creative art therapy. In D. Dokter (Ed.), *Exile: Refugees and the arts therapies*. University of Hertfordshire Press.

Vertovec, S., & Wessendorf, S. (Eds.). (2010). *The multiculturalism backlash: European discourses, policies and practices* (1st ed.). Routledge. https://doi.org/10.4324/9780203867549

Vietze, D. L., Jones, J. M., & Dovidio, J. F. (2013). *The psychology of diversity: Beyond prejudice and racism*. John Wiley & Sons.

Vlachos, H., & Williams, E. (1994). *Orthodox psychotherapy: (The science of the fathers)*. Levadia.

Volkas, A. (2009). Healing the wounds of history: Drama therapy in collective trauma and intercultural conflict resolution. In D. Johnson & R. Emunah (Eds.), *Current approaches in drama therapy* (2nd ed., pp. 145–171). Charles C. Thomas.

Walby, S., Armstrong, J., & Strid, S. (2012). Intersectionality: Multiple inequalities in social theory. *Sociology, 46*(2), 224–240. https://doi.org/10.1177/0038038511416164

Wallace, S., Nazroo, J., & Bécares, L. (2016). Cumulative effect of racial discrimination on the mental health of ethnic minorities in the United Kingdom. *American Journal of Public Health, 106*(7), 1294–1300. https://doi.org/10.2105/ajph.2016.303121

Walsh, K., & Nare, L. (Eds.). (2016). *Transnational migration and home in older age*. Routledge

Ward, J. (2018). 'Prove it' working with LBGTQ+ asylum seekers who must prove their sexuality to stay in the UK. *Dramatherapy, 39*(3), 141–151. https://doi.org/10.1080/02630672.2018.1524503

Weaks, D. (2002). Unlocking the secrets of 'good supervision': A phenomenological exploration of experienced counsellors' perceptions of good supervision. *Counselling and Psychotherapy Research, 2*(1), 33–39. https://doi.org/10.1080/14733140212331384968

Weisse, C. S., Sorum, P. C., Sanders, K. N., & Syat, B. L. (2001). Do gender and race affect decisions about pain management?. *Journal of general internal medicine, 16*(4), 211–217. https://doi.org/10.1046/j.1525-1497.2001.016004211.x

Wengrower, H. (1994). The roots of the expressive therapies in the social field: Immigrants and the host society. In H. Smitskamp & Z. Fibert (Eds.), *Proceedings of the third European arts therapies conference* (Vol. 3, pp. 14–17). Ferrara.

Wente, M. (2014, February 27). The phony crisis of the middle class. *The Globe and Mail.* https://www.theglobeandmail.com/opinion/the-phony-crisis-of-the-middle-class/article17124154/

White-Davis, T., Stein, E., & Karasz, A. (2016). The elephant in the room: Dialogues about race within cross-cultural supervisory relationships. *International Journal of Psychiatry in Medicine*, 51(4), 347 356. https://doi.org/10.1177/0091217416659271

Whitehead-Pleaux, A., Donnenwerth, A., Robinson, B., Hardy, S., Oswanski, L., Forinash, M., Hearns, M., Anderson, N., & Tan, X. (2013). Music therapists' attitudes and actions regarding the LGBTQ community: A preliminary report. *The Arts in Psychotherapy*, 40, 409–414. https://doi.org/10.1016/j.aip.2013.05.006

Wilkinson, G. (2018). Dramatherapy and gender: Shattering norms and unearthing possibilities. *Dramatherapy*, 39(3), 152–162. https://doi.org/10.1080/02630672.2018.1511815

Wilkinson, R. G., & Pickett, K. E. (2009). Income inequality and social dysfunction. *Annual Review of Sociology*, 35, 493–511. https://doi.org/10.1146/annurev-soc-070308-115926

Willemsen, M. (2020). Reclaiming the body and restoring a bodily self in Dramatherapy. A case study of sensory focussed trauma centered developmental transformations for survivors of father-daughter incest. *Dramatherapy Review*, 6(1), 203–219.

Williams, B. (2016a). Minding our own biases: Using drama therapeutic tools to identify and challenge assumptions, biases and stereotypes. *Drama Therapy Review*, 2(1), 9–24.

Williams, B. (2018a). Unapologetically black: Seven questions and poems that explore how race performs in clinical practice. *Drama Therapy Review*, 4(2), 223–232. https://doi.org/10.1386/dtr.4.2.223_1

Williams, B., (2020). The R-RAP revisited: Current conceptualizations and applications. *Drama Therapy Review*, 6(2), 183–201. https://doi.org/10.1386/dtr_00027_1

Williams, D. R. (2018b). Stress and the mental health of populations of color: Advancing our understanding of race-related stressors. *Journal of Health and Social Behavior*, 59(4), 466–485. https://doi.org/10.1177/0022146518814251

Williams, Y. (2017). *Classism in America: Definition & examples*. https://study.com/academy/lesson/classism-in-america-definition-examples.html

Wilmer-Barbrook, C. (2013). Adolescence, asperger's and acting: Can dramatherapy improve social and communication skills for young people with asperger's syndrome?. *Dramatherapy*, 35(1), 43–56. https://doi.org/10.1080/02630672.2013.77313

Wilson, G. (2000). *Understanding old age: Critical and global perspectives*. SAGE Publications.

Wilson, W. J. (1999). *The bridge over the racial divide: Rising inequality and coalition politics*. University of California Press.

Wilt, D. (1993). Treatment of anger. In S. P. Thomas (Ed.), *Women and anger*. Springer.

Winder, R. (2004*)*. *Bloody foreigners: The story of immigration to Britain*. Little, Brown.

Winter, N., & Cole, A. (2021). The silent intermediary: A co-authored exploration of a client's experience of art psychotherapy for C-PTSD. *International Journal of Art therapy*, 26(1–2). https://doi.org/10.1080/17454832.2021.1898425

Wolford, L., & Schechner, R. (1997). *The Grotowski sourcebook*. Routledge.

Wong, A. (Ed.). (2020). *Disability visibility: First person stories from the twenty-first centuries*. Vintage Books.

Wood, L. (2018). Impact of punitive immigration policies, parent-child separation and child detention on the mental health and development of children. *BMJ Pediatrics Open, 2*(1), e000338. https://doi.org/10.1136/bmjpo-2018-000338

World Alliance of Drama Therapy (WADth). (2021). *Association and representatives*. https://www.worldallianceofdramatherapy.com/collaborating-members

World Health Organisation. (2014). *Social determinants of mental health*. https://apps.who.int/iris/bitstream/handle/10665/112828/9789241506809_eng.pdf

World Health Organization. (2015). *World report on ageing and health*. https://apps.who.int/iris/handle/10665/186463

World Health Organization. (2021). *Disability and health*. https://www.who.int/news-room/fact-sheets/detail/disability-and-health

Yarbrough, E. (2018). *Transgender mental health*. American Psychiatric Association Publishing.

Yep, G. A., & Mutua, E. M. (2015). Intersectionality, identity, and positionality. In K. Sorrells & S. Sekimoto (Eds.), *Globalizing intercultural communication* (pp. 85–102). Sage Publications.

Young, I. M. (2000). *Inclusion and democracy*. Oxford University Press.

Young, L. (2009). Multicultural issues encountered in the supervision of music therapy internships in the USA and Canada. *Arts in Psychotherapy, 36*(4), 191–201. https://doi.org/10.1016/j.aip.2009.01.004

Zane, N., Hall, G. C. N., Sue, S., Young, K., & Nunez, J. (2004). Research on psychotherapy with culturally diverse populations. In M. Lambert (Ed.), *Bergin and Garfield's handbook of psychotherapy and behavior change* (pp. 767–804). John Wiley and Sons.

Zoabi, A., & Damouni, N. (2016). The contribution of dramatherapy to the reconnection of abused Palestinian females with their bodies and feelings. In S. Jennings & C. Holmwood (Eds.), *International handbook of dramatherapy* (pp. 191–199). Routledge.

Zwart, M., & Nieuwenhuis, L. (1998). Mourning rituals in non-verbal therapy with traumatised refugees. In. D. Dokter (Ed.), *Art therapists, refugees, and migrants reaching across borders* (1st ed, pp. 62–80). Jessica Kingsley Publishers.

Index